SCHROON LAKE

SCHROON LAKE

by

LUEZA THIRKIELD GELB

PULPIT HARBOR PRESS

NEW YORK

2006

ISBN: 978-09778800-2-7

Design by Jerry Kelly
Printing by Capital Offset, Concord, NH

To the memory of my parents

Constance Harris Thirkield 1897-1984
&
Eden Buckley Thirkield 1892-1970

and to my husband
Bruce

Prologue

I'm looking into my father's ear. It's a beautiful shape, asymmetrical and somehow mysterious.

I'm sitting on the wicker stool to the right of the fireplace while he builds the fire. He is kneeling on one knee, the other leg bent at a right angle, his green Hood boot just touching the right andiron. His right ear is six inches from my nose. It's a big ear, somewhat longer than it is wide. It fills the space exactly right between the frayed top of his flannel shirt collar and his slanting gray hair. He smells like wood when it's been split. I breathe him in as he moves around on the hearth.

I know his fire-building motions by heart: his bare hands snapping dry twigs, then tenting them together into a tepee shape. Three times he snaps and twists to form a larger triangular shape. Then he turns to me. "You do one more bunch," he says, the words I've been waiting to hear.

I ignore the sting as the stiff twigs snap suddenly. I bend and twist, adding my fire-starting pile to the growing tepee. He watches with no comment. Then he gets back to work.

Above the tepee, supported by the two legs of the andirons, he places four or five small sticks of kindling, which I hand to him. He arranges them to allow the fire to breathe.

"Now the forestick," he says in his low, quiet voice, turning to glance at me. I know he wants me to hand him the correct piece of wood to act as a bulwark behind which he'll build the burning part of the fire. I stand up and reach for a knotty piece of maple he propped against the outside of the fireplace. I have to use two hands to carry this piece of wood that feels more like a chunk of granite. Foresticks have to be hardwood. I won't forget that from yesterday's fire-building lesson when, in a hurry to please him, I grabbed for the piece of wood closest at hand – a piece of split pine, fat but lightweight.

"No fire-builder uses softwood for a forestick," he told me. "Burns through lickety-split. Besides, pine sparks too much. Use it in back."

I felt rejected when my choice was found wanting. Now he takes my offered heavy, solid piece of maple with enthusiasm. "Now that's a forestick," he says. "We won't have to worry about this fire for more than an hour." With one big hand, he lays the well-chosen log gently in place. "Now pine to get 'er going."

I can carry four to five pieces of fast-burning softwood on my out-stretched arms. I make two trips to the woodpile in the old woodshed off the living room, stacking the wood carefully as I've watched him do ever since I was old enough to notice anything. When I come back with my second load and deposit it in the wood-holder without bang-ing it, he's already sweeping the hearth and the rug in front clear of wood bits. When all is tidy, he squats down to me, puts a hand on my shoulder.

"Do you want to light the fire?" he asks. "You'll keep us warm all evening." By this invitation I know I have earned his highest praise.

The door of Aunt Charlotte's bedroom squeaks open.

"I feel a terrible chill," Aunt Charlotte says. "Who left a door open?" She looks accusingly over the top of her pince-nez in the direc-tion of the woodshed door. "Can't you keep a fire going, E.B.?" she grumbles. "I've been cold all afternoon."

"I know you don't like to be too hot when you nap," he answers. "It's been above freezing till the sun went down." He's brushing his hands together, shaking off bits of sawdust. "Scout here can now lay a fire."

"She might remember to shut the door behind her." Aunt Charlotte backs slowly into her room. She wants the final word. "As long as she knows enough not to play with matches," she says, and she closes the door.

I force myself not to say anything, even after she's gone. I look up into Daddy's face. He's on his feet, brushing off the knees of his breeches. Now his eyes are blue like an early March sky when the snow starts to melt. Sometimes I've seen them go more to gray, fright-ening and hard, like the way I think a Damascus steel blade must look. Now he's squeezing my arm. I flex my biceps under his grip.

"Keep yourself strong, so you can take care of yourself," he says. I already know this is one of the things he thinks is important; he's told me this ever since I can remember; and I believe in it too. He reaches for his worn fedora, picks it up by pinching the crown and settles it squarely on his head. "Time to think about dinner," he says. "I hear your mother's step."

Mother comes from the front room, walking her quickstep walk, headed for the kitchen. "I could use some help setting the table, Weezie," she says. She glances into the fireplace. "What a beautiful fire you've made, E.B."

"Why don't you really look at it?" he says invitingly. "Weezie knows how to build a fire now."

"Oh, that's lovely," Mother says without slowing her pace as she turns to pass through the breakfast room. "Is Charlotte up? Jeannette's having some tea."

My father leaves a pause. Then he says, "Thank you, Lueza."

My chest swells with pride. He uses my full name when he's very serious about something, both good and bad.

I hate going to the kitchen, helping with women's chores – a bore compared to carrying wood or building a fire. I look at our fire. It's snapping and crackling and hissing happily, increasing its warmth every second.

I reach for Daddy's great hand. I love his hands, rough and always fascinating to me with their big veins that move across the backs and disappear into his powerful knuckles. His hands are always warm. I kiss the back of his hand and at that same moment he grabs my head with his other hand, holds me tight to his side for a few seconds.

"I have to put the car in the barn," he says. "Help your mother. She needs you."

One

Dwight is wrong. I take this as my adage. He believes what he believes, but I know that what I remember is as true as what he remembers. I've thought we each had a different set of parents, partly because of the four years between us, and partly because of who we each were and the ways our very different personalities played within the family. I know he's not lying. I know everything he told me happened to him, even that frightening thing, probably more than once. But how is it I never knew anything about it when we were growing up? And where was Mother?

All I want to do is to preserve some of my treasured memories of that place and time and those people. I want to try to see them, the people who shaped me, as fully rounded as I can; a deeper and more sympathetic vision.

As I straightened my kitchen this morning I was beginning to go back to Schroon Lake and I found myself sitting on my father's lap. I used to like exploring his pockets, pulling out his glasses case (although in the earliest days he wore no glasses; he could spot a fly on the branch of a tree at a hundred yards).

I inspect his face up close, follow the line of the blue vein running just in front of his hairline, then disappearing under his crisp hair. I loved to put my cheek against his cheek, rub up against the stiffness of his beard. I lie against his chest, feeling his heart beat next to mine. We don't have to talk.

I was going to get to his wallet. Thin, worn to a reddish-brown. I feel sure I could have seen my face in it. And it was curved from the shape of his body. He always kept it in his rear left pants pocket. "In the city, aren't you afraid somebody might try to pick your pocket?" I ask.

He turns his head, gives me one of his fierce looks. "Let someone try." He flexes the huge bicep in his right arm, clenches his rock-like fist. I can feel his entire body ready for a fight.

Sometimes I would come into his lap on my own, sometimes he would catch me running past his big chair and stop me still, his arm too quick to escape. I would pretend to struggle. I remember the feeling of being lifted for a long time by his iron-strong arm, and then he would draw me close, my back to the warmth and solidity of his chest.

Surrendering, I would shift, turn and fit my head deep under his jaw, one arm hooked around his neck, the other hand free to gauge the roughness of his beard, the contours of his ears, to straighten the wild, wiry hairs sprouting from his eyebrows. The most unruly ones were turning white, though the colonies of eyebrow hair were still black like the hair on his head had once been. I used to try to imagine all of his hair black again as it was in the old snapshots of him on his horse, Topsy, or with his sisters on the beach, in his old-fashioned Charlie Chaplin bathing suit. And my favorite, standing straight, oblivious in the fuming, foaming surf of the breakers.

I see myself now. I turn to his pockets: two battered flap pockets in his checkered flannel work shirt, in one a squashed pack of Camels, damp from his sweat, strike-anywhere matches inserted for easy access. "Only smoke in moderation," he used to tell me. He was a man of adages. "Too many of these can kill you." I believed him.

I DIDN'T WANT to displease my father. You always had to be careful not to displease him. But for me, once I had understood, when I was three or four years old, how to be good, I developed the habit of trying to please him.

In later years I've wished I had asked him about his side of the story. We had all those long drives to college, and back from college, with him going forty-two miles per hour, and we didn't talk about anything. I wish I had used that opportunity to talk to him. Once I was out of the house, married, I used to say things I knew hurt him. Like, "Oh, I don't want that old thing," if he had offered me some piece of furniture from the house. I didn't set out to hurt him, but I had lost that particular discipline of trying not to displease him.

He could be very irritating with his set ways. But I was always proud of him for sticking to his own principles. He had a certain level of taste, and he had no desire to let that level slacken. He would stick to what he believed and what he wanted, no matter what the circumstances were, and this is why he never really succeeded in his life. Dwight says he should just have taken any job, as a clerk in a grocery store, or a factory worker. But Dwight sees him only with anger, and the myth of E.B. being injured by the world provokes him. I think that in those days if you had been used to a certain standard, you couldn't lower that standard. I realize now that my father never would have succeeded. He was injured; he was sensitive.

It's a terrible shame that he was unable to go out and get a job and provide properly for his family, and it's a sad fact that he always believed he could parlay this or that amount of money into more and it turned out the opposite. But there was something else to him that Dwight never saw. I saw it because I was always looking for it, coaxing him, in a way, by taking an interest in the things he was interested in, and by knowing how to be the child he wanted.

MY FATHER DIDN'T CARE about being sought after; he didn't care whether people liked him or not. Mother always said, He's too sensitive, gets hurt feelings too easily, over seemingly trivial things like differences of opinion or other ways of doing things. He would close down. I think now he didn't know how to get along with people. He was always ready to turn and walk away the minute he was misunderstood. And he was bound to be misunderstood. It was built into who he was. He walked away all the time, all his life. That unbending, proud streak he had, made me proud of him. But he also annoyed me. I was embarrassed by him because of it.

I THINK he fostered my imagination. When I went with him for a walk in the woods, which was always strictly silent, I would notice everything around me in order to talk to him about it later. As a side effect of this, I took in everything. I believed everything was important. I believed everything he said, when I was a kid. I loved the woods and the wildlife. I was unhappy because my parents were unhappy, but we lived in this beautiful place that I felt was my own. I think it was my father who gave me the sensitivity for that place, beginning when I was tiny.

Now I move around the city in the same way I used to roam The Place (as we called Grandpa's place), with the same absorption. My father knew the city and loved it too. I regret that I didn't walk it more with him. We were boon companions in those childhood years, but once I got to be twelve or thirteen, I left all that. And he was away a lot, working in Albany and then in New York, and out on recognizance trips to try to make deals or realize prospects.

At fifteen, when I went away to school, I left my family and adopted another family, my roommate's. It was a family that liked me; they thought I was funny and full of enthusiasm. They used to tease me because I believed everything they told me.

WHEN MY FATHER DIED, I was in Vermont with my husband and our children. It was Thanksgiving weekend. I'd gone off and left my mother at her post at Mt. Sinai at E.B.'s bedside. Once he had the stroke he was never able to communicate with us again, except for one time when my husband walked into the hospital room. E.B. opened his eyes and mouthed Hello, Bruce. There was a huge distance between where we were and wherever he was inside his stricken body and mind. I ran away. Mother said go ahead, and I went. We didn't know when he would die, but that didn't have anything to do with my going off that Thanksgiving. I couldn't stand seeing him that way. He was so inert, so utterly helpless. I didn't see my father, I saw a failure and a ruin, and I didn't want to see that.

Dwight wrote:

> Mother knew, how could she not have known, and she didn't help me. Sometimes I believed everyone knew; sometimes I believed it was a secret. The shame was there, either way, and it still makes me wince with anger.

Two

HER ASHES were in an unadorned, sealed cardboard box, heavy as if it contained a gold ingot. I hadn't known ashes could be so heavy. (When I lifted it there were four small v-shaped wedges etched into the passenger seat of my car. I wished those marks would stay there, a continuing sign of my mother's presence.)

The drive to Schroon Lake, less than six hours these days, felt too short for collecting myself to go back to this place alone. Mother's earliest trips to the Adirondacks had taken over twenty-four hours. It always sounded like a thrilling journey from Westerleigh, on Staten Island, to the wilderness of upstate New York. I loved to hear her tell the story of the ferry ride to one of the West Side piers, then the overnight Hudson River steamer, the *Algonquin*, carrying passengers and freight up the river to Albany. Then on land again, Mother would watch the sunrise from the train rattling north into the foothills of the Adirondacks, and change to a Toonerville Trolley of a train at Warrensburg for the final push to Riverside. A poky buckboard would be waiting at Riverside, and she and her brother Dwight would run alongside the bumping wagon, glad to stretch their legs. At the south end of Schroon Lake, with ten miles still to go, they boarded a lake steamer, the *Evelyn*. Finally, late in the second day, they would arrive at The Place.

Now the miles raced by. The old road had been rebuilt and it was still raw, unsettled-looking, unfamiliar. I was stiff from driving, exhausted already by this homecoming. A fragment of last night's dream hung in my thoughts. Winter. I was walking up the porch steps in the back, leaving footprints in newly fallen snow. No one had shoveled. I knew something was terribly wrong. I was in the kitchen, my feet wet and cold. The room was chilly, no fire in the range. Mother and Daddy were both there, but no one spoke. They moved silently, separately, unaware of me, of each other.

I had woken up before dawn this morning in my bed in New York, tears running across my nose.

For the second time in less than a hundred miles, I saw flashing red lights in my rearview mirror. My mind had wandered again. Another big fat speeding ticket. Daddy never had a ticket in sixty-five years. He'd been driving since long before speeding tickets had been invented. Think of the money the state – meaning all of us – would save if people respected the speed limit. Fewer gruesome deaths too. This is what he always said as some crazy nut (a speeder – myself, I thought) whizzed past us while Daddy maintained a steady forty-two. Keep it in mind when you have your license, he would say. You'll get there just as fast if you maintain a steady forty-five, Lueza.

My final year at home, when I was legally an adult, I dared to tease him gently. "Okay, Daddy darling, I'm keeping track of your little lessons in my little black book." He didn't explode; he was delighted. He took his right hand away from its one-o'clock position on the wheel for long enough to ruffle my hair in fatherly approval, even appreciation. Why had I been so intimidated by him for so many years? Now it was too late. I would be a married woman in six months.

I remember that ride better than most, because I acted like a grownup for a change, unafraid to challenge him at least mildly, and the sky didn't fall in on top of me.

Now the State Trooper's shape approaching in my side mirror reminded me of my father. He was solidly built, not tall but commanding none the less, with broad shoulders, a powerful chest straining at his shirt, huge hands as he accepted my license and registration.

Once I had my ticket, I continued the drive at a more leisurely pace.

Okay, Daddy, I'll drive the rest of the way without rushing. I said it out loud. Driving was restful at this pace. I could see the mountains gradually getting bigger; sometimes I got a glimpse to the north of a cluster of higher peaks. The road crossed Schroon River a few times. Every curve was more familiar.

I wondered why I wasn't thinking more about Mother. I wished so much that I had asked more questions. There were too many gaps in the story.

Why did it matter?

This was a question I had asked myself many times these last six months, since she died.

MOTHER AND DADDY fell in love in a romantic spot. Grandma and Grandpa's place was still a camp in those days, with tents for extra guests pitched on what in my day had always been a fairway-like lawn, but was rougher in those early years. The town was a remote little North Country village, elms lining both sides of the streets, Grandpa's car one of only a few in the whole county. They still used horses and a wagon for most errands and excursions. I've always wished I could have seen it back then.

I know they were very much in love. Mother said so and they look it in the photographs, Daddy holding Mother's hand in that grip of his, Mother shy and innocent in a World War I dress, her hair shingled that summer for the first time. Already he was becoming possessive. "E.B. was disappointed I'd bobbed my hair," she told me. She was so uncertain of herself. She said, "I was afraid he'd call off our engagement. I gave him a big coil of my hair. He kept it."

When she told me these things it made me happier and sadder at the same time. What went wrong? Why did they become so formal and distant with each other? It was as if some unspoken rupture had taken place but it was too frightful, too shameful to speak of.

Mother told me many times, "I adored E.B. And I know he loved me, but . . ." And then she'd add nonsequiturs. "He was so hard to talk to." or "He said he didn't want children until he was well established in business." or "I didn't know anything." These statements came out in our bathroom talks – hurried conversations while Mother, Maya (pronounced like the month), and I took turns using the toilet, the sink, the tub.

I know it's pointless rerunning these scenes through my mind. They all wander into a dead end like a path that disappears in the deep woods. The forest has become a secret place, the path unknown.

THEY WERE apart but together. They were loyal to each other and yet there was a distance. It was as if they were each speaking a slightly different dialect of the same language and neither of them could ever fully understand the other's words. Daddy's silent angers estranged Mother; I know she felt abandoned even when he was home. Those angers – his barely controlled rage – drove her to petty sniping and carping about trivial things I'm sure would not have bothered her if she'd been made to feel cherished and loved by at least some demonstration of affection.

I felt a leitmotiv of sadness through all the years of my childhood and I always wished and hoped and even prayed they would find the closeness that had brought them together in the beginning.

THE MORE slowly and steadily I drove, the calmer I felt. The chore facing me would get done. I would wind up this part of my life. I had the hope, faint but there under the surface of all my memories of this place where I had grown up, of being able, finally, to trace the hidden track of the paths my parents had taken so many years ago when they had wandered away from each other. I wanted to search the house for those obscure clues. I hoped Dwight would want to help me.

I was looking forward to stretching, breathing sweet Adirondack air. Everyone always said how incredible it smelled. Now I opened the window and noticed it, too, spring air rushing in, whirling my hair around my head. Made me think of flying with Dwight, letting him show off over the lonely islands in the straits of San Juan de Fuca. He had moved as far as possible from Schroon Lake, almost out into the Pacific Ocean. The natural beauty of the place reminded him of the Adirondacks, he told me, made him feel he was connected in spite of the distance.

The house looked as it always looked after the long winter and spring. I carried the box of ashes, balanced on my left hip where I used to settle my children, up the porch steps to the door, and put the key in the lock. I had forgotten it took two hands to open the front door, sticking as it had for years, one more thing never fixed. I set the box down on the porch floor and noticed the gray paint on the boards, cracked and flaking. The door creaked open and dead inside air mixed with the fresh spring smells. I carried my precious cargo inside, set it on the piano. There was Mother's music on the piano's music stand, waiting.

I turned aside. There was a lot to do. The house had to be gone through. Closets, bureaus, desks, the kitchen, two attics, and two woodsheds, cellars, barns, chicken house, boathouses, The Lounge down by the lake. It was too much to think of. I went up the stairs and my legs remembered how steep they were. Almost at the top, ahead of me I saw the pink bricks of Daddy's chimney, coming up from the fireplace he built from bricks he rescued, aged and mellow, when they were replaced by newer ones in the walls of Grandma's cutting garden. Grandpa had thrown them out. Daddy asked for them and Grandpa said, "Take 'em, E.B., if you want 'em." There, near the bottom of the chimney, set off by the pale pink brick, was a black iron grate. From this grate, in the cold seasons, there issued a comforting flow of warm air vented upstairs from the fireplace below. Daddy's invention. He kept a fire going from early frosts till mid-May, sometimes even on crisp summer evenings.

At the top of the stairs I was out of breath. Years ago I did them two at a time, with Dwight in pursuit. I would be glad when Dwight got here.

THE FIRST BEDROOM, the cold one, was where Dwight and Mother slept. I could see four dents worn into the floor by his crib legs all those years ago. My bedroom, Maya's and mine, was next, with our shared bureau, closet, desk, twin beds crowding the room. Four or five feet across the hall was Aunt Netsie's room on the lake side, only one window.

I pushed the bathroom door open. Funny old bathroom, facing the lake, too. It served all of us upstairs. The slope of the floor made the door glide shut automatically. I looked down at the old metal wastebasket we always used as a door prop. It was rusted on the bottom, scene of a rose garden almost faded away. I used to stare at it, hope I would see the White Rabbit. You knew when someone was coming out of the bathroom because you would hear this wastebasket being slid into place to keep the door open. We kept it open so anyone coming upstairs would know the bathroom was available, and because it stayed warmer. My foot moved the wastebasket into its proper spot by long habit.

I crossed to the window, looked out toward the lake obscured now by tall trees, pale green spring foliage. On winter mornings, thick frost coated this window with intricate patterns, left only a small space at the top for a glimpse of the whiteness of the back yard. I lifted the sash, automatically clicked the old-fashioned spring pulls into their slots to suspend the bottom half. A warm breeze brushed my face, stirred the close inside air. I felt a pang, looking onto the aluminum roof of the porch. "More practical," said Daddy, to save face. "Much cheaper," he should have said, like the country people, who could not afford handsome shake shingles either.

Low like the window sat a dark-stained armchair, its soft cushion flattened to pancake thinness, yellow and brown so faded I could hardly make out the Paisley print. I sat in the chair, leaned back and looked up at the worn beige window shade with its random pattern of black spots near the top where Dwight and I had trapped lazy fall flies. Reflexively, I still knew how to let the shade roll up fast, flies buzzing furiously inside. We didn't need to pull the shade for privacy once the boys left the camp next door at the end of August; there was no one else around to see in.

This bathroom never looked like a real bathroom, not like the smart, modern bathrooms pictured in the ads in *Life* and *The Saturday Evening Post* after the war. It had a wooden floor the same as the rest of the house, bare places worn almost to the white of the original wood. In front of the sink was a small oriental prayer rug. The sink was lower than any sink I had ever seen. Separate hot and cold spigots. It was not easy to get hands and face washed, bending over this sink cupping water, splashing. For serious washing in the coldest weather, we filled the sink partway, bathed only the most important parts. We were always cautioned, "Don't waste water."

One small radiator barely took the chill off this big room. Electric heaters used too much power for the ancient wiring, and would have been a serious fire hazard in this old farmhouse. For the worst cold spells, we had a low-power electric heater. It was enormous, copper colored, with a white porcelain core surrounded by wires that glowed bright red, threw out delicious warmth at least an arm's length. The heater was a presence to be feared. Every time it was turned on we were warned never to touch any of the metal if we were wet or we would be electrocuted. I gave the heater a wide berth.

The claw-footed bathtub sat out from the wall almost in the middle of the room. The tub, with its high, straight sides, required a large quantity of water, every drop of which had to be heated by the cooking range in the kitchen. In summer we often had lukewarm baths since no one wanted the kitchen warmed by a blazing fire. And in the hottest weather baths weren't much needed; we spent good days mostly in the lake and we often included a lake bath during a swim.

On the rare evenings when it was hot and muggy, a lukewarm bath felt soothing and got rid of the dirt, the grass stains and the itchiness of the day's activities. Days when the grass was cut, Dwight and I would roll around in the soft mountains of grass ends, throwing handfuls of it over each other and diving into the sweet-smelling piles stacked in rows to be picked up by Harold, Grandpa's gardener, early the next morning. We two younger ones got into the same bath; there would be little bits of grass floating around on top of the water. Standing in the bathroom now, I could smell that water coming out of the tub faucet; it had a warm lake smell, like the water that lapped the beach.

We used lake water pumped up to the house by a pump sheltered in its own small brown-shingled house along the lower path through the woods to Aunt Rae and Uncle Joe's cabin. Dwight and I used to go to the pump house with Harold and watch while he serviced the powerful engine.

I thought about Dwight: we would go there one more time. I forced myself to get up. Time to get back to the moment.

I HAD to call Dwight, let him know I had arrived, how much I was looking forward to seeing him. Although there had been phone calls and brief visits, and we had met at various funerals over the years, we hadn't ever really talked about ourselves, our childhoods, our parents. I was curious about him, wanted to talk, finally. And I had to make arrangements for a Schroon Lake memorial service for the friends who were still left. I had already made an appointment with the auctioneer, who would drive up with a truck after Dwight and I had done our sorting and weeding and culling. Mother would finally get her wish; she always wanted to get rid of the accumulation in one clean stroke.

I walked through the entire house, making a list of the rooms and areas to be sorted through. At least I would be able to show Dwight something I had accomplished waiting for him to arrive. There were several lifetimes of accumulation in this house and its outbuildings. Mother and I had tried to make a start but the pack-rat habit was too strong and we accomplished very little except to have a lot of laughs. Nobody in my family had ever been able to part with anything. I looked through rooms, closets, bureaus; found newspapers, furniture, piles of *Life* magazines and *National Geographic*s, yellowing linens, mirrors with ornate frames, opera programs from before World War I, boxes of china, moth-eaten blankets. I closed another door.

I was determined to do something, though, to make a tiny start. Up the narrow stairs in the hot little attic over the kitchen, always referred to as the downstairs attic, I rooted out several labeled boxes of clothes and photos, small enough to be dealt with by me alone. I set myself to identify as many photos as possible and unpack at least one box.

So many squinting strangers. Now and then a familiar face peered back at me, wrinkle-free, with hair much darker than I remembered. Under the loose photos I found some framed ones turned upside down, hanging-wires rusted from the damp. And under these, I found a heavy photograph album. I took the album and the framed pictures and headed for the back porch.

I sat in the late afternoon Adirondack air and looked at my mother in her wedding portrait. She was holding an enormous bouquet that obscured her body from shoulder to hip. Her long veil was attached to a lace headband that crossed her forehead American Indian style, just above eye level. Her knee-length dress was in the flapper mode. It had no waist, and there was a band of lace below the hipline. The photographer had draped yards of veil across the front of the dress, giving a more traditional look at first glance. Peeking out from under the veil were two very pointed flapper's slippers. Was she beautiful? She looked pure, stylish, hopeful. Or maybe I read those things into her at that moment right before everything changed.

There was no formal bride-and-groom portrait. Mixed in with the smaller snapshots I found a casual shot of the two of them, summer of 1918, the year they got engaged. He was holding her at arm's length – I could feel the grip of his big hands – looking more serious than happy; she was smiling broadly, her head bent, her eyes cast down shyly.

There was a formal portrait of him, his hair parted a little off-center, his arms folded. He was looking sideways into the camera. His high collar rose toward a large, perfectly shaped left ear flush against his head. His mouth was straight, not a suggestion of a smile. He refused to take a smiling picture, even a snapshot. "People look ridiculous, grinning at the camera," he would say, baring his teeth in a cartoonish grin. His jaw was square, set with determination. He was movie-star handsome but he loathed that word, handsome.

I turned over the biggest framed photo and I was looking at the whole family group. It was now 1937 and I was in the picture too (six years old). There we all were in front of Harris Fort, a three-sided, rock-walled enclosure, with benches set back into deep niches. Grandpa had built it as one of his many surprises for Grandma, a background for more of her flower gardens. The photo was black and white, of course, but I could see the cornflowers and blue delphinium, white and pink phlox, lobelia nestled along the edges, all the colors more intense against the dark gray granite walls.

There was my father, on Uncle Joe's left. He stood a bit in front of Uncle Joe, and was making no contact with Mother, who stood next in line with a space between. He was wearing a wool sport coat, dark tie with narrow diagonal stripes anchored by a tie pin against his white shirt. His face was unreadable. The right side of his mouth went down slightly, the left side was straight. His expression was like the one in the engagement snapshot only he looked older. His hair was gray here, and he had the beginning of jowls. He was still the best-looking man in the group.

Mother stood turned slightly toward him but looking over toward baby Dwight. She had a worried expression, no smile. She was wearing a light-colored summer dress that had a bow right over her bosom, another above it. Her hair was done in a marcelled bob, and stirred freely in the breeze. Mother hated hairnets.

I had been happy to be next to Muriel that day. Muriel was my favorite cousin in those years. I was squeezed between her and Grandma, sitting on the bench with Grandma's arm around my waist and my small elbow pressed into her thigh. I could feel her stiff corset pressing into my hip bone. I had to sit on the front edge of the bench to make room for both grandparents. I was holding the loop of a souvenir whip from the circus we had been taken to that spring. I had only just learned, after hours of practice, to crack the whip with a smart snap. (Grandma took it away from me not long after the picture was taken, for cracking it too close to Dwight's face.) I was wearing a lime-green dress with peach accents; it had two cherries with leaves attached to their stems appliquéd on the collar.

Looking at the photograph now, I remembered the dress. I remembered Grandpa trying to get everyone ready that day, hustling them all from Grandma's Sunday birthday dinner, across the porch and down the steps to the Fort, happy organizing that big group. "Let's not dilly-dally. Mr. Steegall doesn't have all day," he said several times. "This is for posterity."

I looked at Maya. All I could think of was the word posterior. I had just learned that it meant your fanny and I kept starting to laugh. Maya and I giggled, looking at each other across Grandpa's stomach. Grandma said, "Shush, girls, you'll spoil the picture." Grandpa said, "Look at the camera. Smile, everybody – for posterity." Finally Mr. Steegall's flash went off – for posterior!

Three

My musing about the child on her father's lap did not go far, but it helps me to know I can begin to dip into that ancient well of memory and then take off from there.

I've started to think of a nicely alphabetical roster of Daddy's things, like the shaving mug. He was a person who had very few things. I like the idea of an alphabetical order and the idea of the way he would always explain that the object was important to him and the way it worked if it was a tool, and so on. Makes me think of Primo Levi's *Periodic Table*.

Here are a few just for a start: his address book, that beautiful, dark dark blue, almost black leather, and the tissue-thin blue pages with his sharp, vertical handwriting; his adze, an ancient tool that I never really saw him use; his axe, which he used with the skill and strength of a born woodsman; a pair of silver-backed hairbrushes, the initials G.B.T. (his father's) intertwined in Victorian script; a Gladstone bag, all he ever traveled with, English leather, the straps worn so thin only he was allowed to touch them, the handle burnished almost black from his grip, also his father's from his days as a silk factor; heavy work gloves and a pair of dove gray dress gloves, also his father's.

Books: all of his mother's Dickens; she'd read every single one of Dickens's works. Thackeray and George Eliot and most of Shakespeare; his mother knew many of Shakespeare's sonnets. The works of William Cullen Bryant. "Thanatopsis" was my father's favorite poem, I think. He often recited it low, under his breath. More books. I can't remember now what they were. And the Bible. His mother could quote from the Bible, knew many of the Psalms. Daddy often quoted Psalms too as we walked through the woods. I shall lift mine eyes up unto the hills from whence cometh my help, and A thousand years in thy sight . . .

I haven't even gotten to G for guns. His Winchester .32 rifle was his favorite, but he also had a shotgun – can't remember the gauge –

and a pistol for which he actually got a permit, so he was allowed to carry a concealed weapon. I remember seeing the license from the State of New York, maybe also one from the City of New York.

I MIGHT HAVE been cannier than I can remember, aware of my ability to adjust to the subtle signals I got when I was playing it just right for both my mother and my father. I might have been a sort of pivot, in the middle, apparently able to please both Daddy and Mother, win their favor. Maya and Dwight inevitably made inappropriate choices and moves.

Children can have an instinct about how to play grownups to their advantage, and perhaps I had such an instinct. It would seem so, since I was able to thread my way through the family minefield. And Maya and Dwight seemed to set off explosions almost as if they intended to. I believe my sister was an innocent, a person stubbornly genuine though seemingly unable to understand the world with any application of experience or wisdom. As far as I can remember, she never gave off any vibrations of hostility. Or maybe I didn't want to read such signals.

I think it's possible my mother acted as Dwight's champion in the Dwight-Weezie wars and that she came down harder on me since I was four years older. Or because she knew I knew better. If I was as much my father's child as it now feels I was, my mother might have been slightly edgy around me in general. And there could be a very tiny sense in her of thinking that if I was going to be such a perfect little Daddy's girl, then I oughtn't to be mean to Dwight and always try to beat him. My father would certainly never condone such behavior. And what upset me the most, when I had been bad, was the idea of my father hearing of it. I knew his standards, and I was always proving to him I was worthy of them. In a way it was a betrayal of Daddy for me to be mean to Dwight.

IT DOESN'T take a burst of anger. It's the anticipation of the burst of anger, or of anger at all, that separates me from my self. You can chastise me in the nicest, kindest way, and something closes down. I panic. My mind goes blank. I feel helpless, like an infant.

My father was given to outbursts, and there was always the possibility of disapproval lurking right under the surface. I learned how to avoid having any outbursts directed at me, but the disapproval was universal. I wouldn't have thought of it this way when I was growing up, but I think now that it didn't so much have to do with our being wrong as with his being right. You could see it in the context of the aunts, his sisters. They were sixteen and eighteen years older than he was, they had set ways and beliefs and they never ceased to let you know it. I think my father spent his whole life proving he knew something. It was part of his personality. It could make him seem strong. He was quiet and dignified, and he really did know a lot about a lot of things. But I can see now how it got in his way.

At the end of his life, one of the last things he said to me was, "I've been a failure." It made me feel terrible. He had always been so sure of what he knew, of what he was doing, I had never paid enough attention to the things that didn't happen.

He was not a man who said, I should have done this, or, I meant to do that. For him, it was more likely to be, If only this had happened, I would have been able to do that. Now I can see that he saw himself as someone to whom things happened or didn't happen. He didn't think of what he might have done, but of what he might have done if things had gone as they ought to have gone.

Where does the feeling of entitlement come from? It isn't one of my afflictions, but I fear Dwight suffers from it. Same parents, same household, same background, but not quite: parents four years further into their marriage and their disappointments; the war; being a boy; born imperfect (he had a hernia) and his birth causing serious damage to Mother.

FROM MY FATHER I learned to be interested in the way things worked. I also learned how to behave. I learned how to be a certain person, how to please a certain kind of person. My father always said, Keep your own counsel. I learned this through and through. I learned to keep my self to myself. I strove to make sure my father only saw the good Weezie. I reveled in being that person, the good Weezie.

I kicked him in the face.

I remember the sudden upwelling of rage, as if I had no control over my own thoughts and actions. I wanted him to tie my shoes. I sat on the couch, one foot in his lap, holding my other leg up with both hands, resting that foot on his big chest. He was making a perfect, even bow, looking hard at my shoelace, concentrating intently, as he did on any task. I still feel it happening. I pulled my free foot down and kicked full force, right into his mouth. The next second I felt shock and terror. I had really hurt him. I wanted to take it back, that hateful kick. Too late.

He spanked me hard. He roared, "Go to your room."

I was frightened of myself. Why had I hurt him? Why had I bitten baby Dwight? What if Daddy found out? Something evil in me took over. I felt tainted and bad. I didn't want to hear his overpowering voice, raging in anger, ever again.

It was only many years later that I began to recognize what I was doing. By then my father was long gone.

HE WAS heroic. He was enigmatic. He was solid. He could answer any factual question you could ever put to him. I used to ask him questions just because I could see it made him happy. It was a way I could shine. My sister and brother didn't want to hear his detailed answers; they didn't want to have to pay keen attention. I wanted to be his adjutant, his acolyte. I asked and I made sure I listened, and I showed him I had learned.

WHEN IT CAME to writing about my childhood, I only wanted to write about the idyllic parts. But there was the worm, the snake. By the time I was old enough to be aware of all the bad feelings, the cross-currents, in the family, they had me in their tow as well. A friend in my present life to whom I have told many of my stories laughed at the idea of cross-currents. "Those were riptides," she said. I know that now, but growing up, I developed my navigational skills for those particular tides, those particular sets of conditions.

The years of being exposed to my parents' strange marriage taught me all too well the necessity of protecting oneself.

I NEVER SAW my mother and father in the same bed together. I never saw them in a posture of affection toward each other. By the time I was twelve, I'd been told many times by Mother, Your father said years ago, "I've gotten all over that love stuff." I saw he meant it. If she looked as if she meant to touch him, he'd withdraw, pull his arm away abruptly, jerk his head back, his body braced as if for a blow instead of a caress. "Caress" was a word that embarrassed me when I read it in a book or heard it in a song. It sounded dirty, not to be said and certainly not to be done, in public or anywhere.

My parents never shared a room, as far back as I can remember. Mother slept in the room with Dwight when he was a baby. Daddy was somewhere else if he was in the house at all. He was on the back porch in summer, in the attic in winter, away on business most of the time. Did he hate the fact that Grandpa had sold the old farmhouse to Mother (for one dollar)? Did it make him feel beholden to Grandpa for his largesse? Was he jealous that Rae, Mother's older sister, got the big house, the one closer to the lake?

Why do I want to write something, anything, about parents who seemed unhappy with each other through all the years I was conscious enough to notice? I have no answer. I want to remember that I loved them, each of them, and that I had dreams that they would wake up one morning and be glad with each other. But they never did.

Mother said, "Daddy always sees the flaws, the hole in the doughnut. He takes everything too seriously. He can't seem to have any silly fun in life."

Daddy never said what was wrong with Mother, from his point of view. He had an attitude that she was incapable of doing things right, as if there were only one exact way of clearing the table or running the water for the dishpan or doing dishes or driving a car or putting a stick on the fire. She might get it almost right but never exactly right. Instead of speaking up and saying, "Let's not be late for church this morning, Connie" (he didn't go inside, he drove us to the church), he'd get the car out of the barn at least an hour ahead of the time it was needed, drive it across the street to the driveway in the side yard of the house, and wait, his head back on the seat, sleeping. She said, "It makes him look like a martyr. Why does he do that?" He said nothing but he looked pained, if a person can look pained while sleeping.

Mother told Daddy things he didn't need to be told. Please wear a tie. Let me wash that shirt. Or she asked him to do something he was about to do, like get more wood for the stove in the kitchen, bigger logs for the fireplace in the living room. Or even worse, she would say, I think the furnace needs some coal, wood, shaking down. And she would add an extra unnecessary note, Don't forget to take out the ashes.

If Mother got to the sink first, Daddy monitored every drop and trickle of water out of the faucets. Sometimes the critique was in the form of a question. Do you need to leave the bar of soap in the dishpan the entire time? or: Wouldn't it make sense to wash the glasses first? He could also convey the critique clearly in a flat, declarative sentence: I could wash the dishes from a Thanksgiving dinner with the water you've allowed to run down the drain.

Four

D WIGHT WROTE:

I have this memory of a time when I think I was about five years old. I was coming down the path toward The Lounge (at the lake), eager to see Daddy (as I called him then), and I heard him yelling as he strode back and forth in the downstairs part of The Lounge, throwing the fishing reel back and forth, picking it up again and again after each time he threw it, stripping line off the reel and breaking it, then throwing it again. When he saw me he began shouting at me about how bad I was, that I didn't take care of or care about anything. How the reel had been given to him when he was a boy and how well he had taken care of it. How he passed it on to me thinking I was ready to take as good care of it as he had, and on and on and on. I hadn't broken it by being careless. One of the little knob-handles that the user would hold onto with thumb and forefinger to wind up the line had broken off – I had fallen when I was carrying it. This memory is one of my earliest of what an asshole our father could be and was, at least with me, all too often during my childhood.

At odd times when I had seen my brother through the years, I had tried to glean from him whatever memories he still carried with him. Although he seemed not to remember being with Mother in that northwest bedroom in our old farmhouse, he said he had been haunted by an overheard whispered conversation between our parents, after he was supposed to be asleep. He barely heard Mother's voice, but Daddy's whisper carried across the pitch-dark room into his crib.

"I'd like to go as far away as I can get and never come back," he heard Daddy say. Dwight said that because of those words, he felt afraid every time Daddy left for Albany or New York; he was never certain he would see him again, but he couldn't voice this fear.

He said he must have heard these words in the middle of the night because he remembered hanging on tight to the cold metal bars of his crib hearing Mother's quiet sobbing, and Daddy's step on the stairs.

We found we had a joint memory of Daddy in the passenger seat of the high old touring car, a favorite of Grandpa's for our far-ranging picnic excursions. The back seat and the floor were crammed with picnic hampers, buckets with ice in them, assorted thermoses – everything covered with white sheets to guard against dust and bright sunshine. Grandpa was driving and he expected E.B. to direct this lead vehicle in the caravan of family cars by knowing every obscure, unmarked country road, paved and unpaved. Dwight and I were still small enough to share Daddy's lap, one of us on each knee, and were thrilled to be at the front of the family outing.

Out of the blue, Daddy jumped to his feet, holding each of us clamped to his chest, as we met an unexpected car coming toward us at a remote four-way crossing. "Hello, Texas!" he shouted at the other driver, who shifted gears heading in the opposite direction. Daddy turned quickly and stood us on the seat, facing backward while he waved his arms over his head at the startled driver disappearing rapidly in Adirondack dust.

"Now why in the Sam Hill would you do a darned fool thing like that, E.B.?" Grandpa sputtered. "You could've caused an accident jumping up so fast."

Daddy settled us back astride his knees. "I had to give a friendly wave to those folks from the Lone Star State," he said. "They were good to us."

Did our father perhaps want to run away from Schroon Lake and its household of women and problems, back to a place where something, who knows what, called to him. Had he felt more at home in Texas? Was it the era of his life that he longed for? Or some opportunity he still felt he had lost or missed, maybe?

E.B.'s sisters, Charlotte (b. 1874) and Jeanette (b. 1876), Franklin, Ohio, 1897

Connie age 1, Staten Island, 1898   E.B. age 6, Franklin, Ohio, 1898

George Balentine Thirkield, E.B.'s father, Franklin, Ohio

Connie, age 6, Schroon Lake, N.Y., 1903, captioned by my grandfather Harris, "A lone fisher girl"

George and Sally Belle Denise Thirkield, E.B.'s parents, date unknown

E.B., Boonton, New Jersey, on his horse Topsy, ca. 1906

Thirkield family: Sally Belle and George, 3rd & 4th from left; E.B., age 10, approx.,
holding rifle, 1902

Grandpa with Connie and Fritz, Schroon Lake, 1907

Rae and Connie, Schroon Lake, 1908, captioned by my grandfather, "Old Glory – The Glorious Bird"

E.B., Boonton, N.J., 1916 or '17

E.B. with Topsy, Boonton, 1916 or '17

E.B., Boonton, 1916 or '17

E.B. on the farmhouse roof, Boonton, 1916 or '17

Sally Belle in widow's weeds, Sea Girt, N.J., sometime between 1917 and 1922

Grandma Harris, Schroon Lake, 1909, captioned by my grandfather, "Duckie watching D. & R. at tennis"

Connie's sister Rae, captioned by my grandfather, "Rae beating Dwight, Aug. 1910"

Connie and her mother, 1911

Connie (second from left) with friends, Schroon Lake, 1914

Virginia Smith, Connie's Oberlin
roommate, Schroon Lake, 1917

Uncle Dwight in his army uniform
before going overseas to France, World
War I, and his bride, Ann Law, 1917

E.B.'s first visit to Schroon Lake, 1917, accompanied by his sister Jeanette, seated in middle seat, wearing bird hat; E.B. in middle of rear seat; Connie to his left; Connie's mother in front seat; (chauffeur's name unknown)

E.B., Jersey shore, visiting his sister Charlotte, 1917

E.B. and Connie, possibly just engaged, Schroon, summer 1918

Jeanette, 1920

E.B. on a visit to Charlotte and her husband Walter Pearson. Left to right: E.B, Jeanette, Walter, probably Sea Girt, perhaps just before E.B. was married

E.B. and Connie with Jeanette (left), Jersey shore, probably Sea Girt, 1921 or '22

E.B. and Charlotte, Jersey shore, 1921 or '22

Left to right: Jeannette, Walter, Charlotte

E.B., Sea Girt – date unknown

Family group, taken at my Harris grandparents' house in Plainfield, N.J.; left to right: Walter, Grandma, Connie, Charlotte, EB, Jeanette, probably 1922

Family group, same location as above, left to right: Charlotte and Walter, Rae, E.B.'s mother (Sally Belle), Connie's mother, (Mary Alma), 1922

E.B., possibly taken in Philadelphia during the time when Connie and E.B. shared an apartment in Germantown with Dwight and Ann, 1923

My grandfather, Arthur M. Harris, at the bank, with his secretary, Miss McKay; fall, 1923. Photo on table is of Norman W. Harris, founder of Harris Trust & Savings Bank, 1880s, Chicago, IL.

Family group: Connie's mother, E.B., Great Aunt Mattie Harris, (my grandfather's unmarried sister), Connie, 1924

Family group, probably Schroon Lake, summer, 1930; left to right: Rae, Joe, Joe's daughter (by his deceased first wife) Muriel; Ann, Dwight, Jeannette, E.B., Connie, Grandma, Grandpa; front row: Dwight and Ann's daughter Mary, my sister Mary Belle (Maya)

My grandparents getting ready to leave
Schroon Lake, September 1930.

My mother holding me, with my sister,
age 5, glum, Plainfield, 1932

My first summer at Schroon Lake, in
front of my grandparents' house,
Almanole, 1932

I examine the view from my mother's
lap; my sister is hidden by the beach
chair; Spring Lake, N.J. 1933

On Grandpa's lawn, Schroon Lake, 1934

Posing for Grandma, Schroon, 1934

With my sister, Schroon, 1934

With my sister in front of Aunt Charlotte and Uncle Walter's house, Spring Lake, before we left for Texas, January 1935

Five

THE STORY I tell myself:

My grandparents on both sides grew up in families that had just come through the Civil War – assorted uncles, fathers, and cousins serving in the Union Army from Ohio. My father was born the year before the Panic of 1893; one of his sisters got married during the Spanish-American War. As a child, my mother was carried in a torchlight parade to celebrate the re-election of President McKinley in 1900. Soon afterward, when McKinley had been assassinated, she and her family watched Teddy Roosevelt's hunting party pass by her family's summer camp hours after he had been sworn in as president further north on an Adirondack mountainside.

Grandpa Harris, my mother's father, established his camp in 1900 on the west shore of Schroon Lake. He named it Almanole for his wife, Mary Alma, though it was always referred to as The Place. Gradually the tents gave way to a cabin, and the cabin gave way to a house surrounded by gardens, lawns, fields, pastures, and woods.

All the family were gold-standard, rock-ribbed Republicans, Protestant to the bone – Methodist, Baptist, finally Episcopalian. They had been Americans a long time. Sometimes they didn't have nice things to say about other people, especially new immigrants. "We've let in enough people already," was the general consensus, with now and then a dissenting voice. Outsider Irish Catholic Uncle Joe's comment as he chewed his cigar, spat into his spittoon was, "Should've only let in Einstein's brain." Grandpa would slap his thigh, shout, "Joe, that's a corker."

We made no end of moves. We lived in the New Jersey suburbs, Florida, on the New Jersey coast, in Florida again, Texas, back up north, New Jersey again, Brooklyn. The one constant was summers in Schroon Lake, at The Place. Just before World War II we moved up there to stay, living in the old farmhouse that had been the tenant farmer/caretaker's house on Almanole's grounds.

My father had no money of his own, and he never earned much. We lived on Mother's inheritance from her grandfather. Daddy's father, who had run the family dry-goods store in Ohio, had gone bankrupt when Daddy was one year old. The atmosphere of disgrace must have pervaded my father's soul right from the beginning. And there was no money for his education. The story was, he was supposed to go to Princeton. Instead, to help support his parents, he went to work at fourteen in the Chalmers Automobile Factory for five dollars per week. His mother was a bulldog of a woman, stern-looking in the photographs. None of her children ever forgot her, even long after she was gone. We took in two of Daddy's sisters, Aunt Charlotte and Aunt Jeannette, and they were always hurling or muttering their mother's standards at each other, and at everyone else in the household as well.

My father was a solemn and stern man, and could be ferocious without warning. I used to imagine he had an ailment that made him mean sometimes, the way a stomachache made me. He could be wonderful, too. That was my secret, my belief that he was everything. I would try to sit close to him, breathe in his smell of kerosene, male sweat, and wood. I would watch his hard, leathery hands full of nicks and scratches. But his temper flared without warning, especially at Mother and at Dwight. As a small child I was afraid of him unless I was good, exactly the little girl he wanted me to be. I figured out how to do it, but I couldn't do it all the time. A lot of times I would try just to keep silent, learning how to do things right. I used to make a story out of it. Grownups were the enemy, and I was a spy. I made myself blend in. It was easy to do that at Schroon Lake. I would make myself disappear into the woods, or go out on the lake in a boat, once I was old enough – escape scrutiny for a while.

The people who worked for Grandpa and Grandma were part of my escape, too. They came from a different world, right off the boat, as it was said in those days. They were from Ireland, Poland, Bohemia; and there was one Negro, as we were supposed to say then. Their world seemed more easygoing than mine; people let out their real feelings, and didn't seem to stay secretly mad. When I was with the people who worked at The Place, I was myself, and I wasn't interrupted or scolded or reminded to speak correct English or act like a little lady.

I loved being with the local country people, too, as a small child. When they were called in to help with haying, or with the animals – my grandfather had chickens, pigs, sheep, cows, and horses – or with big parties, and extra spring and fall chores, I would hang around them, listening to their short answers, their straight way of speaking their feelings, and their lore about woodland creatures and plants, and about the weather.

My grandparents created the setting. The family gathered every summer for dinners and picnics; Fourth of July fireworks; family birthdays; hikes in the woods and up the mountains; excursions and fishing trips in Grandpa's motor boats. There were drives to vistas and historic places. Plenty of free time, games, treasure hunts, sports. It seems to me now that nobody peeked, cheated, boasted, or took the name of the Lord in vain. Sportsmanship counted, not winning. These summers were lessons for life learned by living.

This ideal time for me lasted about ten years. Then the war came. Things began to unravel. I started to grow up and I could no longer run from the dark areas, the clashes of personalities, tastes, and tem-peraments. My mother acted as peacemaker in the midst of increas-ing hostility, working to maintain a home for a mix of relatives with nowhere else to go. My father was in and out, away more and more of the time trying to earn a living at this and that. He couldn't seem to find the right niche. As the years went on he got harder and harder on himself and on everyone else. He was happiest in the woods, alone, chopping down trees.

How would it have been, in those days? What do I know about my mother and father's early acquaintanceship? What can I put together? How would they have gotten to the point where he might have said to her, as I know he did, "How would you like to live on a farm?" and she would have taken that as a proposal of marriage and later wondered if she had been mistaken, and he hadn't meant it as a proposal at all.

What do I possibly know about them? I know they were in love, to begin with. I know the story. They met at Oberlin. But go back to the moment before they met. My father and his sister Henrietta – Nettie (later to be called Jeannette, sometimes also Netsie) – are on the train. They're going to visit their sister Pearl, who is married to Philip, a professor of English literature.

I can begin to see them on the train. I knew them both only later, but push back and I can see them: my father, the only son of the family, baby brother to Henrietta, the middle girl; she is sixteen years older.

The windows go black. The noise of the train's progress intensifies. It's the last tunnel, a short one before Dayton. They sit facing forward, close, not touching. She is looking out now at her own reflection, he is methodically scanning every page of the newspaper, left to right, top to bottom. Their clothes are conservative, of good quality, their bags overhead monogrammed but well worn.

Henrietta straightens to her full height. She reaches toward a strand of hair that has escaped her smooth upswept arrangement. She shifts her position slightly and addresses the window. Her face returns her glance, her brother's profile behind her. He turns another page. She concentrates on her quick toilette. With a tortoise-shell comb pulled from the top of her head, she re-anchors a roll of copper-colored strands with a practiced hand.

She removes from a hatbox a dark blue straw hat with veil, and settles the hat in place, giving it a slight dip over her forehead. She secures it with a long, jet-tipped hatpin, weaving the hatpin into the knot.

The train explodes into the sunlight at the other end of the tunnel, smoke momentarily hazing the brightness of the morning.

"What time do you have?" she asked in her quiet voice.

He closed the newspaper, folded it neatly in half, and quartered it, squeezing it firmly into a compressed oblong. He slipped it into his left coat pocket, then reached for his heavy gold watch chain looped across his vest, and pulled forth his thick timepiece. He clicked it open. Roman numerals on a white face. Five minutes of eight. "We're right on time," he said. He knew these schedules like his own name. "We'll be there by 10:07, on the dot, or I'll be a monkey's uncle." He snapped the watch shut, and rubbed the cover slowly in a circular motion above his pocket. "Works like a charm," he said. "Father took care of his things."

She reached out to touch his arm. "I'm worried," she said. "How do you think we'll find our sister?"

Pearl's letter had sounded cheerful enough, but that was because she didn't want to worry their mother. The train whistle blew and in her mind's eye she saw her younger sister, a new bride, boarding the train at the very station where they were heading today. She saw her reaching out a gloved hand toward her new husband, Philip, who was leaning down, with a look at the edge of disapproval, to help her up the high step into the train and her new life with him. Even at the wedding, Philip had looked stern, unmoved, judging them all as wanting, Nettie was sure. Pearl had described his look as professorial, put it down to his strict intellectual rigor in judging and ranking the great works of English literature; she had been one of his students, so she spoke with authority.

Their wedding day had been as chill as his manner, gray, a wet snow whitening the slightly greening grass on the mid-April day. With Pearl already pregnant. Ten years ago, now.

Soon E.B. and Jeannette would be boarding the local train for Oberlin. In the meantime, E.B. needed quiet, and preferred not to discuss Pearl's misfortunes – a favorite topic of Nettie's. They had all tried to make the best of the situation, for the most part avoiding the subject, but now it was clear Pearl was suffering. Their mother couldn't be told a word of it, so Nettie discussed it with him endlessly. How could they all have been so taken in by that professor, and on and on.

Nettie had showed him Pearl's begging letter. Pearl had written to the sister everyone turned to for help and guidance, the middle sister of solid competence. Truly, Nettie gave the family a sense that they would all pull through whatever adversity came along.

There would be enough talk later. Now, he stretched his legs in front of him, laid his head against the seat-back. In the night his mind had been racing as fast as the train, preventing the deep, luxurious sleep he normally enjoyed on a train. There were too many conflicting questions, and he was disturbed by the fact that he had allowed Nettie to pay for both their round-trip tickets with her own money. She had insisted, saying it was only up-to-date to allow a working woman to pay her way, and to help her brother. He agreed in theory. And he knew she wanted to make it possible for them both to have a visit with Pearl. But it went against his pride.

The lush countryside spread out in green folds undulating away from them. Telegraph poles snapped past with the regularity of a metronome, linked by looping telephone wires, in an off-beat rhythm with the wheels. The miles clicked by, bringing them closer and closer to the unpleasant visit ahead of them.

Next to him, Nettie spread her fingers in front of her, strong fingers with large knuckles, hands that had known gardens and horses. She dropped her hands into her lap.

"Tell me honestly, E.B., did I do the right thing?" she asked.

She was referring to a sum of money she had told him more than once she had borrowed to pay the family bills, and incidentally also to pay for this trip. He didn't see why she had to keep harking back to it. She had already started paying it back.

"We all need the money," he said. He had no intention of discussing it again.

"I know I'm needed by this firm," she said. "I'll get a raise."

Ah, she was fretting for his approval. He summoned what he needed, speaking in a murmur so that no one else would hear him. "You must work, Nettie. For your sake. And it would be the death of our dear mother to leave that farm. It was Father's dying wish for her to stay there."

Nettie nodded. "I know all that, but I still don't feel right leaving her alone. I know she's got the servant girl, but it's not the same. But I do love my work."

E.B. stood up. He squared his shoulders and cleared his throat. He looked at his watch again, then snapped it shut. "That's that. There's no argument. You need to be using your mind. You won't only get a raise, you'll get a promotion, you mark my words." He turned abruptly and headed out into the aisle to find the porter. They would need help with their bags.

Barely touching the brass fittings on the upper corners of the seatbacks to steady himself, he made his way through the train. He calculated that this powerful juggernaut must now be at its peak speed of seventy-five to eighty miles an hour, lapping up the miles across the rich farmland of his native state. There were few grade crossings in this open, nearly flat territory, which meant the engineer could go full steam ahead. The phrase thrilled him. The ease and smoothness of this magnificently designed means of transportation filled him with awe.

He could have summoned a porter by touching the bell near his seat but this errand gave him the satisfaction of walking the length of this splendid train. His measured pace brought him quickly to the comfortable, all-male setting of the parlor car. For a few exhilarating moments he stood outside on the final platform, feeling the rushing air around him, enjoying the thrill of the scenery racing away from him. Then he re-entered the nearly empty parlor car. He took a seat and swiveled it so he could gaze out at the passing landscape.

Reaching into the breast pocket of his vest, he withdrew a thick cigar. With the pleasure of anticipation he passed the cigar under his nose and inhaled the aroma. Before he could reach for his matchbox, a white-coated porter was at his elbow, lighted match flaring at exactly the right distance to light the Havana masterpiece. He drew several long drafts of the flame, slowly rotating the tightly rolled cigar with each draft.

He nodded to dismiss the porter and settled back to enjoy the pleasure of a smoke. Pearl's wasn't the first misfortune in the family. There were misfortunes going back into his grandfather's generation. His grandfather had recovered from business reversals, but his father, now gone, had never been able to catch up, try as he did.

The story had been told to him many times, harking back to the hazy days of his babyhood. His family had once lived in an august house on the banks of the Great Miami River in southwestern Ohio, with his father's parents. The family had been in the dry-goods business. Very successful. His father, the oldest son, carried on the family name and traditions. E.B. was the only son in his generation, a baby – so he had been told – so unexpected in his mother's late childbearing years that she thought she was growing a tumor. That was only a few years before the business disgrace that had caused them to move to an obscure town in central Ohio, far away from the place where they were known. As a child, E.B. had heard this story whispered behind the upheld hands of his three grownup sisters when he was supposed to have been too young to understand what they were saying.

He knew they had left their hometown under a cloud of unspoken, never explained shame. To him, growing up overhearing the stories, he and his family had always appeared to be under a sentence of exile from the town and from the business where it seemed as if all the men in the family had worked for unending generations. He remembered the great brooding dry-goods store at the center of town, that sacred temple of commerce from which his father had been banished. E.B.'s ambition was to make up to his mother what his father hadn't been able to accomplish in the world. He was always on the lookout for opportunities.

The thrill of the fine Cuban cigar did not dwindle as he worked his way through thoughts of a future different from his father's. A good cigar was an antidote to morbid reflections. When he had come to the end of it, he stubbed it out in the ashtray, then dropped it into the brass spittoon and leaned back, stretched out his legs, and gave himself forty winks.

THE TRAIN to Oberlin would have flashed through my father's hometown, Delaware, Ohio, already smaller than the twelve hundred souls who had populated it when he lived there. Those souls had supported three churches, the public school, one small grocery, a butcher, a wheelwright, a carriage and buggy maker, a coal, grain and feed store, a livery stable and blacksmith. The one variety store – cheap yard goods, some simple tools and kitchen gadgets, notions including ribbon, thread, needles, and darning wool – was run by his father, though he did not own it. I imagine his father sitting at the kitchen table every night, green eyeshade giving his face an odd tinge, adding and re-adding the day's figures, never pleased with them. There was always the cloud, the sense of shame hovering around him. If my father ever mentioned him, or when my aunts spoke of him, which they did rarely, it was always in that same hushed tone.

My father's stories of his boyhood days came to me as lessons in the way things were done, and the way things ought to be done. Those days carried a golden halo for him. One thing I remember particularly is his description of the excitement he felt when the morning or evening train streaked through town. He grew up longing to travel to far places on trains, to go all over the country from one coast to the other, from Canada to Mexico. It was always a dream of his.

For some reason his father was fired from the running of the small store. I don't know why, but I've always suspected the father didn't belong in merchandising. By this time he was not well, and in order to minimize the shame of staying in that close-knit town for a second public disgrace, the family left for the east. My grandfather was once again set up by the Franklin relatives, this time to be their silk buyer in New Jersey, near the silk mills of Paterson. That was when E.B., now fourteen, took the Chalmers job, working as a day laborer to put food on the table till his father's new position might bring in some money. E.B. at fourteen would have been proud of his ability to earn a man's wage, bitter at being forced to end so abruptly his academic studies. A vestigial bitterness about his curtailed education stayed with him all his life.

Daddy's way of understanding life was Edenic. Things had been perfect before, and that golden time was his standard for judging anything that came along. I remember finding an ad for ladies' spun-rayon undergarments in an old magazine and showing it to him. "Enjoy the luxury but not the cost of the finest silks fit for a Princess, at a fraction the cost" was the line. "Rayon," Daddy muttered. "A sleazy, man-made fiber not fit to put on a dog." Rayon, he told me, had been the first of two death blows to the silk industry. (The second was the massive strike whipped up by that strident woman, as he called her, that socialist, Elizabeth Gurley Flynn. He was convinced that this woman had hastened his father's death.)

History, for me, was infused with life by my father's stories, always backed up by fact and detail. This was part of my early education, and I still smile when I come upon one of the people or events I first learned about in connection with his own and the family's history.

HE WAKES UP, checks his watch, and heads back to rejoin his sister. As he reaches her, the train is slowing, with loud exhalations of steam, its forward motion sharply punctuated by jerks and jolts as it enters the outer railroad yards of Dayton. He watches Nettie as she sits upright, pats her hair, makes sure her hat is secure. Someone has opened a window a few seats forward. He can taste the grit of coal dust, feel it on his skin.

"E.B., you've been in that club car. Don't I smell cigar smoke?" Nettie said. "You know how allergic Pearl is to tobacco."

He ignored her remark, gave final instructions to the porter, and gently herded his sister off the train. There was still the connecting train to catch for Oberlin.

"I wish we'd asked for them to meet us here," Nettie said fretfully. "I'd much prefer a buggy ride in the open air after being cooped up for so long."

"Now Nettie, you know there's not a Chinaman's chance of our brother-in-law making an ounce of effort on our behalf. I'm sure he's got far more important things on his mind and Pearl would never dream of asking him."

On the local train, Nettie dozed again, and E.B. studied the financial pages of the Dayton *Daily Record* for the previous day's stock quotations. Another hour and they squealed to a stop at Oberlin. Tears and embraces. Pearl's exclamations. "How's Mother? You must be exhausted. You're right on time. The child can hardly wait to see you both. We're having a little soiree this evening."

More commotion as the bags were stowed in the back of the buggy and everyone settled down for a cooling drive along tree-shaded streets. Pearl made a nervous attempt to keep light conversation going, speaking of events leading up to the commencement festivities in another week. Dark circles showed under Pearl's violet eyes, and small lines on either side of her mouth.

The party at the house that evening, she told them, was for some of the first-year students, the ones in Philip's English composition course. It would be supper, and a recital by conservatory pupils.

They drove into the driveway and underneath the broad porte-cochere.

Baths were drawn, bags unpacked.

NETTIE CAME downstairs first. Pearl was in the spacious kitchen, pots bubbling on the stove, with two hired girls peeling and chopping. Pearl ran to her and grabbed her hands.

"You go sit on the porch," she insisted. "I'll bring something to drink. Don't fuss. We'll talk later." Pearl propelled her back through the pantry and into the central hall. The floor creaked gently under their feet as they made their way along the cool hallway toward the front of the house. Philip's mellifluous voice emanated from his Student Study, one of the former front parlors, which he had converted. The door was ajar, and Nettie could see the slim ankles of a young woman sitting opposite him, her pale yellow skirt bright on the dark floor.

Pearl settled her gently but firmly into a rocker. "Now you sit right here and watch the badminton. I'll bring you some iced tea. We'll have a real chat by and by." She bent over and kissed her, and ran off back into the house.

Henrietta eased herself into the welcome chair. She was glad to sit on a stable surface after all those miles hurtling along at high speed. The slow pace of the porch rocker was what she needed right now, since she had not chosen to nap at this early hour.

She watched the young women swatting at the shuttlecock. She and E.B. had set up a badminton net in their back yard. She liked playing this game. It took a subtle kind of skill that tended to equalize male and female. When she returned her brother's furious smashes it piqued him, and her sneaky drop shots often scored points, to his distinct annoyance. Now, in this lovely shaded spot she had meant to rock and perhaps to snooze, but she felt herself becoming more and more interested in the outcome of the hard-fought match only a few yards away from her.

I HEARD THIS story more than once, with Aunt Netsie and my mother telling it together, each from her own point of view; and then from my mother later, when a lot of the clarifying details were added.

IT WAS a round-robin contest, with the longest-lasting contestant to be judged the final winner. Nettie found herself rooting silently for one young woman who seemed to throw herself into each game with a passion, leaping to make near-impossible deep shots, scooping to save and win floaters that barely skimmed the net, racing from one corner of the playing area to the other. She kept winning, trouncing the tall and the short, no matter what shots were delivered to her. And she won with outright joy, devoid of gloating, which made the spectators crowding around, the girls who had lost and the ones waiting to play, cheer the loudest for this small blond dynamo. She was dressed in blue bloomers and a white middy blouse, its broad sailor collar flapping behind all her exertions. She was young, fresh, enthusiastic. Nettie was quite charmed by her.

At the crucial moment when the final match was to be decided, Nettie heard Philip's voice behind her at the front door. "Miss Harris, it's time for your conference," he said, and then he came out onto the porch and greeted Nettie. Nettie immediately started to explain that this young lady simply had to play the final moments of the contest.

Philip was not the least impatient. "Why of course," he said. "These little athletic interludes are quite appropriate." The young woman – she looked childlike in her athletic costume, her face flushed and damp from exertion – had run over to the porch steps.

"I hope you don't mind if we just finish this one point, sir," she said, smiling up at him. "I think I can do it and then I'll be right in for my conference."

"Of course, my dear. I'd love to see the victory." He pulled up a rocker and sat down next to Nettie.

Miss Harris whipped over a quick and accurate serve. Her opponent returned it but in a few more quick strokes the match was over. The surrounding girls cheered, and Nettie silently cheered with them. Miss Harris, flushed and pleased with her triumph, left the crowd of young women and came up the steps onto the porch.

Philip was on his feet, and E.B. was out the screen door, where he, too, had been watching the last point. Philip was saying Miss Harris was one of his most promising young students. "Miss Harris, please meet my sister-in-law, Miss Henrietta Thirkield. And this is my brother-in-law, Mr. E.B. Thirkield. They've come all the way from New York to pay us a visit."

There was a shaking of hands and the exchange of polite greetings and then Philip was cupping the elbow of the young girl with one hand, while the other hand reached out to pull open the screen door.

Pearl had come out onto the porch, and E.B. sat quietly with the two women, half-listening to their talk, half-dreaming. When Miss Harris emerged from the house after her conference, he offered to drive her to her dorm in the trap. She had a recital to play that evening, she said, and she would be glad for the ride.

The two of them walked quickly down the front steps and made their way around the house. He noticed that she kept up with his pace very easily, perhaps less constrained by those loose, floppy bloomers than she would have been by a fashionably narrow skirt.

He felt he had to speak, to break the ice.

"You must have been playing a great deal of badminton to be so good, Miss Harris," he said.

"Oh, we play all the time," she answered. "And I'm used to playing with my brother and his friends so I guess playing against girls is pretty easy." She said this modestly, as if there were nothing to beating out probably a dozen young women. Then she looked up at him and said, "But please don't call me 'Miss.' It makes me feel like an old woman of thirty."

He nodded. "But what name do you prefer?" he asked. "Should I call you Constance?"

"Just call me Connie. And what's your real name?"

He was somewhat sensitive about his name. He had always felt Eden sounded girlish; he'd been teased horribly as a boy. "I was named for my distinguished grandfather, Eden Buckley," he said, "called by my initials from birth. I'd rather have a more ordinary-sounding name."

"I know, I'll call you Eden B.," she said, "if that's all right with you. I like the idea of having a special name for the first man who ever cheered me on from the sidelines." She looked up at him with a sweet, open expectancy, and he felt his own formality. Her frank smile made him feel out of place, as if she thought he was someone to swoon over.

He was at a bit of a loss how he should reply. This girl was so much more casual than the ladies to whom he had been accustomed – mainly friends of his much older sisters. He had no ready reply. Connie for her part seemed to pull back a bit, blushing slightly. She hopped up into the trap without his help, light and sure-footed as a cat.

For a few minutes they were silent as they busied themselves getting settled next to each other in the back seat. E.B. told Frank that they would drive to Miss Harris's dorm and that they would wait for Miss Harris and then drive back.

"You're Mrs. Sherman's brother?" Connie said. "And that other lady's your sister too? But they seem—" She stopped herself, again blushing slightly. "Your sisters seem so much older," she ventured.

"Yes," he said, amused. "And I have another sister, long married, who lives in Cincinnati. I'm the baby."

Then she smiled again. "I'm the youngest in my family, too, and my brother and sister seem absolutely ancient to me. Rae won't even run races with me anymore."

"Your brother?"

"Oh gracious, no," she said with a burst of laughter. "Rae's my sister and she's already twenty-five."

"I never knew a girl with the name of Rae." he said, and then she told him her sister had been named for a boyhood chum of her father's who had been thrown from his horse and killed. E.B. watched her while she told the story of the friendship. He was taken with the natural and forthright way she spoke. There was no artifice as she let the story flow out, nothing flirtatious or calculating. He found her refreshing; he didn't care what she was saying as long as she seemed pleased to be with him. When she paused, he realized she was waiting for him to say something, and he had no idea where she had left off.

He waited, hoping she would help him, but she seemed to have run out of conversation. He felt reticent about speaking too intimately of his own background. They rode in silence for a block or two, the horse keeping a steady trot that threw a hazy cloud around them in the soft afternoon light. Was she hoping he would say something about his sisters?

"Are you at all acquainted with my sister Pearl – Mrs. Sherman?" he asked.

"She's awfully sweet," Connie said. "And she makes the professor's students feel right at home. But I really don't know her. I'm in awe of the professor." She laughed at herself. "I sit as far back as possible in class, and I always try to frame my answers to reflect his judgments of the English poets."

E.B. watched the way she turned her head to look past him as she talked. He saw the slightly dampened hairs that she pushed behind her ear. "I would like to hear more about your badminton games with your brother and sister," he said. "I had no idea a young lady could have such stamina."

She told him they spent their summers in the Adirondacks. "My father loves all kinds of contests," she said. "He thinks it's good for us to compete with each other, because that's the way of the world."

That sounded very appealing to E.B. "I love the out-of-doors," he said. "I like to hike." He preferred hiking, not games, but he didn't want to say that was because he had been working since he was fourteen and had not had time for games.

"And where do you spend your winters?" he asked. The more he listened the more he realized she must come from a wealthy family. No one he knew spent summers in a place other than their home.

But she picked him up on something else, in her lovely spontaneous way, leaving his question unanswered. "Oh, we love hikes," she exclaimed. "We climb all the mountains and hills around our place and Father gives a little prize to whoever gets to the top first. Where do you go hiking?"

"I like to take long hikes up the Watchung Mountains. It's not far from our farm."

Connie clapped her hands with pleasure. "Oh goodness, you're so lucky to live on a farm. I love all the sweet animals, especially the calves, and the sheep. We have some in summer to take care of. And we have a horse."

He couldn't help chuckling at the sheer ebullience of her. He turned his face away for a moment so she wouldn't think he was laughing at her. "We live in Boonton," he said when he had recovered.

"You're in New Jersey too." She was clearly pleased. "We're in Plainfield. We've taken Sunday drives out to Boonton."

E.B. was surprised. He had been sure she was an Ohio girl. He felt a great rush of pleasure at having this lovely young girl so close to him. He tried to speak calmly.

"We have a modest working farm," he said. "I live there with my sister Henrietta and my aging mother."

"Do you do all the farm work? You must be very strong."

He had an insane urge to take off his jacket – he was too warm anyway – roll up his shirtsleeves and flex his muscles. "I wish I could," he said. "It's so satisfying. Backbreaking and never done, but I love it." His current job selling soap to grocers did not seem worth mentioning just at the moment.

She said they had a tenant farmer up at the place in the Adirondacks. "Father says he did enough farm work as a boy to last him a lifetime."

"May I ask what your father does?"

"He's a banker."

"Ah," escaped him as a flicker of pleasure ran up his backbone. He had dreams of becoming a banker – surely the soundest way to earn one's living in this expanding country, and one with a great deal of dignity to it. And the Adirondacks was a region he was drawn to by Winslow Homer's paintings, the mountains bathed in a light like no other he had ever seen. "I've wanted to see the Adirondacks for many years," he said, with all the eagerness he had kept in check until now. "Do you go up there every summer?"

They went every summer, yes, all the family. Her father came up with them to help them get settled in June, then they all stayed and he went back to the city. "He comes up later, in August, to stay until we have to go back," she said, turning a face to him lit up with pleasure and enthusiasm.

Before he could reply, she spoke again. "You should come up and visit us." She stopped, perhaps thinking better of her premature invitation. Then, with a slight shrug, she went on. "I know my sister sometimes invites young men, brothers of her friends, to come up for a house party. Maybe you could come sometime for one of our house parties."

He nodded. "You could explain to your parents that you know my sister. I believe my brother-in-law spoke of meeting your father when you first came to Oberlin."

Connie nodded vigorously, going along with his train of thought. Her hair, in disarray as it was from the badminton match, glinted in the sun coming onto it between the pale leaves of the overreaching elms. "Oh yes, Father had quite a talk with the professor," she said, unsuccessfully trying to suppress a little smile of amusement. "I think he told Father perhaps a little more about the English poets than Father was ready for that day."

E.B. had to smile too. "We might as well admit that the great professor can go on at length on the subject of his favorite poets," he observed.

Connie put out her hand. "We're allies," she said, as they shook hands. "Do you come often to visit your sister?"

Another flicker of pleasure. She was so sincere. And she liked him, he could tell. "I hope we'll come again soon," he said, as naturally as if he had been saying things like this to beautiful young girls all his life. "But in the meantime, would it be possible for me to call on you after your return home for the summer holidays?"

At this moment Connie asked Frank to pull up the trap in front of a turreted, three-story house wrapped around with a deep porch. As she stood up she reached her hand out to get her balance. "Oh yes," she said, eye to eye with E.B. for a moment before she moved to jump down from the trap. "I'd love to have you come and call. I'll bring down my card after I've changed." She hopped down and took off toward the porch steps. "Back in a jiffy," she called over her shoulder, and she disappeared inside the house.

LATER THAT EVENING, after Miss Harris's – Connie's – concert, E.B. walked down the porch steps eager for air. He had to escape the crowded living room, the chatter of meaningless comments spoken in haste, the insincere meetings and greetings of more Philip-like academic bores, slick and political in their jockeying. He walked far enough from the lighted rooms to avoid their glare on the dark lawn, and withdrew a cigar from the inside pocket of his jacket. As he lit up, the anticipated pleasure of a mellow cigar mixed with his feeling of excitement about the charming young woman with whom he had had such a delightful interlude. Here, below the dark arches of the elms, he could think about her undisturbed.

She had played the Chopin études exquisitely. But he had been truly stirred by the explosive passion in her performance of Beethoven's *Appassionata* Sonata, one of his great favorites. It had been a thrilling climax to what had been a most memorable day for him.

He had looked for her in the crowded front parlors chock-a-block with fluttering students and stolid professors and their proper wives. He was glad not to find her engaged in inconsequential conversation with one of those matrons. He couldn't help thinking of them as a flock of plump hens, clucking and self-satisfied at their solid places in the pecking order of academia. How ready to squawk at an errant husband each would be, he was sure, all except his acquiescent sister Pearl. She was too patient and forbearing, all too ready to give that slimy Philip the benefit of the doubt when it came to his questionably long conferences. How could she be so blind, especially when one of his innocent young lady students emerged from his sanctum sanctorum flustered, in disarray and sometimes even in tears? Surely it was not always because of a disappointing grade. Unfortunate campus rumors would suggest otherwise.

He knew his mother would be bitterly disappointed if he and Nettie did not bring back some firsthand word on Pearl's mental condition. Sometimes he thought perhaps his mother should have been a little more concerned with his father's mental condition, maybe he would still be alive. But he would not allow his mind to drift in this direction. He buried his cigar in a shallow grave under the spirea, along with his disturbed thoughts, eager now to return to the party.

He walked up the steps on the south side of the house, enjoying the stillness of the sweet spring evening, savoring it for a few more minutes before he plunged back into the social whirl inside. As he reached the top of the steps, he heard an odd sound coming from the dark recesses at the far back end of the porch. He was sure it was muffled crying, interrupted by the very low tones of a man whose voice sounded all too familiar. E.B. was in a fighting mood. He would like nothing better than to expose this vile man, the cause of so much distress to his mother ever since his sister's hasty marriage.

E.B. quieted his tread and came up to them on silent feet. The man's back was to him but he was certain it was his brother-in-law. The young lady was crowded up against the wall, her arms held up as if to act as a shield for the upper part of her body. Her arms partially concealed her face, but E.B. heard her shaking, muffled voice say, "Please let me go, Professor."

He realized they had no sense of his presence. He made his voice steady and low but very firm. "Let the young lady go."

Philip turned. E.B. focused on him so as not to embarrass this clearly innocent young woman. The smooth phrases of explanation were already rolling off Philip's tongue. "Why there's no need, E.B. This troubled young woman begged me to come out onto the porch for a further consultation. You know I had my conference with her just this afternoon, at the moment of her badminton victory. Not to mention her success tonight with Monsieur Chopin. I believe she's had entirely too much excitement for one day."

Constance Harris? Whom he had allowed himself to address as Connie? E.B. pushed down his emotion. He forced himself to lean over his loathesome brother-in-law. "If what you say is true," he said, "why is she crying as if someone's trying to harm her?"

"Why, I couldn't answer that any more than I could tell you why the wind blows. With young ladies at this vulnerable age their sensibilities are so close to the surface their tears are always at the ready. I'm sure this particular young lady is distraught that I might not give her the grade she expects, or that her father expects. And this fear opened the floodgates."

E.B. was taken off guard and as he floundered for words that could rout this man, Philip was turning on the girl, speaking again.

"I might say with this young man, my brother-in-law, as witness, Miss Harris, that this kind of behavior could be brought to the judicial body of the faculty." As he spoke, he straightened his clothes, adjusted his tie. "Any kind of coercion or attempt to persuade a faculty member to alter a grade is subject to immediate expulsion." He smoothed back his fringe of hair. "Perhaps you were not aware of this, as a first-year student. How unfortunate."

And E.B. was struck dumb. That same young woman with whom he had had such a pleasant conversation this afternoon and with whom he was hoping to spend more time in the very near future. He couldn't get his thoughts straight.

Philip was already moving toward the door. "I suggest we drop the entire subject right here and now," he said as he reached to open the screen door. "If Miss Harris will put no further pressures on me to alter her grade, I'm quite willing to forgive and forget." He stepped into the house and turned to E.B. "I caution you to do the same," he said, and he closed the door silently behind him.

E.B. took his handkerchief out and offered the folded square to Miss Harris and she took it with a soft "Thank you so much." He stepped away a few paces to allow her to compose herself.

How could they go back to that easy comradeship they had established so recently, now damaged perhaps irrevocably by the terrible accusation he had just heard? He knew it could not be true but why had she come out onto this dark porch with her professor, far from all the gaiety and conviviality of the party inside? Would she have had no sense of how improper it looked for her to be out here, alone, with this married man?

He was startled to hear her voice coming to him strong, almost normal.

"Eden B., I hope you don't for one single second believe what that awful man just said. I was so frightened before you came I didn't know what to do." She walked over to where he was standing near the railing, what little light there was from the streetlamp falling on the white shoulders of her dress.

"But why in heaven's name would you have come out here," he stuttered, "all alone, with him?" He heard the accusatory tone creep into his voice.

"I hardly thought I had to worry about my old professor," she interrupted. "He insisted we come out onto the porch. He said he had some important information to convey to me." She said the word convey as if it had quotation marks around it. "Why does he have to speak in such flowery terms?" she continued, and she stamped her foot, disgusted.

By God, the girl was fearless. She was attacking a revered campus figure.

"But didn't you think about how it would look?" he couldn't help asking. "You're a beautiful, innocent young woman—" He stopped for a moment as her eyes flared. "Forgive me. I had no intention of being presumptuous. I only meant to say that you must never compromise yourself by putting yourself into such a questionable situation."

"How could it be compromising or questionable," she insisted, "on his own front porch?" She gave a tiny shudder. "He talked about the stars, and he quoted from one of his favorite poets, and then he was pushing me back toward the side of the house and he wouldn't stop." She sounded as though she might start to cry again, but she added, in a thin, fighting voice, "I can't stand him." And she stamped her foot again.

"But you shouldn't have come out here in the dark with him," E.B. insisted. "Or with any man."

She burst out laughing. "I can see you've never been up to a camp in the mountains," she said. "I'm alone with all kinds of men – in the dark. When we play Run, Sheep, Run, and when we walk up from the lake after the fireworks." Her lovely smile flashed at him. "All the time," she said. "We aren't living in the Dark Ages."

He took half a step back. He didn't like to feel she might be laughing at him with her silly pun. Was she so much freer with young men than a properly brought up young lady was expected to be? He didn't want to sound pompous. "I was so worried," he said, "when I heard the sound of a young woman crying, as if she were truly frightened and in danger."

"You were very brave to come and help me." She sounded serious now. "Yes, I was afraid. But I couldn't imagine that such an old man would even think of trying to take advantage of someone like me. He's almost as old as my father. And besides, he has such a beautiful wife."

At that moment, the party seemed to come looking for them. Onto the porch a crowd of people spilled, chanting, "We want Connie! We want Connie!" There were excited cries when Connie was spotted on the porch with a young man. E.B. heard one girl exclaim, "Oh, there she is, with the handsomest man at the party." It made him squirm. He wanted to be substantial, not handsome.

Someone switched on an overhead light, giving a pale yellow glow to the lovely young women suddenly surrounding him and Connie. One of them got the rest to quiet down and proposed a group cheer "for our outstanding classmate, Connie Harris, lion of the badminton court and true artist at the piano." She turned to the others. "All right, girls!" And they broke into a shouting chorus of "For she's a jolly good fellow" followed by three rousing cheers of Hip hip hooray.

After the song and the cheers for Connie had subsided, another person came to the forefront of the crowd and made a quick toast to "Our favorite professor's wife, Mrs. Sherman," and there was another chorus and more Hip hip hoorays.

As the last of the hoorays faded out, Philip came bounding up the steps, a broad smile on his face. His hair was combed, his clothing was in order, tie carefully tied, vest buttoned, watch chain jiggling across his compact paunch, pants knife-creased. Had the sly dog been able to change? Had that been necessary? E.B.'s thoughts churned up disturbing pictures of what had gone on between the professor and Connie before his arrival.

He cleared his head by focusing on the lovely Connie enveloped by this mob of friends and enthusiastic admirers. She had begun to capture his heart with no apparent effort or the slightest plotting. It had simply happened. He gave himself up to feelings and imaginings about when he would be alone with her again.

HERE'S A QUESTION: Why doesn't he just step up to Philip and punch him? Because of his upbringing – I mean because of the outlook of his mother and his sisters, who were so much older than he was, and because of the dark atmosphere in which he was brought up – I think he might have had trouble really understanding things in a straightforward way. In other words, I think he would have been genuinely confused by this scene because even though he hated Philip and didn't trust him at all, in his mind Connie shouldn't have been out there with Philip, period. I think maybe my father didn't know how to trust anyone, and particularly not women, though he might not have seen it that way.

And Connie explains only as much as is absolutely necessary, since she knows she's not guilty in any way and she refuses to be made to feel bad or guilty. I think she lost this certainty as she went on with E.B. When they met she was a young girl who had never yet come up against the plate-glass window that separated my father from the rest of the world. This girl was glorious, honest, upright, clean of mind and body. I believe it wouldn't have occurred to her that E.B. would think she was in any way at fault, simply because she was not.

She laughs, and explains about being alone with men in the dark up at Schroon Lake, at the camp. She doesn't think twice about it. But E.B. wouldn't have been easy at all about this. He was uneasy in his own skin. How could he have thought she was laughing at him? But I feel he was so constrained that he couldn't see beyond his own dignity. It seems to me he was in the dark himself, in some way. When he was with Connie, those first meetings, I think he would have been in life as he had never been in it before. He was right on the periphery of her world of light, looking in and also feeling the radiance.

One thing, an aside, really. Now that I think about it, I'm not sure my father liked people very much. His approach was often scornful or dismissive. It's almost as if he couldn't find a fit for himself in the world. It strikes me only as I write this that it's E.B. who was the misfit, rather than the people who didn't measure up to his very high standards. Again, I feel he must have learned this from his mother and his sisters. It's as though his family was another country, or another order of being, and because of that he had no easy way in the world.

And I think the citizens of his country didn't trust anyone. Their loyalty was all to one another. The rule would be that you put the other person first, before yourself. So E.B. would have been expected to put his mother first. Henrietta expects herself to put E.B. first. Something like this: I see them all trying to be selfless and in the process they lose a kind of generosity and a sense of the truth; everything gets complicated and circumscribed; everyone is constrained.

I suspect that the beauty that was in E.B., the mysterious shining person, was by this time armored over, protected in a way for which Connie would have no experience. She must have felt that magical E.B. who was inside, and she would have wanted to get there, bring that out, get him to put aside or at least suspend some of the protective layers, many of which showed themselves as arrogance, and in hostile and uncharitable ways of thinking and behaving.

Six

Aᴀ FTER A NIGHT in the house alone, I was glad to go out in the dark early morning to the airstrip to meet Dwight.

The sun pushing above the edge of a mountain to the east set the trees ablaze suddenly and slanted over onto the far side of the minute landing strip. A hot-pink windsock veered stiffly, north by northwest; air fresh, with a chill. I pulled my windbreaker on over my sweatshirt, leaned against the car and looked for Dwight's plane. Not a speck in sight in that endless expanse overhead. From some obscure airstrip in the Upper Peninsula of Michigan I had heard his voice through static crackle the night before: "See you between five and six for an early breakfast."

I wanted to see his approach, see his wheels touch down. His childhood dreams had all had to do with planes and flying. To think about Dwight meant thinking planes. My favorite picture of him showed him wearing a boy's version of the old-style Lindbergh flying helmet, brown leather close to the head – a second skin – strap snapped under his chin, goggles at the ready slipping over his eyebrows. Mother had found him a small version of a World War II bombardier's jacket. He wore jacket and helmet year-round, shed them only in the hottest weather. "Young Dwight, you'll wear your hair off," Uncle Joe used to tease him, and, "That helmet will grow to your skull."

Dwight told me, one of the few times he came home on leave after he joined the Air Force, that I was the one who had hooked him on planes in the first place, when he was about four. He remembered being with me on the landing at the top of the stairs and either I had made for him or we had made together the semblance of an airplane out of the sides of gift boxes. From then on he was obsessed with planes, he said. Daddy used to take him to Bogle's dock during the summers even before that, though, to watch the seaplane taking people for rides. I remember them going there starting when I was six, I

[72]

think, so Dwight would only have been two at the time, 1937, '38, '39, and maybe 1940.

I remember making planes for us out of what seems like rolled-up white poster board stuck together with Scotch tape. I drew insignias on them with crayons – American Air Force (white star in a blue circle); British Lancasters and Spitfires (red, white, and blue concentric circles); evil-looking rising suns of Jap Zeroes; Iron Crosses and swastikas on Nazi Messerschmidts and Fokker dive bombers.

He told me he had kept his for years. Why didn't I know that?

We worked out an elaborate game involving marbles, and points for partial damage, direct hits, and shoot-downs. We had a "V for Victory" two-sided map showing the European theater on one side and the Pacific theater on the other, and we knew where all the bomb-blasted cities were, and the places in the Pacific where bloody battles had occurred.

When he was still little he was my eager and welcome sidekick, ready to lend his imagination to any suggestions of mine about locale, time period, choice of weapons, good guys and bad guys. In our World War II games nobody wanted to be a Nazi or a Jap (as they were referred to, then) so we made up what the enemy was doing as we went along. Dwight could throw together, out of the most motley collection of boards, huts and hideouts, tree houses, boats, even an iceboat for the frozen lake. Dwight's iceboat flew across the frozen Russian steppes as the two of us beat back the German army at Leningrad and Stalingrad. The excruciating burning in our toes as they thawed after hours in the frigid snow was the pain of our bloody wounds inflicted by the German Wehrmacht.

Indoors, Dwight's hands would move over the light-as-air balsa sheet stamped with elevator and aileron flaps, his Exacto knife severing precisely the struts of different lengths to create the delicate fuselage and wings. He stuck together these parts with airplane glue dotted onto the joints in precisely the right amounts. Too much, it wouldn't dry solidly; not enough, it wouldn't stick. The trickiest part was using the pieces of colored tissue paper to cover the balsa skeleton, stretching it enough to make a smooth, taut fit but not pulling it too much or the flimsy paper would split. (The model-plane people did not supply extra tissue paper.) When he finished a model, his fingertips would be capped with whitish, transparent crusts of dried glue.

My contribution to the delicate perfection of those planes was to soak the insignia decals free of their backing and hand them to Dwight at the correct moment for placement on fuselage and wings. And I also helped tie a slipknot of black thread carefully around a special small hook glued by him at the exact spot on top of the tiny model that would allow it to hang to best advantage, to move realistically in the living room's air currents. I was proud of those planes of his. I would hug him when he finished. I remember his furry boy-smell mixed with the sickly sweet smell of airplane glue.

When I got into my teens I didn't want anything to do with Dwight, and I would taunt him; I couldn't let him be near me without taunting him. I could stir him to rage with a pointed look, my eyebrows raised, lips pouted into a whistle. I didn't need to make a sound, skipped away blameless every time while Dwight reaped Daddy's wrath.

I remember one day he was in the bathroom too long and I pounded the door open, surprised him shaving. He slammed the door pinching my fingers and I screamed. Daddy's head popped into the stairwell, and up he came.

"Leave your sister alone," he thundered.

Dwight had been using Daddy's shaving cream, in Daddy's father's mug, lathering with Daddy's father's sacred, pure beaver-bristle shaving brush. Hurrying out of the bathroom because of my harassment, he left a guilty trail, which was instantly sized up by Daddy's gimlet eye.

Daddy was meticulous. You had to care properly for your possessions, and if you didn't take care of someone else's things you didn't deserve to use them.

"See me on the back porch, Dwight." Daddy was filled with cold, silent rage. When he was provoked, the air got ominous with tension. The rage never broke, the air never cleared afterward. The rage festered inside him. He stored it deep.

The sound of his rage made me flee the house that day, wishing I hadn't gotten Dwight in so much trouble, wishing I didn't have to hear

Daddy's roar ever again. I stayed away down by the lake for a long time.

WHEN DWIGHT was fourteen he started caddying on the town golf course. He spent his earnings for flying lessons. I was eighteen that summer. I had nothing to do with him by then but he tried to make me his ally. He made a confession to me of these forbidden lessons even though I didn't want to know anything about them. His teacher was a guitar-playing jack-of-all-trades, Jimmy Sanchelle. I knew Jimmy from the roadhouses where I went on dates. He and Dwight had met tinkering with cars. Dwight was every bit as handy as Jimmy at diagnosing sick engines. Jimmy had been married several times and was free with stories about his life. Dwight learned the ways of the world from this dashing fellow who broke hearts the same as he fixed cars.

Jimmy taught Dwight guitar, too, for free, and Dwight took to it fast. Jimmy took him into his band, Sanchelle's Adirondack Rangers, playing local dives. Places that hired Sanchelle's group were liable for fat fines with a fourteen-year-old boy thumping out chords and belting out songs at all hours. Owners took chances because Dwight brought the crowds, warbling heart-breaking country pop tunes in his youthful, dead-on tenor.

Dwight and I did become partners in crime in a way, during those teen years. We would run into each other in the surreptitious parts of our lives. I went to Dwight's joints on clandestine dates. I pretended not to know the hick guitar strummer/country crooner with a stalk of hay behind one ear, who sang with a Texas twang. We ignored each other. I was in my Veronica Lake hair-over-one-eye phase, pouting Fire'n'Ice lips; I was underage to be drinking. We covered for each other back home. We were not friends, but we needed each other's protection.

Dwight had the guts to own a car underage, bought – illegally of course – through the law-flouter Sanchelle. He got it with his gig-earned cash, big money for a kid. He kept the car hidden on an old logging road deep in the woods a mile back of the barn. More than once he rescued me from dates I wanted to escape, letting me hide out in his battered car. And he kept his mouth closed about it. I played good girl at home. Always. He had become openly hostile there, and was never around except by direct command. The two of us maintained a truce; we were cool but civil to each other. The minute I left Schroon Lake, I let go of the idea of Dwight altogether.

Now, in he came with the snap of the wind sock. I heard an engine in the fragrant air. I ran out onto the landing strip for an unobstructed view, shielded my eyes and saw a speck in the blue. I watched the speck get bigger as the sound of the engine got louder. The plane banked and circled, waggling its wings at me. I thought I could see Dwight waving. Suddenly I couldn't wait to see him.

He touched down without a sound, a perfect three-point landing. My eyes watered and I ran out feeling we were in a romantic movie. Dwight was even wearing a white scarf. It had escaped from his jacket, and ruffled bravely behind him in the breeze. Pushed back from his forehead he wore his fifty-mission crush World War II Army Air Force hat, Steve Canyon style. His unplugged earphones were around his neck. He pulled them off and I ran into his arms. He smelled almost exactly like the little boy I had loved and hated so much, but now there was no more airplane glue, just the smell of gasoline.

"That was a pretty nice landing," I said, as I stepped back to get another look at this brother I hadn't seen for too many years. He took his hat off and clamped it under his arm, ran his other hand through salt-and-pepper hair darker than I remembered it. He was grinning.

"How do you like my memory-lane get-up?" he said. "Thought you'd get a kick out of it." He wound his white silk scarf around his hand and stuffed it into an inside pocket of his jacket.

"I love your beard. Makes you look so mature." It sounded stupid as soon as the words came out of my mouth.

"Well I hope so," he said. "About time." He reached toward me, gave me a hug around the shoulders and laughed, showing his teeth. His grip felt powerful, assured. He had gestures, ways of moving his hands in smooth, deliberate motions that reminded me instantly of Daddy. The easy, warm smile, though, showing his excellent, perfect square teeth, was completely unlike Daddy.

He opened the tiny door on the side of the plane, reached in and hooked his headphones around the controls. I watched him flip a few switches, press a button or two. His hands were those same big, capable hands I would never forget from watching Daddy all those years.

"Now I've got to get this crate of mine squared away," he said. "Anyone around?" He nodded in the direction of the tiny corrugated-aluminum shack that was the maintenance building, where a beat-up truck had just pulled in.

We matched our strides, crossing the concrete amidst daisies and black-eyed Susans that had forced their way through the cracks. We didn't talk. I didn't know what to say, and stopped myself from chattering to break the silence as we went around to the rear of the shack. In a lean-to hangar, a weathered old chap was working on the engine of an ancient Piper Cub. (I knew my airplanes, thanks to early years with Dwight.)

"Hi there," Dwight called out, offering a casual military salute. "I need to park my Moonie for maybe a week, ten days. You got tie-downs? What's your routine?"

"Pretty little craft," the man said. "Nice landing." He tossed away a dead butt. "Here, I'll help you roll her to the parking lot."

They headed for the plane. It looked in the distance very much like one of Dwight's balsa models. Back at my car, I watched as they moved it to an apron of the airstrip equipped with heavy metal eyes sunk in the concrete. Dwight looked dashing. I was taken by surprise. He was full now, manly. And every bit as handsome as Daddy. As I watched him secure the cables, limber as ever but solid, with the wiry hair and beard, I realized what I had meant by mature. I saw that he would have turned my head if he hadn't been my brother.

When they had tethered the fragile-looking silver bird, Dwight covered the engine with a tarp, locked the tiny door, and headed in my direction.

"When did you finally get your license?" he asked, getting into the car. I could see he was ready to tease me as I backed up, faster than I meant to, and bumped over potholes in the concrete. Once I got going, I drove as smoothly as I could, girlishly trying to impress him.

"I remember a big fight between you and Mother," he said, settled back beside me. "She said the roads were too treacherous for you to drive between November and April." He was chuckling. "You yelled at the top of your lungs, 'You'd keep me a baby forever.' And you slammed the storm door onto the front porch. Cracked the glass. Our father was furious."

"Funny, I only remember fights you had with her," I said, for some reason mildly irritated. "She wasn't too nice about your pals – those wild guys from the band. Only made you stick up for them more."

"Now if you'd only associate with different boys," he said in falsetto. "You'll outgrow this obsession with the underdog, wait and see."

She had said the same thing to Maya, but Maya to the day of her death was still trying to heal the world.

"And I seem to remember she never wanted you to fly," I said.

"You're right on that one. She used to lay guilt trips on me. She would tell me about every crash of an airplane she had ever heard or read about, then tell me how it would just destroy her if that happened to me. 'You wouldn't want to make me suffer like that, would you?' she'd say." He paused, shrugged. For a moment his anger was palpable. Then it dispersed, and he laughed. "The guilt was laid on thick," he said with a little cackle.

I wanted to say something, give him something, praise. "I couldn't help thinking when you made your three-point landing," I said, "I wish Daddy'd been around to see it."

Dwight stared out the window, cracked his knuckles between his knees. We drove along in silence for a few minutes.

"Wouldn't have made a rat's ass worth of difference," he finally said. "He was dead set against my flying. Period. Nothing would've changed his mind."

"Why do parents do that?" I said. "Feel they know what kids should do with their lives?" I had done it myself.

He squared his shoulders, puffed up his chest. "Son, I wanted to be a train engineer when I was a lad," he said in an exaggerated Papa Bear voice, imitating Daddy. "What kind of a life would that have been? Absurd." He dropped the imitation abruptly. "He'd get that sneer into his voice. I wanted to kill him."

I slowed down and glanced over at him. He folded his arms, squeezed his lips together.

"Damn," he said. "You got me going."

"Sorry."

I knew he blamed them; I just couldn't figure out why he hadn't left all that behind. Not that I planned to say anything about it.

But he said it for me.

"I'm too old to be angry."

I wondered if he was angry at me, too. "And it's such a waste of energy," I added, hoping to lift us out of it.

We were climbing now, rising from the lower elevation south of the county seat of Elizabethtown up toward the East Branch of the Ausable River. The valley fell away to the east of the highest peaks of the Adirondacks. We had a clear view of Haystack, Whiteface, Nippletop (I couldn't say Nippletop as a kid; too embarrassing), and the biggest of them all, Mt. Marcy.

I thought what a shame the war had come along. After that Daddy had never taken us climbing again. We had never climbed the big ones.

"I've always wondered why he took us up Crane Mountain," I said. "Supposed to be a tougher climb, and you weren't even seven."

"Because nobody else did it," Dwight said right away. "He'd brag about how tough his kids were. He bragged about the damnedest things. Once, I sneaked off to camp with my buddies out past Crane Pond. I hiked there, backpack on my back. Must have been ten miles to the lake, and then along the Mt. Pharaoh trail, and finally through the woods to the other side of the lake. I didn't get in trouble for going on the camping excursion. He bragged about how I had hiked all the way from our house to Crane Pond." There was a hint of wonder in Dwight's voice. "I guess it was kind of an accomplishment," he said, "but I didn't think of it that way, I just did it because I wanted to go camping and when I asked Mother her response was, as always, an emphatic no."

I have to admit it was true, Mother tended to say no, first. But I don't remember it holding me back. I just didn't ask, and I didn't tell either.

"I was thinking," I said. "It was different with me. Probably because I was a girl," I added. But I didn't think it was because of that.

He made a movement of impatience. "Let's change the subject," he said. "How are things at the house?"

I started to protest, but skipped it. I didn't want to fight. "I've made lists," I said. "So far I haven't done much else. Too overwhelming alone. I'm so glad you're here."

"At your service. Are you still planning a memorial service? Don't expect me to speak."

"She had a lot of people around here who loved her, no matter what you may think." For a second I felt like crying. I kept my eyes on the road. We were winding and climbing, and there was a plunge straight down at my left, into the Ausable River. Dwight said nothing.

"I've got some remarks," I said when I could trust my voice. "I'd like your opinion, if you can stand it." What I wanted was his approval. I wanted him to agree with me, and I knew he knew it. The road straightened ahead for a ways. I looked over at him with my most pleading expression and saw him wince.

"Sure, why not?" he said with a shrug. "Keep your eyes on the road, Sis. Mind if I nap?" He stuffed his leather jacket between the seat and the door, tipped his head over, and was asleep in seconds.

I drove along past unchanging rocks, looking and not looking back at the past, and was relieved when the road straightened out and leveled off, and Dwight opened his eyes. We were coming into Moriah.

"Used to play here, the Wolf Bar," he said, sitting up. "I feel like one now. Let's eat."

We ate a country breakfast of ham and eggs sunny side up, toast, juice, and plenty of good strong coffee. I was happy to eat; it gave me something to do during his silences. Daddy used to be like that, too. I learned early not to talk for the sake of talking.

"You haven't lost your appetite," Dwight said approvingly. "Thought maybe city living would've made you eat like a bird." He stopped buttering his toast and pointed at me with his knife. "You know, I haven't the slightest idea what you're like."

"Same goes for me. When you took off for the Air Force I thought we didn't have a word to say to each other. And I didn't much care. Awful, isn't it?"

He had left home at seventeen, convincing our parents he would get into an officers' training program, though he had told me all such avenues had closed down not long after the end of World War II. He had been wanting to get out of the house for years. Daddy and Mother, with other problems pressing harder, finally gave in and signed the permission papers. I wasn't interested in what Dwight did at that point, or what anyone else in the family did, either; I was gone from Schroon Lake by then.

"Oh, I don't know," Dwight was saying. "Lots of families go separate ways, seems to me." He washed down a mouthful of toast with a gulp of coffee. "So, what about the ashes you talked about?"

I told him what Mother had wanted – half the ashes scattered, the rest buried in the plot next to Daddy. She had been worried about the empty space next to Daddy in the graveyard. I had checked with the cemetery people and they had no objections. I told him I had set up the memorial service for a week from the following Wednesday, at eleven in the morning, and that I had talked to a Glens Falls auction outfit.

"Whatever we don't want, they'll dump unless it's worth selling."

"And what do we do? Look at every blasted thing?" He was scowling. Then he shook it off. "I don't care, let's dump," he said. I watched him stir milk into a fresh cup of coffee. He tapped the spoon against the side of the cup, put it to his mouth, upside down, and licked it like a cat. "That used to drive Mother up the wall," he said with satisfaction. "Bad manners. If she hadn't told me that I probably would never have done it again."

We both laughed out loud.

"Hang on," I said. "We've got to go through the stuff. What about the bonds?" We laughed harder. It was an old joke, one that had come about when we heard Mother talking about some bonds years ago as if they would wipe away the financial gloom. At this point I wasn't sure Mother hadn't been talking about them as a joke herself. She had never mentioned them to me.

"We'll keep our eyes open," Dwight said. "Had enough? I'm stuffed."

Seven

BIRDS WERE tuning up around the house. Sunlight slanted into the bedroom at an early angle through the bathroom across the tiny hall.

Maya and I had shared this room. Last night I had found her navy blue nurse's cape, first lieutenant's bars, an orange, red, and green Korean theater bar, her RN pin. She hadn't bothered to take them into marriage, so crowded with babies one after the other, and moving from one place to another as her husband tried to find a permanent teaching post. Paul, a man she had known for three months when she married him. Maya wasn't sentimental, not after she graduated into real life.

This is what I wanted to write: Maya and I are running down an endless lawn, our shadows stretching down the hill beckoning us on. We're running in golden light and I'm able to keep up with her, my shorter legs working harder and harder. She lets me keep up, stops, turns, sweeps me into her arms. I inhale her clean clothes smell. She holds me around the waist, my cheek pressed to hers, her golden hair tickling my face, my feet dangling above the grass. The collar of her dress stands away from her neck; I can see the brown circle of a mole halfway between her dress and her chin, freckles across her nose, tiny ones sprinkled across her cheeks. Her teeth are straight, even, white. She's always smiling.

We had a world. We had special names. I was Suba, she was Beeba. Our games, Subabeeba games. I would be Miss Sirkie, great explorer, going across the trackless desert, befriending wild Arab tribes swooping across the sands. Suba and Beeba spoke all languages, felt at home anywhere, with Eskimo of the Arctic Circle or Kalahari Bushmen, whirling dervishes of the Caucasus or the Golden Horde sweeping over the Mongolian steppe. Miss Sirkie was an excellent horsewoman, a crack shot. She was also known as Wifeuh, married with many chilluhs, but she traveled everywhere because the children's father, Huzzah (Beeba, of course), did exactly what she, Miss Sirkie (aka

Wifeuh), told him to do. Besides, she had Maidlets Beedlets (Beeba again) to take care of them. Maidlets Beedlets was nurse, doctor, a perfect nanny with magical powers. Cooklet was in command of the kitchen. Often Suba, Miss Sirkie, took several of the chilluhs along on trips of exploration, their adventures adding to the excitement.

I was also Quaybec Corsinscones, noted actress and femme fatale, whose dearest and closest friend Chellun (Beeba again, of course), was a brilliant writer, movie director, impresario. Quaybec starred in movie productions all over the world; more travel, more adventures. They were always on the move.

Beeba could make everything come out all right as it never failed to do for Miss Sirkie or Wifeuh and her many chilluhs.

It's as if, next thing I knew, we were walking through a cavernous train station. I, Suba, held tight to Beeba's hand; Beeba was holding Mother's hand. Daddy went ahead, found our compartment on the train. There was a lot of noise, sudden squeals, shrieks, loud jets of steam. I was lifted high onto the platform between cars of the train. Who lifted me? I was not quite four years old. We walked down the narrow passageway, following close behind Mother. Suddenly there was Daddy, in a small living room, where two green couches faced each other, with a table between them. Daddy said goodbye; he said he would bring our toys to Texas. Then he was outside, waving at us outside the window beyond the table. The loudest, most piercing squeal of all, a grinding lurch and the train began to move. We waved and waved. Daddy walked down the platform and then it was black outside the window.

Snowy fields rushed by, then no snow, just gray-brown fields, purple hills far off. And always telegraph poles looped together endlessly. The porter came in to turn the couches into beds at night, back into couches in the morning while we ate breakfast in the dining car. We stopped at stations in big cities. Maya and I looked down on ladies' hats, feathers sticking up, brims down over faces, fur collars hiding chins. The porter took our shoes from outside the door at night; the shoes came back in the morning shined like new.

I liked the rocking motion at night when I went to sleep, the continual clickCLACK clickCLACK of the wheels. When we went around a long curve I would press my face against the window to see the engine, smoke puffing out of the smokestack. The train whistle sounded like a wail, made me feel far away from everywhere I knew.

Getting off the train. The ground moved. Daddy was there with our car. I remember he showed us an indentation on the back seat where our trunk of doll clothes had marked the gray upholstery. Texas was hot, flat, dusty; there were no clouds in the sky and there was no water of any kind in sight. We went to a small house, a bungalow, one floor, with a pink walkway that curved from the sidewalk up to the door and orange-red tiles on the roof. The grass in front of the bungalow was rough and brown. Inside, our trunks filled up a lot of the space.

Why were we there? Daddy must have had some kind of job, or he was hoping to get one. There were oil jobs, Maya said. I didn't understand what an oil job was. Daddy went out some days, some days he didn't. Maya and I stayed outside as much as we could.

I WANTED to write about how bright and full of magic life seemed to me, in the first years of my life, with Maya. She shared everything with me. I remember that winter in Texas, soon after we got there, she got a birthday check from Grandpa and Grandma Harris. She said she would have a big surprise for me, Suba. One morning I found a heavy box on the breakfast table. Inside the box was a pair of roller skates, bought by Maya with her birthday check. She got a pair for herself and a pair for me.

It was already hot sitting on the bottom step of the porch. I remember the way you could feel the warmth through your skirt, your underpants. My skates were shining new on the pink concrete. Maya squatted in front of me, her skates already attached to her shoes. She took my ankle, slid my foot onto its skate. Then the other one. She pulled the stiff leather strap out full length. It was almost as long as my arm. She poked the end of it through its buckle. She had to pull all the way to the last hole so it was tight enough and the skate wouldn't wobble on my foot. She did the same with the other skate, then she tightened the clamps grabbing the toes of my shoes. I see her bending over me, her lower lip caught in concentration beneath her straight white upper teeth as she turned the skate key tighter and tighter.

I fell more than I stood for a while.

"You can do it, Suba," Beeba called out to me again and again. "You're skating." She made smooth turns to stop. How did she know how to skate?

We skated all morning, quit for lunch, went out and skated till Daddy came home and made us go in for supper. But first he watched us skate, and at supper he told Mother how well I had made the turn at the end of the driveway.

SUNDAYS WE were taken on long drives in the country, miles from San Antonio. Maya and I were in the back seat. It was our own tiny room. We each had half the seat, half the floor. We sat on small seats that folded out from the back of the front seat, facing our dolls lined up on the back seat. We leaned our arms on the backrests of the jump seats, talked like grownups. I, Wifeuh, and she, Huzzah, and the chilluhs were on a trip across the desert to Timbuktu.

Something terrible happened. Huzzah said Rosa had been kidnapped. Wifeuh looked at the row of dolls, her chilluhs. Rosa was missing. Wifeuh was so upset. She called the police, asked them to come right over, start looking for her favorite daughter. A man with a loud voice made terrible threats, said he wanted a big ransom, her jewels, if she wanted to see her darling daughter Rosa ever again.

Wifeuh yelled at the police officer, told him about the man on the phone, his demands. Huzzah searched with the police, tracked down the bad man, brought Rosa back safe and sound. Suddenly Rosa was there, peeking from the top of the front seat. What a relief! Wifeuh grabbed her and kissed her happily.

I remember singing with Maya, holding Rosa close, and looking through the window across empty stretches of prairie, a lone tree here and there, piles of rocks far in the distance. Big balls of tumbleweed bounced across the deep ditch at the side of the highway and blew wildly across the black road. There were no cars. We were driving alone, under a great bowl of fierce blue sky. Then a car was coming toward us, headlights bright.

"Why waste lights in broad daylight?" Daddy said as the car passed.

"What's that dark line, E.B.?" Mother asked, pointing. There was a reddish-brown cloud rolling and growing, spreading along the prairie, up into the sky. Trees disappeared in the swirling mass. The sky turned from bright blue to a hazy gray-brown; the sun faded and for a minute glowed like a fiery ball, then it was out, gone. It was black as night.

Wifeuh couldn't see the chilluhs. Her teeth were gritty. Huzzah's face right next to hers was pale and dim.

"Roll the windows up tight, it's a dust storm," Daddy said calmly. "We'll wait." He had pulled over, stopped the engine.

"Quick, Wifeuh." Huzzah's voice was loud in my ear. "We must get the chilluhs inside before they're blown away. Help me."

Wifeuh wasn't scared. She had to take care of her chilluhs, protect them from the terrible storm, make sure none of them got kidnapped again. She and Huzzah and Maidlets Beedlets ran to the yard and grabbed them where they were playing. They got them inside before it was too late. Huzzah told her and the chilluhs the story of Rose Red and Snow White.

I dozed off, woke with a jump when Daddy got out of the car. The sun was shining again. I felt gritty all over. Daddy was sweeping sand from the windshield with a whisk broom. It was piled halfway up the windshield and on all the windows that faced away from the wind. When we were on our way again we left a huge cloud behind us as we moved. The road had almost disappeared beneath the sand draped across it.

Without Maya's villainous characters and hair-raising adventures, I might not have remembered a dust storm, one of hundreds those years that destroyed thousands of acres of farmland and sent families trekking westward across the country, fleeing starvation. We were oblivious of the consequences, out for a Sunday drive, saving our dolls.

WE LIVED in Texas for eighteen months. What I remember is having to be careful around Dwight.

To me Dwight was a spoiled baby who would never grow up. Born too early down in Texas, he had kept Mother in the hospital for weeks, made her very sick after what Daddy described as an extended labor. Then she had needed a repair job – a suspension, she called it to me and Maya. When she and Dwight finally came home, Maya and I weren't allowed to make a sound. The puny baby wasn't supposed to cry. He had a hernia and crying made it pop out. When Mother changed his diaper, it made me feel sick to my stomach to see her hook into place a wide pink elastic belt with a gray rubbery ball that pushed the hideous bulge back inside.

I knew I shouldn't hate him but I did. I made him cry very hard one day. He was in his carriage outdoors having a nap. He woke, started to whimper, waved his arms in the air. I looked over the side of the carriage, right at eye level. His tiny hand was under my nose. I grabbed one arm and bit his thumb as hard as I could. He screamed. I was terrified, flooded with guilt.

"Don't tell Daddy," I begged my sister. I knew she wouldn't. She never tattled.

STILL IN TEXAS. I'm four now. We move to a bigger house, bigger rooms, a long staircase. I'm walking upstairs, alone. Maya is in school. Carpet in the middle of the stairs, bare floor on the sides, a landing. Mustn't step on bare floor, don't make a sound, no noise. Must walk just right or they'll get me for being so evil. Dangerous not to do it exactly right. Almost at the top. No bad places so far. Bad shoe ... good shoe ... bad shoe ... good shoe ... Daddy's voice thunders, out of sight, then Mother's higher voice, but it's drowned out by his roar. I have to get out, get away. Don't let him know you heard anything. Tears burn, my eyes are too blurry to see. I'm out the back door. Nobody must see me. I hide under bushes, tears fall on ants crawling in the dirt. I squeeze the dirt, trap the ants inside.

"Weezie. Lu-eee-za! Where are you?" It was Maya, home from school. Shivery after-sobs. I don't want anybody to know I'm crying. Only babies cry, babies like Dwight. More hatred for him fills me. I'm not supposed to hate him. "Be sweet to your baby brother. Why do you make him cry? Be gentle, like Maya. She's so sweet with everybody. Why aren't you sweet like her? You have a mean streak."

[87]

I imagine a wide yellow band crossing my soul – my mean streak. Can other people see it? God will punish me for my mean streak, for hating; it's not Christian, Mother says. Even if I don't act mean, I feel mean. Something's wrong with me. Maya isn't mean. "What a sweet child," everyone says. And, "Poor, dear, sweet Maya, she has that dreadful asthma but she never complains. So patient, waking in the middle of the night, unable to get her breath."

Mother gets up with Dwight; she gets up with Maya in the middle of the night. She creeps around our dark room, the lamp shaded, a smell like church incense in the air, my poor sister breathing heavily, propped up in bed on a pile of pillows. "Poor, dear Mary Belle," says Mother. She lies down beside her. In the morning she shushes me. "Don't wake Mary Belle; she had another bad night. And don't wake the baby."

Nobody worried about waking me. I worried about myself; my evil feelings, my lack of sweetness. And catching Maya's asthma, one of my biggest fears. If I got a cold it might go into pneumonia. Then I'd get asthma. That was what had happened to Maya before I was born. That was why she was so delicate. My fault.

I didn't want to be delicate like my sister. I didn't even want to be a girl. I hated being a girl. I knew it was better to be a boy, more fun, less fussy. I hated dresses, patent leather shoes on Sunday, being told to sit properly like a little lady, with my knees together. I hated curtsying to Grandma's and Aunt Charlotte's friends. I hated their fussing and cooing over me. Their exclamations. "How sweet she is." I knew I wasn't. I knew it was false, just me with a fake smile of sweetness so I wouldn't be scolded.

I wanted to be tough. After I finally started school, I got tired of Maya's games of make-believe. I think it made her sad but she didn't say so. She still called me Suba but I'd pretend I hadn't heard. I wouldn't call her Beeba anymore. She started throwing me kisses when we passed each other in the house. It felt false to me. Did I hurt her? I began not to care. I began to go my own way, seek out boys to play with or tough girls like Antzie, next door. She was tougher than most boys, with those five older brothers. Other girls were sissies. They giggled, acted silly, cried if they fell down or got a little bump or their dresses got dirty. Mother bought me a pair of blue-jean overalls when I was seven. I think she liked my toughness. She said she'd been a tomboy when she was growing up. Aunt Rae had been the little lady. I stopped wearing a dress except when I had to – for school or church and Sunday dinner.

Gradually I began to know I was not evil, I was probably no meaner than anybody else – except Maya. Other kids said they hated their brothers and sisters most of the time. I was not a freak. There was no such thing as a mean streak. I got better at pretending to be sweet, and people believed me. I learned to act. Underneath, I knew some day I'd run away and see the world.

I DON'T KNOW why we went to Texas. Mother was never able to tell me. I think it was a fresh start for Daddy. She told me, though, about things that had mattered to her at the time, and over the course of a lifetime of talking to me she transferred to me the scenes, bit by bit, that affected all our lives.

MOTHER IN Nix Hospital in San Antonio where Dwight was born in the spring of 1935. It would look like this:

A small bump, the door flies open. A welcome interruption. An orderly comes in rolling a cart. More mail, the afternoon delivery. Connie reaches eagerly for several envelopes. She opens one she sees is from Charlotte. Luncheons, card parties, some teas, a wild northeaster that flooded the basement. Walter still working on his biblical study, Nana and dear Virginia are well, a few minor colds. Spring is there to stay.

A letter from Charlotte:

> Jeannette is keen to help you out, Connie. You know she's a great help to us but we do have Adelaide, and her daughter comes in a pinch. Just ask! Don't hesitate! [underlined several times with Charlotte's hasty pen]. We'd have to ask you to wire her train fare or perhaps E.B. could make the reservation there and mail her all necessary tickets, etc. for the journey. Connie, you mustn't overdo [more underlinings], and Jeannette is strong as a horse and we know she is eager to go to you and E.B.

[89]

There was a note scribbled by Jeannette at the bottom of Charlotte's letter saying she would love to come and help out.

Connie thought, why not invite Jeannette to come down? She was so sweet with the two girls, it would be wonderful to have family with them and not more strange help to train or direct. Connie couldn't keep herself from letting the thought insinuate itself that Jeannette could help them and it would not involve money. And she was sure Jeannette would want to come down.

She rang for the nurse. She must write immediately. E.B. would be sure to agree. She arranged the rolling table with fountain pen, ink, several sheets of paper. For the first time, she began to feel good about going home, instead of dreading all the hard work and still feeling sore and weak.

She urged Jeannette to come. She wrote about what a welcome change it would be for Jeannette, a different part of the country, the train ride a thrilling experience. She wrote about how much the girls would benefit while their mother was still recuperating from such a major operation. She mentioned the darling baby, and hastened to assure Jeannette that he was to have his own nursemaid since he had had such complications from being born prematurely.

Her energy began to flag. She pushed herself to write, feeling an urgency to finish before E.B.'s late afternoon visit. She didn't want to be distracted. She felt sure her sister-in-law would not refuse her invitation. Above all, she didn't want E.B. to dissuade her.

When the letter was in its envelope ready to be mailed, she relaxed back onto the pillows. She knew she should have mentioned this to E.B. first, but how could it matter? He would surely be delighted with her initiative.

She let her thoughts drift comfortably hither and yon, now that she wouldn't have to face going home alone; now that she would have a congenial woman beside her who could help pick up the loose ends. She dozed off.

SHE OPENED her eyes as E.B. was reaching for her hands. His hands were always so warm. She squeezed them and smiled, happy he was there.

[90]

He reached over and ruffled her hair. "I bring good news from your doctors. You should be allowed to go home in a week, or ten days at the most." He gave her shoulder a pat and sat down on the edge of the bed. "And Dwight weighs over five pounds," he added, "so they say it's up to us from here on in."

She straightened her hair where he had mussed it. He was going on about what the doctors had said. "The only precaution is not to do too much when you get home. I've hired a woman to help around the house."

"I had the sweetest note today from Charlotte," she said. She wanted to tell him she had invited Jeannette to come to them. "She says they're all fine," she continued, "especially now that spring's come at last." Then she allowed herself to get sidetracked. "Oh, I do miss a real spring with some cool days before summer is upon us," she burst out.

E.B. moved off the bed and went over to the window. He pushed it halfway up. Cool air filled the warm hospital room. He stood looking out over the gardens below. "The men at the office tell me this is the finest time in Texas," he said without turning. "Thousands of flowers blooming all over the prairie. We'll take some drives as soon as you feel up to it."

"I look forward to one of our drives, E.B. It'll be good to get out in the countryside again."

He took a turn around the room, from one side of her bed to the other. "One of the men told me about some property not far out of town," he remarked, offhand. "We'll have a look at it when you feel up to it. I'm told it's fine ranching country."

Connie was annoyed with herself for letting the right moment to tell him about her invitation to Jeannette slip past. She realized she hadn't been paying attention to what he was saying. "That sounds lovely, dear," she said, hoping her inattention hadn't been obvious. "And how are the girls doing?" she asked. Maybe she could steer the conversation back toward her need for Jeannette's help with Weezie and Maya.

He was still pacing, preoccupied, his hands in his pockets. He glanced over at her. "I've told the girls something about ranch life and they said they'd love to have a horse. We were looking at those old photos of me on Topsy. Remember those, Connie?"

She looked up, quickly attentive. Something in the way he said her name. Had he been out to see a ranch? "I'd love to drive out with you," she said. "Perhaps the girls could have a pony ride. Did you see the baby?" she asked.

"They told me he was sleeping. I said I'd have a look on my way out."

He turned toward the small rolling table near the foot of her bed, and she saw him catch sight of the letter to his sister, in its envelope. Relieved, she told him she had written to invite Jeannette. "It would be a help to me, E.B."

He walked across the room and perched on the edge of the chair cushion. He looked as if he would spring to his feet momentarily. He ran his hand across his hair. With his other hand he gripped the arm of the chair.

"You don't have to go right away, do you?" she asked.

"I've brought work home from the office."

She reached for her letter. "Would you mail this for me?" she asked. "I'd like it to go right out."

He rose to his feet. He came again to the side of the bed. Connie tried to keep her voice cheerful. "You be sure to tell those precious girls their mother misses them very much. And tell them Aunt Jeannette will be coming down within a few weeks."

"I really must be going, Connie dear," he said without emotion. "I'm thankful you're looking so chipper today. I'll stop by the nursery on my way out and wave a kiss to the baby." That was kind. He didn't seem able to break through further than that yet. When the baby was out of the incubator, Connie was sure E.B. would see what a beautiful boy he was. The baby's hernia could be fixed as soon as he had gained enough strength. Very soon, she was sure.

"Now eat plenty of good wholesome food to build up your strength," he admonished her. He leaned over and gave her a quick kiss on her cheek, patted her arm, and turned and left the room, the letter ignored.

Connie threw herself back onto her pillows. She closed her eyes for a few minutes. Then she sat up and summoned the nurse, and gave her the letter to mail on her way home from work.

MAYA TOLD ME, "Mother's bringing home a baby."

I remember asking, "A baby what?"

Maya couldn't understand that I didn't get the importance of her announcement. I thought she meant a baby dog or cat, something we could play with.

"No, Weezie. A little baby person," she said. "A baby boy. Isn't that wonderful?"

I didn't think it was wonderful. It made me angry that Mother and Daddy should want anyone besides me and Maya, and when Dwight came home and Mother was sick, I hated the whole idea of him.

I was alone that fall for the first time. Maya had to go to school; she was eight. I was too young even for kindergarten. Mother was sick from having Dwight, and Dwight needed all the attention. Aunt Netsie came for an open-ended stay. She had abandoned a brief career as a bookkeeper because the family expected her to help out when needed in the households of her siblings. She did all the domestic work, and she also read aloud in a dramatic tone. She could forecast weather – she knew every cloud formation; she acted as our nurse, did gardening, and could identify flowers, birds, weeds, and bugs. Her information came out quietly, casually, no fanfare. She seemed to love the world.

Aunt Netsie took me for long walks so the house would be quiet for Mother. No fun without Maya, weeks were endless. I remember seeing kids playing in bunches in other yards. I never went to play with them.

Daddy took Maya and me to the movies on Saturdays. The theater was packed with kids pushing and shoving each other around, shouting, eating Crackerjack, candy bars, Fro-joys; drinking soda.

"That stuff's bad for you," Daddy always said. I used to wish I was one of those kids, free, loud, left alone. It was a long show: cartoons, news, the serial, and then the movie. I was wobbly when I came out, sunlight too bright. And I would be desperate for the bathroom, afraid I would wet my pants and ruin the seat in Daddy's car.

"Not till we're home," he would say. "Public toilets are filthy."

In our high car, he made us rinse our mouths with Listerine, spit out the window into the gutter. I timed my spits between groups of kids so no one would see me do it. Why did Daddy have to be this way? I wanted to be part of the gangs of kids. What good was a baby brother?

Aunt Netsie took us to the zoo in San Antonio many times. Maya loved the zoo, and she never would go without me even though I walked slowly. I held her hand. I can remember the feel of my hand inside hers, and trying to keep up. My legs would get tired and she would give me a piggyback ride. I would bury my nose in her hair. I hated zoo smell.

Only once, we went to see the snakes.

We went into a dark tunnel, the zoo smell strong, and came out looking down into a round pit, red sand raked neatly in rows. We found seats at the edge of the pit. Beeba let me, Suba, sit on her lap so I could see better. No snakes yet.

A man holding a big basket walked into the middle of the pit. He bowed and introduced himself. Sam the Snake Trainer. "And now, ladies and gentlemen—" He cracked his long whip. Snakes curled up and over the side of the basket, snakes came untangled and curled and uncurled very fast back into their basket. Everybody clapped. More snakes oozed from the basket into the pit.

I, Suba, got sleepy, leaned back on Beeba, missed the pythons. To make me feel better, Maya told me she and Aunt Netsie couldn't watch. Another crack of the whip, two sharp blasts of a whistle brought me wide awake.

"Ladies and gentlemen! A legend in our lifetime, the incomparable Lex Langhorne, who controls the most dangerous creatures in the entire animal kingdom!" Everyone clapped hard.

The tallest man I had ever seen walked slowly into the pit. His clothes were black from cowboy hat to pants stuffed into cowboy boots, to the boots themselves. His spurs flashed as he moved. He had very white teeth that shone out from under a long black mustache as he grinned in greeting his audience. His eyebrows were dark black. He held a short black whip in one hand, a long pointed stick in the other. He walked around the center of the pit, looking down at four square baskets. Moving fast, he lifted off the covers of the baskets with his pointed stick. Then he cracked his whip once. Right away, snakes started to come out of the baskets, pouring themselves over the sides, down onto the sand. They glided outward toward the seats, curling and uncurling.

I looked right into the eyes of the snake coming toward me. It seems to me now that his eyes were so black they looked like deep holes in his head. He stuck his long forked tongue out very fast and pulled it back in again. When he was close to the edge of the pit, the man cracked his whip again. The snake stopped. He was right near me. I didn't want to look at him but I couldn't help it. His head was high and he was darting his tongue in and out fast. I started to cry.

Suddenly the tall man in black had put one leg and then the other over the short fence between me and the snake. Hanging around his neck was the biggest rattlesnake of all. The man came toward me, his teeth white under his mustache.

"Don't be afraid, ladies and gentlemen," he said in a loud, showy voice. "These snakes do only what I command them to do." He laughed in a mean way.

I was still on Beeba's lap, and he was standing right in front of me. He had a hand on either end of the huge snake draped around his neck. He patted the snake gently. That snake, too, lifted his head, and stared at me, flicking his tongue in and out.

"Now, little lady, this snake is absolutely harmless," the snake man said. "He's had his poison sac and fangs removed by yours truly. Look how friendly even a deadly diamondback rattler can be, if you know how to handle him."

The snake man squatted down in front of me so that the head of the snake was almost in my face. "Show the crowd how brave you are," he said, and he lifted the snake from around his neck and held it toward me. It writhed and twisted, its tongue going in and out faster and faster. Then the man gripped it right in back of its eyes, holding its head tight. He put the awful head right against my leg. I felt its forked tongue touching my thigh. I screamed, pulled away as far as I could. I buried my face in Beeba's chest.

Beeba was shouting, "Stop hurting my sister." I felt her leg shoot up and out, and I bounced off her lap. The man groaned, bent over. The snake fell to the cement floor and disappeared under the seats.

People screamed and jumped up. Aunt Netsie grabbed me up in her arms and ran, Maya racing after. We didn't stop until we were outside the black iron gate.

Aunt Netsie was saying under her breath, over and over, "That vile, vile man. How could he do such a thing?"

We were next to a fence that had llamas on the other side of it. They were all chewing and chewing, mouths going around and around. They looked as if they were smiling crooked smiles. Near the path one of them stared at Aunt Netsie. He stopped chewing and looked at her first with one big brown eye, then with the other. He made his lips into an O and blew thick yellow cud right at her. He splattered her straw hat.

She shrieked, but it turned into a laugh. She took the hat off and sailed it into a garbage can and we headed home laughing.

I LEARNED LATER to put pieces together. I can recite Texas by heart.

It would begin with my mother sitting in the car next to my grand-father, and keeping her hands pressed together in her lap. She told me her father couldn't tolerate nail-biting. In his opinion it was self-indulgent, and possibly even sinful to inflict such destruction on one's own body. She hoped her whole life long that she could discipline her-self enough to break the habit. I never saw her bite her nails. If I look at her hands now, in my mind, the evidence is there, but the actual bit-ing was a private and shameful act.

My grandparents came out to Texas from Florida sometime in early fall of 1935. We had been living there about eight or nine months by then. Dwight was seven months old, and doing all right.

No, IT STARTS at the dinner table, with Connie worrying about any number of things with her parents as guests.

The maid carried in a quivering lemon meringue pie and the patri-arch clapped his hands like an excited child.

"Now, Jeannette, you shouldn't have," he said. "But I'd like a gen-erous slice when it comes to my turn. You know I love your pie."

There was a brief pause as Netsie's famous pie was divided, the maid turning each piece so that its pointed end aimed directly at the person she was serving. The girls held their forks poised, hesitating as Connie had taught them just long enough to allow their grandparents to make the first move. Now everyone was eating the pie.

"This pie of yours, Jeannette, was divided into perfect eighths, I'm positive," Connie's father said. "I'd like a guarantee to get the dividend." Already he was carefully lifting the last bite of his piece to his mouth. Then he looked across the table at his son-in-law and added. "But of course, E.B., under your roof it's your prerogative to distribute the treats. Now I'd like your thoughts on a possible trip to Europe, which Mother and I would like to give you. I think Connie needs a change."

Before Connie could say anything, E.B. began to describe, in glowing detail, the beauties of various drives within the city limits and out into what he referred to as real ranch country.

"If I didn't have some obligations tomorrow, Father Harris, I'd be delighted to accompany you and Mother and Connie on a drive. We certainly appreciate your most generous offer but I don't think anything Europe has to offer could be quite like the tonic of this pure, fine air."

Connie half heard what E.B. was saying. She concentrated on finishing her own helping of Jeannette's masterpiece. Why wouldn't it be a good idea to take up her father's generous offer of a European tour, she wondered. But her heart was not engaged at all by the prospect. She could not pull herself away from her precious baby son. He was filling out, finally, and she knew E.B. wouldn't want her even to think of being away. She couldn't shake the sense that she hadn't heard the end of E.B.'s plans for moving to a ranch.

EARLY THE NEXT MORNING she was in the car, waiting for her father to emerge from the house for their promised drive. Images of her brisk and generous sister, her easygoing brother slid across her inner vision. Her throat filled. She forced herself to look out the window. Their dried-out lawn looked burned. Shrubs and trees had withered and now looked shrunken, tan leaves brittle, still clinging. But there was no palette of fall colors. She was thankful to have her parents here at

[97]

least and she would not allow herself to feel sad during their visit.

The screen door slammed. Her father walked as briskly as he always had, covering the path down to the street. James had the door wide open in time.

"Good morning, Constance," her father said. "Your mother decided to have an extra forty winks. She says the heat gets to her." They exchanged kisses over the armrest.

Connie was relieved. She knew she shouldn't have such an unkind thought but she couldn't help feeling glad to have her father's cheerful company to herself. Around the house it was far easier to be alone with a mother than with a father. She was thankful he had seized the opportunity as soon as E.B. had announced he had to go to his office.

"Now tell me where we're going. You'll have to give directions to James." Her father rolled down the glass partition that separated the back seat from the chauffeur. Connie was pleased and somewhat surprised to have her father ask her to take charge. They rolled along the quiet streets, and she told him what she knew about San Antonio's part in the war with Mexico and during the brief period of independence for the Lone Star State. She was determined to sound enthusiastic and to be as accurate as she could be. Her father never wanted to go anyplace without being thoroughly informed.

The dim coolness inside the Alamo calmed her. She knew her father wouldn't trouble her with personal questions as long as there were facts to absorb. She was thankful to walk along like a child beside him, her spirits borne up by his enthusiasm.

At lunchtime they found a cool picnic spot in a park where there was a small children's zoo. "I want to know how you and E.B. are enjoying your new life down here in Texas," her father said. "Dear Jeannette has packed a lovely lunch."

Hastily she began to arrange her thoughts. Pleasant things at the forefront, all negative ones pushed far to the back of her mind.

"I'm so glad to see this park," she said. "I've wanted to bring the girls to the zoo." She had never had the time or the energy to get her Texas driver's license. But she didn't mean to admit this to her father. (She had mastered driving years before her older sister. And she knew it had tickled her father.) E.B. had told her any number of times that he would bring home the necessary papers for her to begin the process but so far she hadn't seen them. He didn't like to be reminded, either.

How lucky to have Jeannette's picnic lunch to deflect Father's attention. And she found she felt truly hungry. The terrible heat had made her lose all desire for food through the endless summer months. This was one of those crisp perfect fall days she'd heard about.

Picnic hamper, thermos case, car blanket to sit on, an umbrella, at Father's insistence, to shield her from the sun. James settled them under a spreading live oak that gave a welcome canopy of shade. Assorted waxed-paper-wrapped turkey sandwiches, carrot sticks and celery, black olives and green ones stuffed with pimento, and small mounds of potato chips. Father filled a large brown paper bag with a generous helping of everything for James and sent him off.

Now her father would start his probing questions to get the lay of the land, as he always put it. She bowed her head as he said grace, then watched him attack the picnic sandwiches with his usual gusto, saying no one could make a turkey sandwich like Jeannette.

The first questions were general – about the climate, the neighbors, school, the baby. This seemed to be a neutral area until suddenly he was saying he had recently mailed off a check to her gynecologist to cover the outstanding bill for her complicated post-delivery surgery. He was unwrapping another turkey sandwich, the waxed paper crackling. She hoped she was not hearing him exactly right.

"But Father," she said, "how could he have sent you the bill? I know E.B. was planning to pay that before you and Mother came down here." This was something of a white lie. She knew the bill hadn't been paid because she had spotted the unopened statement sitting on the hall table her first day downstairs. She was worried, had to know how much it was, so she had opened it, and she had been shocked to learn that almost four months had gone by without E.B.'s taking care of it. She didn't want to remember the scene when he had come home that evening. Now, she tried to hide her agitation. E.B. would be enraged if he thought her father was interfering in their affairs.

The lemonade was cool and soothing on her throat and helped her feel she could control her urge to cry.

Her father spoke with his usual serious, hearty tone. "I telephoned

E.B. several months ago," he was saying. "I didn't like the sound of those complications. We felt we wanted you to have the finest medical care available and we all but demanded that you go up to New York."

He had talked to E.B.? E.B. hadn't said a word to her about it. Her father had had words with E.B. over her delicate condition?

"The most important thing is that you're well again," he said, using a carrot stick he was eating to emphasize his point. "I had a long talk with Dr. Burton and he assured me you're 100% now. And at the same time, I told him I wanted to take care of the bill. I knew we were coming down here and I'd tell you both. And that's that." The carrot disappeared into his mouth.

"Have you told E.B.?" She tried to keep her voice at a normal level but she could feel it start to quaver.

"That shouldn't be any problem. Surely all E.B. is concerned about is that you're now fit as a fiddle. Tell me, where does he work? Shall we surprise him at his office?"

This was the question she had been dreading. She named the brokerage firm where E.B. spent most of the day – or at least that was what she understood – and of course her father knew the name; it was well-known in the Street.

"And he got himself a seat on the Exchange after you moved down here?"

"Why yes, I suppose so," she said. Had he gotten himself a seat? The answer was no. But she didn't have the heart to say it; it felt too much like betraying E.B.

"Now, what kind of an answer is that? Don't you know if your husband has a seat?" He was angry. "Don't you know where E.B. works?" He was holding a brownie in his hand, halfway between the fallen waxed paper and his mouth.

"Father, I don't know. I know he goes there every day to watch the ticker. And he does some trading." She picked up her paper cup and started taking tiny sips of lemonade, trying hard to stay in control of herself. It was very still in the park. There were no sounds of the city.

"I've been meaning to write you a long letter to explain E.B.'s plans," she said. She made an effort to speak directly and carefully. "He told me he felt that spending any of my inheritance from

Grandfather toward a seat on the Stock Exchange would be an extravagance. He was confident that by moving to Texas, we could live much more economically, and ever since we got here he has kept his eye open for a working ranch to buy. He has his eye on some property. We'll be closing on it just as soon as the new well has been sunk." It was only as she spoke that she realized how truly she was speaking about the ranch. She felt the flush of all it would mean, and ducked her head, hoping her father wouldn't see it.

He took a minute or two before he was ready to answer. "I can appreciate E.B.'s desire to hold onto the bulk of your inheritance," he said. "But what I don't understand is what income you're living on. Your expenses may be much lower here than up North, but still and all, one must pay the grocery and the milkman and buy gas for the car and pay your help at least enough to hold body and soul together. Where's your income?"

"He's set aside a small amount of the inheritance to trade with and he's been making money buying and selling, recently. And he says once we're receiving income from the cattle ranch, we'll be all set." She made this last sound almost promising, even to her own ears.

Just at that moment, James came back.

They arose from the ground and headed for the convenience, on the way back to the car. She went in, and found a black, furred tarantula crouching in the corner of the cubicle. How had she gotten to such a wild, hostile region? Everything here was hot, dry, poisonous. Or it was too big, like the long-range withered vistas reaching out to where your eyes were fooled by shimmering mirages, or the rolling dust storms that buried you in darkness on a simple Sunday-afternoon drive. She hurried out of the facility and joined her father.

"And now, Miss Constance," he said, "I would like to drive out of this lovely southwestern city into what I've heard E.B. refer to as real ranch country. I want to see some true long-horned Texas cattle." And he began to sing a popular western ballad in his pleasant Sunday baritone. "Oh, give me a home, where the buffalo roam."

CONNIE DOZED in the back seat of the car. When she woke up, her father was in the front seat with a map spread out on his lap. She leaned forward and looked at the map. They must be close to the ranch E.B. wanted to buy, had probably put some money down on, and where, right now, he was still drilling a new well. She knew E.B. had made his buying this ranch contingent on finding water. And the seller, the bank – the folks had packed up and headed for California after three dry years – had agreed. The drilling had been going on for over two months.

If they did find water, what would her life be out here? Miles from anyone, dependent on hands who were willing to work for almost nothing, dependent on the whims of rain clouds – a cloudburst in one county, not a drop a few miles off. Your cattle died. Such a harsh life for her. But E.B. had his heart set on it. He had said, "This is where I can prove myself. This is what I feel I can do."

She saw landmarks. She had only been out here once, and she hadn't been paying attention; she hadn't known, then. Now she saw a windmill – a landmark she remembered – something that showed the hand of man, not simply untamed nature beating you down if you weren't made of rawhide.

She leaned over the back seat. "Turn here," she told James. "I'm sure this is it." They made the turn and she saw that Z lying on its side.

They rumbled over the cattle guard, then between stone pillars onto the property. Her father's car was not made for such rough territory; it was a city and suburban car. They bumped and jolted along at a crawl. They went through a stretch with trees then, and up ahead the house and outbuildings appeared, dusty and abandoned. James pulled the car up to the front porch of the house.

SHE SHOULDN'T have brought her father here. She didn't want him to see such desolation.

He pushed open the car door impatiently and put one foot out onto the running board. "Let's have a look-see," he said. "E.B. has been so darned excited about this place I can't believe it doesn't have some merit."

Who on earth could make a living out here?

Father asked questions. She gave short, direct answers as best she could about the property, the broker, the drilling company, the costs of providing an adequate water supply. They circled the house and she could see him looking from roof to foundation and at each of the windows. He opened the small sloping doors at the back leading down into the cyclone cellar, and went inside.

"These folks left their canned goods behind," he called up to her. "Must've left in a hurry."

Connie reluctantly took several steps down the worn wooden steps and ducked her head to look. Row stood on row of neatly labeled Ball jars of string beans and tomatoes, beets, peas, peaches, and what looked to be dark reddish jams.

She wished he would not be so interested in every detail. "I think the bank foreclosed," she said. "They were evicted." When she thought of the ranch wife putting up all those things from their garden and then being forced out in a hurry, she realized the horror of this action by the bank. On Sunday drives she had seen some of these farm families straggling westward, their cars or trucks piled with all their belongings. She'd never thought of those women putting up canned goods and then having to leave them behind.

Why would she and E.B. be able to do any better?

Her father rejoined her. "Folks can't expect to be coddled along," he said, as if he had read her thoughts. "A bank isn't a charitable organization, Constance."

Back out in the brightness, she noticed the hour. The sun was slipping down. They shouldn't linger too long. The county roads were marked but some of the signs were so faded it would be difficult to read them after dark.

"How's the drilling coming along?" her father asked.

"They said the old well was too shallow and a deeper one will solve the problem. There are lots of artesian wells all around San Antonio." She didn't want to be disloyal, though she wished, standing here now with her father, that there would be no water to be found. "E.B. says we have to keep our fingers crossed."

"I want to take a look at the outbuildings and then we should head back," he said, and he strode off at his usual quick pace. She kept up as best she could, past corrals, into the large, dim barn; past a tractor

[103]

on blocks; pieces of farm equipment in dark corners. He led the way straight through the barn and they emerged out the back, blinking in the bright sunlight.

A tall live oak, a swing waiting there for some child; out past the swing more corrals, and farther, what looked like a well-worn cattle path. When they got to the highest point, out beyond the outbuildings, she looked toward the sun, moving closer to the horizon. They might still have an hour or so before sunset. They had better leave soon. Though the vista was beautiful, the land seemed to stretch endlessly in all directions, beyond any human scale.

Her father stood beside her, quiet, taking in the view. They turned toward each other and she felt his hand take hers.

"You know your mother and I will stick by you whatever kind of life you choose," he said.

She nodded but she had to keep her feelings in check. She suggested that they walk around the far side of the outer corrals and then head back to the car.

Now they walked at a slower pace, preserving the closeness of this day. When they got near a small copse of trees just beyond the last corral, she saw a snaky trail of black, moist-looking soil. Fringing the black moistness was the faintest tinge of green, the hint of tiny new shoots of tender green grass seeking light and air. She was in the lead at this moment and she was the first one to see the brimming ancient bathtub, half sunk into the ground, for cattle to drink. She slowed her pace and waited.

The tub was full of water, water that trickled slowly but steadily from a long pipe leading back into the middle of the small cluster of live oaks and mesquite. The far end of the pipe disappeared into a tiny pump house. Now she could hear a steady KA- CHUNK, KA- CHUNK, KA- CHUNK – the familiar sound of a one-cylinder engine pumping water up from far underground.

The two of them, father and daughter, stood for a few moments without saying anything. She was transfixed by the beauty and rarity of water. She felt a rush of happiness for E.B. But there was a pain inside her, forcing her to draw a sharp breath. Fear. Now there was no longer any question. She and E.B. and the two girls and little Dwight and Juanita – Oh, please let Juanita come with them – and Jeannette, please, would soon be packing up their household and moving out here to this hard life. How could she ever do it?

"Well, my dear," her father said gently, "it seems E.B.'s faith in this place was well founded. You and the children will start a new life." He turned her to face him, putting his hands on her shoulders. "Whatever your mother and I can do to help in this move, we will do for you."

He squeezed her shoulders fondly. She wanted to appear calm as she should be, married now these fifteen years, with three children and a husband who was getting his heart's desire.

"Oh Father," she began softly, and then she just kept going. "I don't know if I can do it. I never encouraged E.B. to look for a ranch. He kept saying how much the girls would love the horses, the riding, the independence. But he didn't really ask me, he never asked me, he never asks me anything—"

She stopped herself. But tears came, tears she had kept dammed up tight, out of sight of E.B. and of her parents. Especially her parents. She didn't want to upset them. They were getting older; both were in their seventies now.

This thought made her distraught. Just thinking of her parents aging far away made her frantic. They were such a very long journey away that she might never see them again, or the rest of her family. And to be forced to live in this harsh, unforgiving climate, baking in the summers, chilled to the bone by the fierce northers of winter lasting for days, out here remote from other people.

She bent her head, put her hands over her eyes, and allowed her tears to flow. There was no possibility of stopping them. She was undone, flattened, without hope once she had seen and heard that water flowing – the life-blood of any ranch or farm or any human endeavor for that matter. She cried without stopping and without a sound.

"Now you may find you like it," her father said kindly. "It's going to be an exciting life. You like to ride." She didn't answer and he gave her shoulders a last squeeze and dropped his hands. "Think of the freedom from the red tape and politics of the business world," he said, "the ability to be your own person, E.B. his own man. I think it will be very good for each and every one of you."

Even he was siding with E.B.

He was speaking again, as they began to move back in the direction of the car. "You know, Connie, I don't think your E.B. really belongs in the business world." His tone was confiding, relieved. "He's got such a thin skin, and that's not good at all. I'd say this may be the ideal life for him."

With this last remark, Connie choked. "But Father," she cried out, "what about me?"

THAT WOULD have been a rare moment in my mother's life, for her to cry out for her own desire. Maybe it was the last time she allowed herself to come to such a juncture. I think something closed in her, in Texas, and that that cry, so humiliating to her, came from somewhere inside she never allowed herself near again. There was one other crisis, when I was about 12, but keeping it from us all, she also kept it from herself – or she kept herself from it. I'll come to that in a little while. There's more to Texas.

The car pulls into the driveway as the last light is fading. There has been no further discussion between Connie and her father. They've stuck to pleasantries during the ride back, and he has dozed off after a while.

E.B. is at his desk in the small alcove area of their bedroom he refers to as his office. He gets up when she comes into the room and they exchange a brief kiss. He knows, she suddenly thinks, he knows there's water – something he surely must have been keeping back from her until he felt the time was exactly right.

"We had a glorious drive," she says in her usual ebullient way. "And we have the best news. The trough out in back of the barn is overflowing with water. You were right, E.B. I wish I'd had the Brownie."

Does he smile? A smile for her enthusiasm? She's running a bath. She comes back into the doorway. "Dinner's at seven. You know how Father likes to eat promptly. I hope you had a good day, E.B." She's off again, closes the bathroom door. She eases into the bath and thinks only about dinner. She will keep dinner a pleasant family time with no unnecessary discussions of ranch plans. She feels sure her father would prefer to concentrate on the food in front of him; a standing rib roast of beef is one of his favorites.

The dinner goes off without a hitch. The conversation moves over national and international issues. Jeannette, a thorough reader of the newspaper, speaks up on several issues of the day.

WHEN THE TABLE was cleared, and the anticipation of one of Charlotte's famous cakes (made by Jeannette, in this case) hung in the air, Connie sat back waiting. If the subject was going to come up, it would be now.

Her father, at the end of the table, and to her left, cleared his throat. He looked down the table at E.B. "I was gratified to see that overflowing tubful of water this afternoon, E.B. It must give you a great sense of satisfaction to know that your judgment has been vindicated."

E.B. straightened in his chair and pushed it out a few inches from the table. "You bet I was mighty happy to hear that good news," he said. He placed his hands flat in front of him and looked straight down toward his father-in-law. "The folks left because of the drought. Now I'm looking for drought relief. It only seems right. After seven lean years, as it says in the Bible, came seven fat ones."

"Connie and I had a Cook's tour of the place, didn't we, Connie," her father continued. He looked over at her.

She felt many pairs of eyes beamed in her direction. She knew she shouldn't lose a chance to speak her mind with her parents there as allies. She hoped that taking a stand against E.B.'s private plan surrounded by her family would be easier than it would be alone, behind closed doors. If this was treason, she would be punished soon enough.

"E.B., I had time this afternoon to give this plan a lot of serious thought," she said. She spoke deliberately, taking time to breathe as normally as possible. "I don't think it's something I can do." She paused briefly, looking down at her hands clasped in her lap. Then she looked up and steadied her gaze on him.

The faces of everyone around the table disappeared. She and E.B. were alone, seated at a long table, and this was the moment in her life as a married woman when she must speak the thoughts that were in her mind. She must not tailor them to E.B.'s wishes.

"I feel we haven't examined all the possible pitfalls," she went on. "We must think of what it would mean to live so far from doctors and neighbors and schools. We can't simply ignore Mary Belle's asthma or the baby's hernia." She paused, forcing herself to keep her voice even and low. "Life on a ranch is hard, E.B., and I don't think I'm up to it."

E.B. cleared his throat with the familiar, deep, two-toned sound – an up note followed by a downward, very deep basso. He spoke calmly but she knew there was anger right inside his mild words.

"Now Connie, this is surely not the time to discuss all the merits and possible demerits of life out on the range. I thought we had been over them a number of times."

She was already nodding. "Perhaps we have," she said. This was too hard. "Let's get the cake." But if they had been over this, she must have been asleep. All she remembered were announcements – bulletins, she called them to herself – from E.B. "I'm having the ranch surveyed today.... The bank is doing an inventory of farm equipment and the contents of the house. . . . Tomorrow I'm interviewing a man who might be willing to work as a head wrangler for us." She had never felt strong enough, throughout her long recuperation, to take a definite stand in opposition to E.B.'s ranch dreams. And for a long time that was all she thought the ranch talk amounted to – some hopes and dreams, but never concrete enough to make her examine her true feelings about such a drastic move.

All this was in her mind as she picked up her bell and summoned the maid. What was taking that angel-food cake so long to make its appearance? Thankfully E.B. hadn't exploded into irrational anger. She didn't look forward to the bedtime hour. But she wasn't going to think about that now. Time to enjoy the cake. Soon, she hoped and prayed.

"Father Harris," E.B. was saying, "I hope you don't think this is a harebrained scheme on my part. Ranching is something I believe I spoke to you about before we left for these parts."

"Why yes, E.B., you and I did have a conversation on this subject, but I'll be confounded if I can remember you talking about you and Connie making it your life. Did I miss something?"

Silence stretched taut around the table. He looked long at E.B. And then the cake appeared. Connie saw it at the same time as her father did, emerging from behind the swinging pantry door. He turned, then everyone turned to watch the white, fluffy perfection of Charlotte's masterpiece. The showdown was over.

After dinner the family gathered in the living room and the nurse came in with the baby.

All rational discussion was dropped as baby Dwight was brought into the family group. He was now solid enough to be passed around the circle of admiring relatives. Each in turn made the usual silly sounds and faces to show their doting approval. Connie watched happily as her father took his tiny grandson in his hands and spoke directly to him.

"And this very next summer," he said, "I'm planning to give you your first swimming lesson in Schroon Lake."

Everyone applauded.

E.B.'s voice broke the spell.

He used his jovial tone.

"Father Harris, I think that's about the time I'll be getting Dwight into the saddle, out on the ranch."

Connie couldn't believe he would do this. Hadn't he heard her direct, straightforward statement?

Several voices competed; questions were fired. The girls were thrilled; Jeannette was skeptical. Connie's gentle mother wondered aloud, "Do you really want to live where your children will be threatened by rattlesnakes and poisonous spiders?" It was as if no one had heard her firm words, not even her own mother; as if she hadn't spoken.

She tried to stay calm, spoke carefully of what a challenge it would be for anyone to get this property back into a working ranch. "I'm not up to it," she said again. Did anyone hear her words?

Then she spoke directly to her mother. The answer she gave was factual. Her reasons went far deeper than any things that crept or crawled on their bellies. She would not bring her children up in isolation, not only from other children but also from her own family. As she spoke, she was praying to find a way to shift the conversation away from the ranch, to make it more general and lighthearted. She knew she would have to face E.B. soon.

The baby got tired and broke into loud howls and Juanita came to whisk him away. Jeannette took the girls off to bed. The radio was turned on for an evening news broadcast.

CONNIE SPENT some time rocking and crooning to the baby, giving him his final bottle of the day. She was gathering her strength, and trying to reformulate her argument before she and E.B. were alone behind closed doors. This day couldn't go by without her taking an absolutely firm stand. She would not let him beat back her objections. If she said nothing more tonight, it would give consent to all his ranch dreams.

And why not try it?

Why not? Because, she suddenly saw, she didn't want to live far from others with only E.B., remote as he was, her only real adult companion. She would be too completely alone. She refused; she would not do it.

She slipped into bed before he came upstairs. Soon enough, the door to the bedroom opened silently and a wide shaft of light slid in, E.B.'s shadow outlined in its path. Then the light was gone, his presence abroad in their room. No one could move as silently as E.B. She lay rigid on her side, telling herself, "Sit up, now, and face this. He has never discussed life on a ranch and it must be my decision too." She would barely allow herself to think, "And it's my money too." That would be an unthinkable and unforgivable thing for her to say, a slap at his manhood.

She tried to breathe evenly to calm her rising panic as she rolled to a sitting position. She turned on the light.

"Why Connie, I thought you were sound asleep." He turned to her from the opposite side of the room, where he had been silently undressing near an easy chair.

"E.B., I feel I'm being railroaded into something," she said, with more of an edge to her voice than she had intended.

"I've been speaking about this for so many months," he said in his methodical way. "I was sure it was clear to anyone who was within the sound of my voice."

"But I thought it was all something you were just thinking about but not – not a serious intention. I certainly didn't think you'd pick out an actual place, a ranch you knew nothing about, and start spending money on—"

"I've made it perfectly clear, from the beginning, that I had a great desire to live on the land," he said. He had gone on with his undressing and she heard the sound of his cufflinks going into their leather box. "Didn't you say you'd like to live on a farm?" He didn't wait for her to answer. "I think it's unfair of you, Connie, to say I haven't discussed this with you and with the girls. You know they're keen on it." He doled out the words evenly, as if he were teaching a young child a Bible lesson, wanting to stress its importance to living one's life here on earth so as to lead, ultimately, to one's heavenly reward.

Try as she might, she couldn't stay quiet, even though that was the only way to get through to him. Her breath came faster and faster, her thoughts scattered about her. "But it's such a serious move and what do we know—"

"I would never enter into something I knew nothing about," he said sternly. "You ought to know me better than that. I've talked to a number of people about this particular ranch. I've traveled the countryside seeking out the most ideal setup with the best possible prospects. How can you think I would enter into such an agreement irresponsibly?"

She had to interrupt, she had to jump in or she would find herself cajoled into agreeing that yes, of course he was responsible and thorough and careful and he would then draw the inference that yes, she would agree to the plan to buy this ranch and move there, when it was absolutely the wrong thing, to her; it was the worst future she could contemplate.

"But when did you ever discuss this seriously with me?" she persisted. "When did you make it clear that you were making decisions, decisions that involved my money – our money?"

He was standing facing her, looking at her with those steel-blue eyes, his face reflecting nothing of what he was feeling. What was he feeling? He was methodically buttoning up an old batiste white business shirt, a shirt too good to throw away, as he said, and he wore it as a pajama top. The way he kept slowly and steadily buttoning those buttons, looking at her with a somewhat pitying, look made her want to scream.

[111]

What could he be thinking? He was like a robot, not showing any emotion but driving her to confusion and distress and rage at his cold control. Was he enraged with her? His words were deadly calm, packed with venom, but anyone overhearing them would have thought she was the shrew. But shouldn't this major issue of where, of how they were going to live have been something for the two of them to discuss before he actually did anything legally binding? And as much as she hated to think this ugly thought, there it was, he had done this with her money, her inheritance, which she had lovingly and willingly turned over to him to manage as if it were an inheritance strictly for his governance. It wasn't right.

But he wouldn't listen. She began to weep.

"Oh, Connie," he said, and then he turned, the two words hanging in the air making her feel like an impossible child who was too willful, too obtuse to listen to reason. He walked slowly away from her toward the door. He opened the door, again without a sound, and just as silently closed it behind him.

She turned off the light and moved herself to the far side of the bed facing away from the door, but she knew he wouldn't come in again tonight. She told herself, "I am alone. I must learn to be alone. I can't tell him anything. I will not move to that ranch." And finally, she forced herself to say it, to whisper it out into the darkened room: "I will not buy that ranch."

Dawn. E.B. stepped over the threshold into the bedroom scrubbing his head vigorously with a towel. His hair spiked out in all directions giving him a wild look. He slung the towel over his shoulder as he advanced into the room to stand over her.

"Here is where I intend to stay," he said, voice low and intense. "You gave your word."

She sat up in bed, looked up at him. She remained silent.

He turned and reached up to grab the towel draped over his shoulder. He moved it back and forth across his back, then with one smooth movement he pulled it in front of him, balled it up, and flung it against the door to their dressing room. The door banged hard against the wall.

Connie jumped. She pushed back the bedclothes and got herself out of the bed. She went over and picked up the damp towel, and then turned to face him.

"I gave my word that I would try living in Texas," she said. She was careful to speak slowly and softly. "And I am trying. All right." She looked him in the eye, and the rest of what she had to say came out in a rush. "But I'm not agreeing to stay here forever, and I never said I would in the first place."

He moved toward her as if he meant to walk through her to get into the dressing room. She saw his cold eyes. She moved out of his path, watched him stand in front of the closet pulling out underwear, socks, a clean shirt, a suit, tie, shoes – methodically, as if he were an automaton, no sign that anyone else was within miles.

"I spoke to a woman I met at the Junior League," she said. "She was quite friendly. She told me Weezie can start at kindergarten in another year. E.B., you see I'm trying to make plans. I just don't want to say I'll stay forever."

He bent and tied his shoes, stood up, buckled his belt, grabbed his hairbrushes and sleeked down his hair on both sides simultaneously. She had seen him do all this thousands of times, but she had never seen how closed his system was, how mechanical his actions were. He put on his shirt, tied his tie to his satisfaction, picked up change, a pen, bills, checkbook, finally his father's watch. Each item found its way to its appropriate pocket.

"I'll be late for my office and I need some breakfast," he said, and he was out the door.

EVERY TIME I write about my mother, Daddy sounds brutal. But she never spoke of him that way. When I try to see how it would have been for her, I think she didn't understand him, couldn't reach him. I know she could be annoying. Sometimes she seemed almost dense with him for moments at a time, as though she must be doing it on purpose.

What if I look at him, not through her, but from what I know?

AT THE BACK DOOR he takes a deep breath of the fragrant air. The eastern sky is turning rosy; the air is still cool. It fills his lungs and his spirit with hope. He takes several deep breaths and throws back his shoulders.

He wanted Connie to understand why he had tried to persuade her, without pushing.

He walked down the back steps wishing he could have said more to her. If he could tell her why he had hoped to establish a life here in Texas, it would be so simple. Nothing was ever simple. He was thankful she'd had the strength the day before to see the results of his faith in that ranch property. It gave him a deep satisfaction imagining Father Harris seeing with his own eyes the vindication of his judgment. He had wanted it to be a surprise. He knew his father-in-law thought he was a fool sometimes.

He moved silently down the steps and around the house toward the street. He just had time for a brisk walk.

He knew the number of strides from the front walk to the first corner. He turned and increased his pace. He wanted to be back in plenty of time to greet his father-in-law's first appearance of the day. Father H. delighted in telling his guests at the lake what he had accomplished while they were still abed, getting a night's refreshing sleep in the pure mountain air. Satisfaction came over E.B. as he remembered early morning encounters with the old man, when he himself had been first at the lake, already getting the fishing launch ready when his father-in-law got there; the first one to arrive at the appointed picnic spot because he followed his instinct and not Father H.'s elaborate directions; the first one to hold places for the family group at Vesper services. Small satisfactions but nevertheless counting as good marks from a firm taskmaster.

If it hadn't been for Connie's complications with the birth of little Dwight, E.B. would have insisted her parents postpone their visit till the spring. Connie would have been fully herself again and the baby would have been more of a little person. E.B. couldn't help bristling as he thought of his father-in-law's comment, "Well, by next spring he'll be more up-and-coming." But Connie had wanted so very much to see her parents after she had been so sick, he had given in. If they could only have been settled on that ranch by the time her parents came.

He had tried to help her accept ranch life, had taken her and the children on drives, cultivated some couples who lived on ranches, people she seemed to enjoy. He had counted on her spirit of adventure; in all the years he had known her she had always been ready for anything. And he had tried to stress how much he wanted to make a new start. Hadn't she heard him?

As he headed onto the home stretch, walking east now, he felt the early sun on his face. The warmth was welcome. The sky stretched overhead, a huge deep blue Texas sky.

He took the back steps two at a time. As he reached the porch, he saw his father-in-law inside spooning oatmeal into his mouth. He pushed the door wide open.

"Top of the morning to you, sir, as Joe would say." E.B. made his greeting as full of enthusiasm as he could to dispel whatever tensions might still linger from the evening before. He tried to imagine what it might be like to have fears for either of his own daughters' lives. Maya's asthma was no better in the Texas air. And Connie – he knew he didn't want her worn down the way some of these hard-driven ranch women looked after only a few years.

Father Harris extended his hand. "Well, my boy, may I serve you some of your sister's excellent porridge? I'm going back for a second helping."

"I hope you and Mother Harris slept well," E.B. said, shaking the small, well-kept hand.

"Like tops," the old man said. He turned to concentrate on pouring thick cream over his oatmeal. "Now E.B., I don't believe in standing on ceremony. I'm digging right in while it's hot."

E.B. brought his own bowlful of oatmeal to the table. The two of them ate in silence for several minutes. Father Harris was the first to push his empty bowl away from him.

"By George, I like sitting in the kitchen for breakfast but Mother does like to be waited on. Now, I've got the floor and I want to propose a little something to you." Sitting back in his wooden kitchen chair, he clasped his hands and rested them on top of his paunch, covered by his beige linen vest.

"I'm getting to the age where I want to make a few plans," he said. "I want to know that things will be taken care of in a proper manner when I'm gone, without any more interference from our friends in

Washington than necessary." He reached over to a large oak-bark folder lying on the table, took out a smaller folder with E.B.'s and Connie's names written on it, and laid it in the middle of the table facing E.B.

"Looky here, E.B." With his thumb he flicked open the cover. Inside was a typewritten sheet with all the words written in capital letters: DIVISION OF THE SCHROON LAKE PROPERTY (HEREIN REFERRED TO AS "ALMANOLE") OF ARTHUR M. HARRIS AND MARY ALMA HARRIS.

E.B. took in the first page at a glance. Before he could say anything, his father-in-law was speaking again, explaining that he had had the papers drawn up by his lawyer a couple of months ago. Before he did that he had had a first-rate surveyor come to survey the property lines and check the deeds against the records in Albany so there would be no question as to what was his and what wasn't. "I don't want somebody trying to pull the wool over anybody's eyes," he said. "Not that you'd let that happen," he added. "But I don't think some people are as careful about dotting their i's and crossing their t's as you or I might be."

E.B. glanced quickly at him, gratified by this last statement. He felt certain that Father Harris regretted not having known about a number of chancy business transactions entered into by his own son in the past. But he said nothing, waiting for the older man to continue.

"It would give me a lot of pleasure if I could turn over to you – and to Connie too, of course – a sizable chunk of the Almanole property. But I'm coming to you first, E.B., because it's for the head of the household to make that decision. It's a man's decision."

E.B. took a deep breath and expelled it. He pushed himself away from the table a few inches and placed his hands on either side of his empty cereal bowl. He looked into his father-in-law's dark brown eyes. They were very nearly the color of his darling Connie's eyes. For a fleeting second he wondered if her father had said anything at all to her about this plan. But no, she would never have been able to keep such a secret from him.

He thought he had been caught. Somehow he began to speak. "Father Harris," he said, too loudly. He adjusted his tone. "I believe you were a witness last night to a deep difference between Connie and myself about our lives continuing here in Texas. You knew when we made the plan to move down here, I had every intention of staying, of making this our permanent home and of setting myself up here in business. It seemed to me I could make a fresh start in this part of the world and I also had some pretty definite ideas about wanting to try ranching." He hesitated, but then continued. "I guess it must seem clear to you also after last night I don't think Connie and I ever realized we weren't seeing eye to eye on this move."

He paused.

"Anyone'd have to be blind as a bat not to have noticed," Father Harris declared. "But had you and Connie not talked about this scheme of yours?"

"I think Connie's idea was we'd try it down here. We both felt it could be the solution to Mary Belle's asthma. We were wrong. I felt I had made it clear to Connie that I meant this move to be permanent. She doesn't think so. I'm bitterly disappointed." He stopped himself before he said something he might regret.

His father-in-law met his eyes and kept him for a long moment, probably sizing him up. "I hope you realize I'm giving property to each one of my children," he finally said. "My lawyer says that to be legally binding, I must sell the place to each of you. So I'm going to do just that." He would sell each of the three shares for one dollar, he explained. E.B. and Connie's share was to be the entire working farm. He would sign over the deed for the property to the two of them. "I beg you to give up this dream of becoming a rancher," he said. "I think it'd kill Connie." He sat back, took another long look at E.B., and added, "I wanted you to hear about this first. It's your decision. I promise not to mention it to Connie."

My decision, indeed. E.B. wanted to laugh with scorn in his father-in-law's face. He had a nerve, using his property and Connie's great love of the Adirondacks to lure her back there. And what of my dream, he thought. He couldn't get over the feeling that he had been abandoned. Connie had never gone against him before in fifteen years. Why had she chosen now, when he might really have made something of himself living on the range, raising cattle and horses; he would have an income from the livestock, and he had planned to open his own investment company in San Antonio. Others had done it. He had thought she was with him. Why had she led him on?

He crushed his napkin in his fist. He wanted to shove his father-in-law's offer down his throat, tell him to get the hell out of his house and go back to his grapefruit trees in Florida – another house, with the croquet court and the goldfish swimming in that muddy pond under the fancy wrought-iron bridge. He hated that place, the place of a rich dilettante who had never had to do a hard day's labor in his life. Everything had come easily for the old man. His own bank had practically been handed to him on a silver platter, all the connections made by his grandfather, nothing to do but tie up the strings.

Then he thought of Connie, and he saw that she had tried to go along with his scheme. She had moved down here, far gone in an already troubling pregnancy. She had never complained.

E.B. came back to himself, suddenly aware of his father-in-law's gaze – those dark eyes, their pupils magnified by his glasses. He was expecting an answer. Now.

He extended his hand across the table. He wanted to say, "You and I both know I can't make the final decision. It's up to Connie, no matter how you try to sugarcoat it. You've got me." Instead, he swallowed and said, "Sir, I think it might be a solution. We'll have to discuss it after Connie's up and about. It's a very generous offer and I don't know quite what to say."

He'd be damned if he'd eat out of the old man's hand. But he kept his feelings in check. When he and Father Harris had shaken hands, he stood up and headed for the door. He had to get back outdoors. "I've got to get myself over to my office," he said over his shoulder. He was out the door, almost running for the garage.

MY FATHER used my mother's health as the excuse for her reluctance to stay in Texas and live on the ranch. She was just not up to it and he couldn't let her take on such a difficult challenge. This gave him a face-saving way of accepting his father-in-law's gift.

My grandfather offered the train tickets for my mother and us children and Jeannette – the best accommodations – and my father accepted. It was decided we had better not move until Maya had finished the school year, and this would give my father a chance to wind up his affairs.

Once they had all shaken hands on it my grandfather said, "All right! That's done!" and he and my grandmother headed for Florida, maybe the very next day.

E.B. didn't mention the ranch again. But it must have rankled, because Mother told me that for the rest of his life he would throw it up to her every now and then, when he was feeling cornered.

I feel it's very important to get across that these two men, E.B. and my grandfather, never could understand each other. It was as if they were speaking a different language. And it was very much like that between E.B. and Connie, too. Connie was most definitely her father's daughter. My guess is that she was much more direct back when she first met E.B., and it was living with him that made her temper her directness by thinking before she spoke. It became a deeply ingrained habit.

My mother said to me many times over the years how direct her father was; he didn't beat around the bush, as she phrased it, while E.B. (and all his family) seemed to put everything indirectly, surrounding the simplest kinds of statements in a haze of verbiage.

It was living with E.B. (and eventually his sisters) that turned Mother into such a soft-speaking, walking-on-eggs diplomat, a role I came to see she learned to play to survive.

Eight

D<small>WIGHT WROTE:</small>

> I remember one time that he was kind of kidding around with me. I was seven years old or so. He seemed to be in a good mood. I remember feeling happy and actually enjoying being with him. I wanted to do something with him and I thought it would please him if I offered to do some of the work that always needed to be done – splitting wood, piling wood, whatever. So I said to him, "Shouldn't we get busy with some of the work that needs to be done?"
>
> We were by the sideboard in the living room. He turned and strode quickly away without a word, stormed out the front door, slammed the screen door behind him, opened the gate, slammed it shut behind him, crossed the road to the driveway that led to the barn, opened the door of the '42 Ford, got into the car, slammed the door, and sat there in the driver's seat.
>
> I was very upset by his behavior and felt guilty that I had made him angry. I left the house through the back porch, went out the Almanole driveway, and crossed the road by Aunt Rae's house when I thought he wasn't looking in that direction. I went straight out through the field behind Aunt Rae's house until I was about even with the barn and then went over to the barn driveway and crept up behind the car so he wouldn't see me. I was trying to sneak up on him and surprise him, hoping that I could get him back into a happy mood. As I came up to the back of the car and crossed to the side, I heard his voice growl out, "I see ya." I knew then that I had better leave him alone. I remember nothing more of the incident.

D<small>WIGHT AND</small> I did all right, working and sometimes talking.

We found we had to vary our work locations to keep ourselves going. Too gloomy to work in the house for too long a stretch. We decided to do mornings inside, then after lunch, move to the outbuildings.

Mother's ashes waited on the piano. I felt she was cheering us on as we plunged into our rooting and sorting and throwing. Dwight argued with me. He felt she was keeping track of our every move on a scorecard, giving gold stars when we eliminated a certain quota of accumulated stuff, pursing her lips disapprovingly – no stars – if we slacked.

When I tried to talk to him about the early days, before he was born, he wouldn't listen. He told me about cold mornings, watching snow fill the north window of his bedroom. We were sitting on the front porch, pushing the old swing back and forth while the sun slid down behind the black pines beyond the barn. The end of a long day.

He got up to close the iron gate, between square stone pillars built by Grandpa. "I hated to see you go out that gate and get on the school bus," he said, sitting back down next to me. The swing creaked.

"Too bad there was no kindergarten back then."

"I thought of the bus as a monster, swallowing you and Maya. I was scared every day you wouldn't be back."

I had never thought of him like that. At least I didn't remember it. I was only thinking about the bus ride, with Antzie, and then school. Dwight tagged after me for years.

"I thought if I kept watching the bus it'd be okay," he said. "So I'd run upstairs and watch till it disappeared, into the snow."

"Didn't you do things with Mother?"

He nodded. "But she worried a lot – about Daddy, Maya's asthma, your ears. Money, too."

"She talked to you about those things? You were only a little kid." She had talked to me of her worries, but I never thought of her saying such things to Dwight, for some reason. He seemed to be in his own world, right from the beginning. "What did you do all day with no other little kids around, two miles from town?"

"I hid from the aunts, had a million places. They never could find me."

I remembered them hovering, scolding, warning of a watchful God who knew my naughty thoughts, saw my deeds, heard every cross word.

Dwight gave a push to the swing. "I thought they were stepmothers who might stuff me in the oven if I wasn't good," he said. "Weren't you scared of them?"

I wasn't scared of them. But I know Aunt Charlotte got crankier once she was living in the house at Schroon. "She must have been so lonely, Walter gone, no more Spring Lake friends," I said mildly. In fact, this only hit me now, as an adult, and I hated to hear Dwight's harsh way of talking about them.

He looked down at his hands, cracked his knuckles one by one. "I hated Aunt Charlotte," he said. "She rapped me on the head with her knuckles. *Tst tst tst*," he mimicked, rapping my head hard enough to hurt.

I pushed him away. He looked mean, as if Aunt Charlotte was about to loom out of the twilight at him.

"And she spit, too," he went on. He was laughing as he warmed to the subject. "The worst. Aunt Netsie was okay but she nagged. On and on about 'your poor dear mother'."

"Poor Dwight." I reached over and hugged him. "Sorry I wasn't a better older sister." I meant it. I hadn't looked after him, hadn't even paid attention to him in those days unless I felt like it. He was conveniently there to play with me. And now? But he seemed only to remember me fondly.

"Water over the dam, Sis." He waved his hand, still chuckling. "Remember when I broke all your Crayolas in half? I thought you'd kill me."

"Yeah. I got back by smashing your balsa-wood model Spitfire." I remembered the two incidents distinctly. "That was awful of me, Dewey." The baby nickname came to my tongue and I let it slip out. I used to call him Dewey for years till finally he twisted my arm back on the dance floor in a dive one night between songs and beers. "I'll break it next time," he muttered.

Now he gave me a look.

"Sorry," I quickly said, but he was mugging.

"Funny how a discarded nickname can come back as an old friend," he said. "I guess I feel you as an ally."

"Should I remind you of the horrible years?"

"Not if you're going to tell me how horrible I was."

I wasn't thinking about him; I was thinking about how mean I had been.

The little boy nipping at my heels made me only that much more determined to occupy the catbird seat. I was canny enough to play hard-to-get with Maya, who was needy; kept her at arm's length. She was always generous and loving but also somewhat smothering.

I was able to make Dwight my close buddy and pal, my companion in crime when I wanted him as a playmate, but then I could be equally hardhearted and ignore him completely. This would happen especially after I'd gotten some game going and then lost interest or decided I'd rather go off and read a book or play with Antzie or, later, Elisabeth.

As an aside: they said this about Aunt Charlotte, too. Mother once told me. Charlotte was known for making big plans for an outing of some sort, a picnic or a drive to the country (horse and buggy) to visit a sweet old relative, take her a pie or something or other, then after she'd gotten Henrietta and Pearl all excited about the outing, she would suddenly drop the plan, say, I've got a headache − or maybe simply, I don't want to do that now, and the others would be left to go by themselves, or drop the whole thing.

I'VE BEEN THINKING about Dwight, and about how our early relationship translated itself into the adult one, in which Dwight is always ready to lay blame and I'm always trying to explain, to make him understand. I always thought I felt guilty toward him, as if I got a better deal than he did, growing up. But now it seems to me that guilt isn't the whole story; there's also a deeply ingrained belief that he could have figured out how to make things better for himself, as I did from an early age. Why wouldn't he protect himself? Even now, knowing so much more, I can sense my irritation that he's still unable to get over something I can't help feeling he could have made different for himself.

I figured out somehow or other, maybe by instinct, how to get along in my family, and I found a way to be someone, within the family. Not that I wasn't rebellious, but from a very young age I struggled to make a person of myself, and to get my father's approval − not by being nice, or being sweet, but by being the kind of child he would have wanted. This could be seen as a negative, but I think of it positively. I think I did my darnedest to be everything I could, to be what I felt my father wanted. I know I played a role for him, tried hard to please him.

He and I related to each other in a big way, for good and for ill. Maya wasn't part of anything. She was always in her own little world.

I have strong memories of loving Dwight, when he was small. I remember it as a fierce kind of love. I wanted to hug him, smell his furry boy smell, but he was not one for much cuddling. He was like quicksilver. He was a small, tough, wiry kid who could run fast, loved to build things, and was full of ideas and imagination.

IN THE MIDDLE of a sentence Dwight walked away into the living room, put his hands on the box that had the urn inside it, and said, "It's time, Sis. Doesn't matter what kind of day it is."

I had wanted a perfect Adirondack day for doing the ashes. Oh don't, I wanted to say. He handled the box as if he were going to toss it. I was standing in the doorway, and I waited. I don't know why. You can't have her, I wanted to say. But he did have her, and she was his, too, whether I liked it or not.

"Mother's disapproving ashes," I said, thinking I was making a joke, and maybe I could get him to put them back. But it came out of me sounding harsh, which threw me off. "Why can't you just–"

"Get rid of all this," he insisted, indicating the rooms around us. "That's the best way to please Mother."

That irritated me.

"You've said for years that you didn't care about pleasing her," I said.

He put down the box, kept his hands on it as if he could feel vibrations from inside.

"I gave up trying," he said. "I realized it wasn't possible."

I looked at him carefully. He looked so sure of himself. I wanted to ask, why are you bitter, this late in life? I shortened it to, "Why?"

"Because she never listened to what I wanted. She–" He stopped himself, and continued in a different tone, less quick with anger. "A few years ago I had to come east on business and I thought of renting a plane and making the few stops I had to make and then flying on to see Mother here. I decided, for various reasons, not to rent the plane, and I flew commercial. During the visit with Mother I mentioned the plan that hadn't happened and her response was, 'Oh, I'm so glad you didn't do that.' That was one of the few times, actually I think the only time, I ever shouted at her. I pretty much exploded."

It was true. Dwight never yelled at Mother. He used to walk away. She would be talking to him and he would already be sidling off. "What did you shout?" I asked. I couldn't imagine shouting at her myself.

"I shouted, 'Why would you say that when you know how much I love to fly?' "

"You think she really understood, about you and flying?"

"Sis, wake up. Everybody who's ever known me has known that much."

"I know. That's not what I mean," I managed to say. This was unknown territory between us, and I wasn't sure where it might lead us. "I mean, she loved you. I'm ... I mean, maybe she was jealous – afraid for you."

"Jealous," he snorted. "That's a laugh. No." He had a way of looking uncannily like Daddy sometimes, just for a second. It happened right then and I had to look away. "I think she loved someone who was her son," he said, "but it was never me." He turned and started sorting through a pile of old *National Geographic*s. The box of ashes was forgotten, for the moment anyway. "You were the only one who knew who I was," he said. "To them I was a constant source of worry and disappointment." He walked out of the room.

Why write about this, why write down every sentence and every exchange, as if there were a way to make something different or to not know what I already know?

The way I remember it, Dwight was not a cause of horrible parental worry, in the early days. What about her relationship with him, when he was little, and also when he was such a difficult adolescent. Did she defend him? Did she talk to him? When he was very little, I know she worried about him. I remember her washing the sheets and putting the mattress out to dry in the sun when he had wet the bed. I do not recall her scolding him on this count. I know he feels she didn't help him, but I know she stood up for him with the aunts, for example. She would get angry at Aunt Charlotte if Charlotte picked on him for making what she considered too much noise. I don't know how she kept her temper with the aunts sometimes, but she managed to. She often said to Charlotte, "He's got to be allowed to let off steam, to play like any other little boy."

I would be willing to bet that my mother never saved up any of either Dwight's or my misdemeanors to recount to my father when he got home. She wouldn't have done that for several reasons. I know she feared E.B.'s wrath going beyond what it should be for minor naughtiness. Also, she didn't want to add to his worries.

(I don't remember anyone ever telephoning E.B. about anything, and particularly not about something as relatively unimportant as disciplinary matters. Of course it may have happened, but we didn't call long distance for anything except conveying important messages.)

Mother didn't like having Charlotte or Netsie putting in their two cents' worth in an issue having to do with us children. She bristled if they criticized us, even if we were in the wrong. She never ganged up with the aunts against us. I have a feeling she was more lenient and forgiving toward all of us – maybe especially toward Dwight, before adolescence set in – because those two women would butt in and scold us, or say something like, How can you worry your Poor Dear Mother? with very long, sober, disapproving faces. This phrase infuriated Mother, but she held her tongue, didn't blurt out, Mind your own business. She would bustle around in the kitchen, maybe slam a pot or two louder than normal. On rare occasions, she stamped her foot, or she might say in a voice slightly louder than normal, Why doesn't she pipe down? after Charlotte or Jeannette had gone out of the room.

There were no overt fights ever that I can remember, only that crackling electrical tension, like the way the air feels when there's about to be a humdinger of a thunderstorm. Full of threat. People muttered under their breath, looked daggers; Charlotte would flounce off to her room, with a parting shot over her shoulder, I remember.

By the time Dwight began to be a serious worry, I was off in boarding school and wanted nothing to do with him. He had turned into a hick, as far as I was concerned. He even talked like the kids in Schroon, pronouncing his name as if it were spelled Dwoight. There was no other kid named Dwight in the entire Adirondacks. He hated his name, and called himself Tex when he started playing guitar.

There was a running conflict between me and Dwight. I did try to bite off his thumb, after all. Mother tended to side with him when she felt he would be subject to too much anger from me. I was so much bigger, stronger, faster, more cagey for so long. I knew this, and I confess it made me meaner.

I remember an incident from when I was ten or eleven. I was at the piano, laboriously reading my way through a Mozart sonata. Every now and then, Mother's voice would come down the stairwell with corrections. "That's a whole note. You must count" or "That should be an F-sharp. Look at your signature" or "Don't play it up to tempo unless you can play all of it that way."

The sound of a slammed door in the direction of the kitchen, running footsteps, Dwight appeared, a small boy, six or seven. He ran into the room, his coat open, his arctics covered with snow that dropped away in lumps leaving wet puddles. Aunt Jeannette called after him from the kitchen, "You know you're to take off your boots on the porch. Don't let your dear mother come down and find that mess." She came in with a string mop and blotted up the puddles.

Dwight ignored her. "You said you'd play with me and you snuck off," he said to me. I went on pounding out the Mozart. He was very angry. I was playing to drown him out.

He pulled off his coat with a force that swung it in my direction and I felt it brush my arm. I continued to ignore him. This infuriated him more and I was glad.

"I want a turn at the piano," he said. "You always hog it and say you're practicing. It's my turn now." He slid onto the edge of the bench and played a rapid, accurate version of Chopsticks, pounding as loud as he could.

I slid over to his end of the bench and shoved him over the edge. He was caught unawares, and fell heavily onto the floor. I laughed at him, and quickly slid back to the middle of the seat and continued playing, this time slowing my tempo to a funereal pace, so I wouldn't make mistakes. And it would take longer to play.

Dwight bellowed in the direction of the stairs. "Weezie ran and hid on me and now she's hogging the piano. It's my turn to practice."

"Can't you two get along?" Mother actually yelled at us. "Stop fighting. Let me have one bath in peace."

Neither of us paid any attention. Dwight was back on the bench, trying to play his fast-paced Chopsticks; I was elbowing him with my right arm, trying to poke him far enough away so he couldn't reach the keyboard, and maybe hurt him while I was at it. With my other hand I continued the piece, concentrating hard on playing it up to tempo without a mistake and as loud as I could.

"That's more like it," Mother called down.

That was too much for Dwight. He picked up his snowy jacket and flung it on top of my playing hands. Instantly I hurled the jacket as far away as I could, and at the same time, I yelled at the top of my lungs, "Mother, Dwight's ruining your piano. He put his wet jacket on the keys."

"She's lying," he shouted. "I put it on her hands and she let it fall on the keys. She won't let me have a turn." He braced himself on the bench.

"All right, baby," I said in my meanest singsong. "Have your way," and I started to get up, my head lifted, with a bored, superior air.

In a flash, he pushed his face against my chest and bit me as hard as he could. He got me right next to my left nipple. I screamed, and we both pushed away from the piano at the same time, tipping over the bench and spilling music all over the floor.

Mother appeared, dripping, a towel held tightly to her.

"What's the matter with you two?" she shouted in the angriest voice I can remember her ever using, before or since. "You're both at fault." She turned to me. "You won't leave him alone, and Dwight, you should be ashamed of yourself, biting your sister. Get upstairs. Both of you. I could paddle you both."

Dwight ran howling past her and out the door, coatless. I lifted my blouse and found a crescent-shaped mark, tiny blood droplets beginning to ooze from the flesh of my budding breast. She pulled me upstairs to the bathroom, and cleaned the blood away with S.T. 37, silent and still angry. Then she sent me to my room.

I THINK Dwight wanted to grow away from his family as fast as he could. He was always quoting what his friends' fathers had to say about everything and he would purposely speak in the local idiom when he did this. He gradually grew more and more attached to the local kids. He told me while we were cleaning out the house that he was certain Mother and Daddy's criticisms of him were based on their being disappointed by him. The way he sees it, they were harder and harder on him because of this. They saw the gap widening as the years went along. The sad thing is that Dwight wouldn't have had any friends if he had looked for kids my parents would have approved of. There was no one of the so-called right type for Dwight in Schroon.

Dwight says our father's criticism of him was always there – in looks of severe disapproval, a tightening of the lips, an abrupt remark that would come out as contempt or scorn. Nothing, Dwight says, was ever good enough from this son of his. And there were explosions. Rage. Once, Dwight told me, when our father had allowed him to use his expensive fishing rod and complicated reel, he got it hopelessly tangled. He was only about five or six – too young for an adult piece of sporting equipment. I would be willing to bet that Daddy had not had the patience to show him how it should be used. Dwight learned early in his life to avoid E.B., to be skittish and nervous in his presence.

Mother's championing of Dwight didn't extend into his older boy and adolescent years. She began to have less and less sympathy with him as he moved from his little boy friendships into ever tighter bonds with the kids whose fathers worked on the road, cut trees for timbering, did odd jobs, drove the snowplow or the school bus. And she detested his country music. I remember her harping on the superior quality of classical music, the importance of education, manners, and especially what she referred to as breeding – a word that was anathema to Dwight (and also to Maya).

Dwight was a very bright kid. He lived up to our parents' hopes and dreams to about age twelve and then everything reversed gear.

His speech copied the local North Country twang; his grades slithered downward. They sent him to Exeter and he ran away after four weeks, came straight home, spoke of all the kids as snobs. And he was overwhelmed by the work. They didn't make him go back.

In Schroon his guitar got him access to older guys who also played, and who fooled around with cars, girls, and beer. He was underage to play in the roadhouses, but everyone liked him and they made allowances. He was home less and less; he made contact with the family as little as possible.

I was moving into the swell circles of New England prep schools and I wanted nothing to do with Dwight and his hayseed friends.

He grew his hair long and wore it in what was known as a ducktail (the polite version of duck's ass and sometimes referred to as a D.A. – long wings of hair glued in place at the nape of the neck, and at the front swooped upward into a pompadour). Ugh! I couldn't stand my little brother at that point, and I don't think my mother could, either. And he had no use for me.

I remember a ride or two up from Glens Falls – at least an hour – when we were both in the car, at ages maybe thirteen and seventeen. Mother was nagging Dwight for the entire drive about his grades, his friends, the way he spoke, the way he dressed, his music (which was not music, to her), and on and on. As much as he annoyed me at that time, I tried to mumble something about not picking on him for the entire drive. But I felt smug.

I MADE Dwight talk to me, while we were up there going through the house. He said why talk about it, it was all so long ago, why dredge it up. I wanted him to say why he was still angry. I asked him that, point blank. I said I needed to know. It seemed like whining, and I needed to know what the problem was.

He said that talking about it would be whining; living his life wasn't whining. But I made him talk.

He said they wouldn't let him fly. They wouldn't pay for lessons. They talked him out of becoming a commercial pilot. They disapproved of his desire to fly.

He told me that in 1958 Daddy had made a trip to Seattle, where

Dwight was living, and had raised the question of what Dwight was going to do with his life. (Dwight was twenty-three, married by this time, with an adopted stepson.) He told Daddy he still hoped to become an airline pilot. Daddy told him he had had a conversation with Eddie Rickenbacker about Dwight's ambition and Rickenbacker had said he would never make it as a commercial pilot if he hadn't been a pilot during the war.

Rickenbacker was a flying ace in both world wars. He had shot down twenty-six German planes in the Second World War.

Dwight told me he later came to believe Daddy had fabricated that story to get him to give up the idea of becoming an airline pilot.

"And even if it wasn't a lie, why did he say anything? It was my life. He should have kept his mouth shut. I thought he was telling the truth. How could he have lied to me? I made the decision to abandon my dream," he said. "Now when I see those big airliners pass overhead I find myself saying to him, You fucking bastard."

The temptation in me has always been to think less of Dwight. Too dramatic. Too emotional for a grown man. I was already starting to do it, to fall into the old habit. I stopped myself. I had asked him. I was the one who wanted to hear it. He might not even want to tell it. I kept listening. He said he remembered thinking they were right when they said that wanting to become an airline pilot was silly; that he should finish college and try to become a vice-president of some corporation. From then on throughout his life, he said, the only reason he had aspired to gain promotions or obtain a better position was to increase his income. So he had mostly just stumbled through his work, never really enjoying it. It wasn't unbearable, but it was always just something he had to do to pay the bills. And he resented it.

He had never really thought about our parents' discouraging him from trying to attain his dream (he insisted on referring to it this way again and again. Never as his ambition, or as his career, always as his dream) until after he wound up buying an airplane through a long-story set of circumstances. Then when he began flying again after nineteen years away from it he realized how much of a passion he had for it. That was when his resentment toward our parents really began to eat at him.

"It pisses me off to this day."

Nineteen years. He called it a hole in his life. The way he saw it, he had gone from the teenage rebel to thinking our parents knew everything, and he had allowed them and their ambitions for him to run his life for too long a time.

"I guess it pisses me off to realize," he said, "that I didn't have the backbone to tell them way back when to kiss my ass, I would do what I wanted with my life, not what they wanted for me."

It's not Dwight's version I want to tell. The story I'm telling will be mine.

We were pitching old newspapers from Daddy's office into piles, stacking them against the wall of the front porch for the auctioneer. Soon enough the truck would drive up empty, get filled to the top, probably spilling out over the sides. I got a thrill imagining it driving away carrying everything we couldn't cope with. We'd come to that moment when we both agreed we'd had it. Printed matter had to go.

Slinging all that newsprint, I thought about the trees that had gone to make it. Something had come back to me. "Hey," I said, "remember the time the tree fell?"

"I thought maybe you'd buried that one for good," he grunted, and he banged down a pile of yellowed newspapers, slamming them onto the porch floor with such force my ears rang. "He nearly killed us."

"What a strange accident," I said. I caught a look on his face.

Dwight and I used to go with Daddy on his chopping expeditions deep in the woods. We went out one day late in the fall, with the leaves long since gone and the ground frozen solid. Because it was nearly the end of November, and would be dark at 4:30 or so, Daddy decided to use the tractor. I remember how much I liked the ride bumping along in the tractor, and I remember the skirmishes between us about holding Daddy's precious axe. We got to the cutting site and Dwight and I ran off deeper into the woods where we'd created a camouflaged fortress. Our plan was to reinforce it enough so it wouldn't collapse under winter snows. As we worked, the *chunk chunk chunk* of Daddy's chopping sounded faintly in the distance.

The afternoon passed quickly, and when it started to get dark we headed back to the chopping ground. But we must have been confused. We kept hearing chopping sounds but they seemed to be from different directions. Echoes maybe. We forged ahead: we were Allied troops trying to sneak through German lines to rescue a cut-off platoon. After a while, we pushed through some thick young firs clumped together, and came out into a somewhat cleared area.

There, not more than fifty yards from us, Daddy stood leaning back, looking straight up. At the same instant a cracking sound tore the silence. Daddy spotted us right then. His voice roared out something we couldn't understand. He was waving his arms wildly toward the left. We began to run. Within seconds the tree, an enormous pine, thundered to the ground, hitting the spot where we had come into the clearing.

I hadn't known enough to be afraid until it was all over. I lay on the hard ground, covered by the pine's small upper branches. Then Daddy was pulling back branches frantically. Neither of us was hurt, but I remember how shaken I felt, and scared.

The ride home was silent, and no one ever said a word about what had happened. I don't remember if Dwight and I ever went back into the woods on a chopping expedition. It's a blank, a hole.

I had never brought it up, had never even mentioned it later that particular day. I don't know if Mother ever knew what had happened. To me, it was too awful for Daddy; there was almost something shameful about it. I had always felt it would be unfair to tell the story. But now I wanted to know, I wanted to ask Dwight. Was he saying it hadn't been an accident? How could it not have been an accident?

"It would mean you believe Daddy meant to kill us," I said.

"Not us," he said with a scornful laugh. "Me."

"That's even more impossible. How could he aim the tree only at you?"

"You don't get it, Sis," he said, but I saw something else in his face.

I felt myself flush. "What don't I get?" I asked, not with anger. Looking at his face, I felt he was right, I felt, just for that moment, that I didn't know anything. I remembered how Daddy had held me when he found me beneath the branches, pressed his cold cheek to mine, his tears wetting my hair. I didn't remember if he had picked Dwight up or not.

Dwight was watching me. "It wasn't the only time he wanted to kill me," he said. "Let's just leave it at that, shall we?"

"But it doesn't make sense," I pleaded. "What kind of person would Daddy have to be, to want to kill his own son?"

"It's funny you never ask yourself how it was for me. You always think of it from his point of view."

"That's because your point of view is impossible. You're angry. Period. But even if I try to imagine how I would have to see things in order to see Daddy as someone who might try to kill me, I find it impossible. He adored me, I know it."

"Not you, not you," he said in a suppressed voice, though he looked as though he might have cried, right then. "It's not always about you, Lueza. He was different to me." He reached out and pinched my arm. "He adored you." He said it mockingly.

Accurate thrilling word, but that wasn't the way Dwight meant it. I felt the tears come up. "He loved us all," I said, but even I knew that wasn't the point, and Dwight ignored it. I wanted to leave, stop this conversation; but I didn't. I had gotten this far, I dared myself to go further.

"Are you sure it's not just jealousy on your part?" I asked, trying not to let it sound like a taunt.

Another scornful laugh. "Of course it was jealousy. But that wasn't it. He taught me to fear him really early in my life."

"But in some way he taught me that, too," I said, only realizing it was true as I said it. I had taken Daddy's challenge as a way of learning, of becoming a bigger person in order to win his love. Dwight had taken it as a defeat. Defeat after defeat, I now guessed. "You always seemed to want to flaunt your hatred to him," I said. "Couldn't you have tried it his way, or something?"

He slammed his hand down on the porch rail. The violence of the sound shocked me. "No!" he shouted. "No. The thing I have, and the only thing I had, was that he never had me, he never made me his."

With a groan I understood that he meant his spirit, he had never yielded his spirit. And had I? Was he saying Daddy had owned my spirit? But that wasn't the way it felt to me. Daddy was a hero to me.

I left the porch. I hated this kind of conversation. But I had asked for it. I went inside and washed the dirt off my hands and splashed my face with cold water. I dried off with the old roller towel in the kitchen. I took a lot of deep breaths and tried to calm down.

Nine

THE DAY we finally faced the ashes, we ate bacon and eggs, toast, juice, coffee for breakfast. "We don't want to fall by the wayside," I said, quoting the warning we had heard from Aunt Netsie almost every day of our childhood. We didn't leave the dishes in the sink. We didn't leave anything undone. But the time came nevertheless.

Dwight picked up the box with the urn inside it. More like a jar. Mother had no patience with the language of undertakers. No reposing of her remains. "My ashes will sit and wait till you and Dwight are good and ready," she said. "No ceremony once I'm dead and gone."

Dwight carried the solid, squarish cardboard box, with me close behind. Through the living room, past Daddy's fireplace and through the breakfast room where we had eaten so many family meals, and then into the kitchen where Mother had hurried and hustled and stoked the fire and cooked and washed up and then done more cooking and more cleaning up – the daily round of life, which she had carried off with such good cheer.

We had agreed to remove the urn from the box on the screened-in back porch, the warm-weather setting for all meals, rain or shine. Dwight set the box on the table. It was tied with a strong white cord wrapped three times around it in both directions. He untied the double bow and unwound the cord, being careful not to tilt the box. I wound the cord around my fingers, as both of us had seen Mother do so many times, and we started reciting her words at the same time: "You never know when you might need a nice piece of string." (How many of those had we already thrown out – and it hadn't been easy, that saving was so ingrained in us.)

That recitation made me feel Dwight might be willing to leave aside his bad feelings about Mother, at least for the day, and it loosened both of us up a little.

He lifted out the greyish-blue urn and set it on the table. Without hesitating, he removed the porcelain stopper from the wide mouth of the urn and set that on the table. There were Mother's ashes. Coarse greyish-white dust.

"Okay, I'll carry the urn," he said, and he picked it up and stepped back from the table. "You go first so you can protect me from snapping branches."

I knew I had to be as practical as he was, or this task would become impossible. I held open the screen door and he went down the back steps and into the yard. When I caught up I led the way across the lawn and around the corner of the old greenhouse, now almost re-absorbed into the ground. We headed toward the lake.

Such a part of our childhoods – the exhilarating run down the vast sloping lawn, then the headlong tumble down the steep hill, and finally trotting down the more gradual pine-needled path that led to the shore. Now we were forced to work our way slowly through thick new undergrowth. Small firs and spindly maple, birch and beech saplings, clumps of trembling baby poplar. Underfoot, tufts of thick heavy grass, mixed with ferns and moss in the shadier places.

Maybe it looked like this when Mother and her brother Dwight blazed a trail to that beckoning lake long before Grandpa's great lawn had come into being. It would soon be a full century since Mother's small feet followed along, trying to keep up with her big brother. Dwight and I had agreed it would be most appropriate to have her ashes adding to this new growth, becoming part of next century's fresh, newborn forest.

Every now and then we stopped, no set plan, and Dwight tipped the urn and let a small amount of ash scatter from its mouth. As we got to the top of the steep hill, I saw the sun, filtering through cloud, glint in patches on the glassy surface of the lake.

At the water's edge we took off our shoes and waded out from the small beach where we used to play in the dark lake sand as children. We started to scatter ashes into the water. But the ash floated. It wasn't absorbed. It lay on the surface as though we had done wrong. We had to stir the water around to get it to disappear. Dwight went on scattering small amounts from the urn, until more solid masses began to slip out; and they sank. That was enough. We never said a word to each other; we just waded back to shore, collected our shoes, and headed up the hill.

Dwight and I had often been so at odds we could hardly agree on the time of day. Now, for this one charged moment, we were united.

The urn was lighter by half. I carried it in the crook of my arm, my other arm around Dwight's waist. He draped his arm along my shoulders and we walked with light feet back up the hill to the house. Our final duty, the digging of a small hole at the gravesite for what was left in the urn, seemed as though it would be far simpler than what we had just accomplished.

As we were eating lunch it started to rain. "Not a day for digging a hole in the ground," Dwight said, calmly finishing the last bite of his sandwich. "I'll get things going." He went out to the woodshed while I washed our few dishes and poured myself a last swallow of coffee. I stood waiting by the screen door with the mug of coffee, wishing the rain could put off this last thing, even by a day.

Dwight brought out all the necessary tools, and two ponchos, which we put on. I brought Daddy's umbrella. We drove in silence to the Schroon Lake cemetery and found our way to Daddy's grave without the exchange of more than two or three words. Dwight seemed cold and separate now and I didn't feel like trying to penetrate his mood.

We paused a minute or two looking down at the grave. The grass was thick and healthy, no hint of a mound after fifteen years' worth of seasons. Dwight selected a sharp spade to get started. I put down the urn and opened Daddy's heavy black umbrella, held it as high as I could over Dwight's head as he got to work. Four times he stabbed the earth in the middle of the plot next to Daddy's, making a square in the tough grass. He removed the square of sod and set it aside, picked up the shovel and started digging. After several minutes he was sweating.

"I can use a little rain," he said without stopping. "Forget the umbrella."

I closed the umbrella and moved back a step to give him more room.

"You don't have to go very far," I said, peering into the deepening hole. I was wishing I could take a turn.

He stopped abruptly and drove his shovel into the top of the mound of dirt as if he were irritated, but all he said was, "Mother always said she liked a rainy day." He looked over at me with a hint of a smile.

I picked up the urn, held it out to him and together we placed it gently in the open earth. I started pushing the black, damp clods of dirt down into the hole with my hands, and he joined me. There were those hands of his again, Daddy's big strong hands, breaking up the clods with me and packing the earth firmly around the cool ceramic vessel. When it was well covered, Dwight filled in the hole and tamped down the dirt with the shovel. Then he replaced the square of grassy sod, stepped on it a few times to press it into the fresh-smelling dirt, and scattered the left-over dirt. I sprinkled a few handfuls of grass seed and raked it smooth.

The rain was softer now, mist hanging low over the lake in the distance. "It's where she belongs, Dwight, next to Daddy."

"Let's not get sentimental, Sis." He picked up the tools and headed for the car.

"You're right," I said. I picked up the umbrella and the bag of grass seed and followed him. "Mother said, 'When I'm good and dead I won't care where you put me.' But she liked the idea of going into that empty plot." I threw the stuff into the trunk and Dwight slammed it shut. "Maybe Yankee thrift, too," I speculated.

He was already getting in behind the wheel. "So I'll quote Uncle Joe," he said, "have it your way," and he started the engine.

I didn't want to be sentimental but I couldn't help thinking that finally, after fifty years of estrangement in which they had stayed married to each other, my parents were side by side. I put my head back as Dwight pulled the car onto the road. I was exhausted.

Dwight headed in the opposite direction from the house. He said we needed gas. We also needed a breather. I knew we would go to the service station Mother and Daddy always used. It was out of the way, north of the village by a couple of miles, but our family had been loyal customers of Cecil's for years.

"Do you remember when Aunt Charlotte and Virginia and Nana moved in?" Dwight asked. "Mother and Daddy must have shared that bedroom before that. It was the best one."

It was the sunniest one, on the first floor, the only one our cousin

Virginia, crippled by cerebral palsy, could have used. She and her nurse, Nana, shared it; her mother, Aunt Charlotte, had the warmest bedroom, a tiny room on the other side of the downstairs bathroom, right in back of the fireplace.

"No, Dwight," I said. "Mother and Daddy never used that bedroom, it was empty till Virginia and Nana moved in." Before Aunt Charlotte came to live with us, Daddy had planned to turn that bedroom into a high-ceilinged living room, pushing the house out south and east. I had seen his sketches. "Daddy told Mother in no uncertain terms, 'I like sleeping alone. It's healthier.'"

"I guess they were never close. When did she tell you these things? Why'd you listen?"

"What was I supposed to do? I knew she didn't have anyone to talk to up here. You know small towns. Tell one person and it goes from here to Plattsburgh." We were moving slowly along Main Street, the only shopping street of the town. Soon the cluster of buildings was behind us; woods closed in again, pine trees shouldering their way to the road.

"Glad I wasn't a girl," Dwight said.

"She told me for years she couldn't talk to Daddy about anything without him freezing up or boiling over like an overheated car. I felt sorry for her."

"Let's not talk about it." He slowed the car. "Look, here's Cecil's Service Center," he hissed, just as we always loved to do when we were children – jetting spit at each other as hard as we could. "I'll treat you," Dwight said, as he pulled in between two battered trucks.

Looking like an afterthought thrown up out of odd lumber, Cecil's Bar/Cafe, run by Cecil's wife Jewel, straggled off to the side of the modern service station. Walking into that place activated memories long buried in me. I stood letting my eyes adjust to the dim light, and felt the early years all around me like Cecil's collection of road signs nailed from wall to ceiling. We had eaten there for years; it was the one place where we could get a less than well-done hamburger.

The aunts didn't approve of any meat with juice running pink so Daddy took us children to Cecil's when he could. Years before anybody had heard of golden arches or of having burgers your way Cecil was piling on lettuce, tomatoes, pickle relish, mayo, mustard, and cheese (poured like lava over the rare meat). Daddy liked the food, and he liked to go home and horrify his sisters with tales of bloody juices oozing into the bun. Guaranteed, I would be hearing terrible tales from the aunts for days after that, about children who had perished from bad meat back before the Pure Food & Drug Act.

Now, Dwight and I started at the same time to recite Cecil's sign, quoted by Daddy for years and still evident over the entrance. "Cecil's hot dogs: better than filet mignon." For some reason Daddy drew the line at hot dogs. "You never know what's in those things," he would say. We slid laughing into a booth.

Some of the men drinking draft beers at the bar looked over at us briefly. Were any of them kids we had been in school with? Did Dwight and I look as old to these men as the men did to me?

Dwight took two old snapshots out of the inside pocket of his jacket and tossed them onto the table. "Found these the other night and put them in my pocket to show you," he said. "Kept forgetting they were in there."

Our parents. The dates were written in pencil on the backs of the photos. 1918 and 1921.

1918 was a courting photo; they weren't married until 1920 – an unusually long engagement. Mother was twenty-one that summer. Her bobbed hair was marcelled, dipping slightly over one eye. She looked hesitant, happy but shy, as if the two of them were about to announce their engagement. Her matronly dress with its dropped waistline didn't detract from her girlishness.

Daddy was serious. Twenty-six that year. His mouth was straight, closed, his eyes crinkled slightly, maybe in the beginning of a smile. Or was it the photographer's light in his eyes? He was dressed formally in a three-piece banker's suit, watch chain and all; perfectly groomed black hair smooth, flat, parted left of center. He stood straight, in charge, facing Mother. I could feel the power in his large hands, one grasping her left wrist and hand, the other reaching for her right arm, down at her side. Their shadows merged, making one dark, long shape stretching away from them.

I wanted more. I kept looking for clues. Dwight had evidently lost interest and was looking around. He waved to Jewel.

Jewel greeted us without surprise, took our order as she always had, nodding and reciting it back to us. "Ayup, burgers, the works." She stuck her pencil into the thick gray knot at the back of her head, reached for our menus. "We'll all miss your mother something terrible," she said. "I'll bring your beers."

I went back to the photo. "She relaxed more after Daddy was gone," I said. "Did she ever tell you how he proposed?"

He shook his head. "Of course not," he said, impatient.

"She said to me one day, 'I wonder if your father meant to propose. He asked me, "How'd you like to live on the farm in Boonton?" And that was it. She said, 'Maybe I jumped the gun.' "

"You mean he never asked, 'Will you marry me?'"

"He never did. Mother took his question as a proposal. Who knows? The next thing he knew, she'd told her parents – she was crazy about him – and that was that."

Dwight picked up the other photo, the one from 1921, and looked at it for a moment. "Maybe he never wanted to marry. He told me more than once, 'Don't marry till you're over forty. Look before you leap.' "

I had always thought Dwight should know the honeymoon story, but now I decided I wouldn't tell him. He didn't want to know about Mother and Daddy, and what I knew would only give him cause to crow.

He held the photo so I could see it too. Summer, a young couple. Funny flapper bathing suits; Daddy's had a top like an undershirt. Mother looked more sure of herself than she did in the earlier picture. Her smile was provocative and she was looking straight into the camera. Daddy's expression was almost the same as in the earlier photo. Such a good-looking man. And Mother was beautiful then. Before the children. Before Maya. Did something change? Or was it never going to work out between them, and the children, like the years themselves, only brought out the differences?

THEIR WEDDING TRIP to Banff and Lake Louise was six weeks. She wouldn't have had to wonder why he didn't have to get back to the bank, back to his job, because the bank belonged to her father. She wouldn't have had any reason to suspect that something had happened. I have a real sense of this young enthusiastic girl, and the unhappiness she begins to feel because her new husband is such a stranger.

Maybe E.B. yields to her a tiny bit and she feels deeply happy and it's in the expression of that happiness that she finally forces him to snap at her. I have a feeling that somehow the shining look filled with love that would suffuse Connie's face as she looked at him in that moment (or any time she looked at him that way) could make him gruff, embarrassed, make him feel cornered, and cause him to rear back and defend himself.

I've been thinking about what's missing. I never had a close friend until adulthood. I loved my chum Elisabeth, daughter of a college friend of my mother's who came to live in Schroon during the war. But I never told her anything, I never confided in her. And when I try to write about her, or about my mother, or the dreadful things Dwight believes, I can't get to any sense of intimacy.

I think I never allowed myself to reveal any of my inner core to anyone. I didn't confide my fears to anyone, not even to my mother. I must have absorbed the terrible emotional tension that always existed between my parents, that made my mother so unhappy and caused her to shut down when she was around my father. She must have been hurt by him again and again, and it wasn't in her nature to lash out at him; it all went underground.

I imagine her being in and out of some kind of emotional state of shock. You become numb to the world. Eventually the hurt becomes less of a crisis, and you settle into a more complex way of being in the world. I imagine them in the car coming back from their wedding journey, when the truth of E.B.'s coldness, his stern silence, was driven home to her.

She has not been sorry to leave Banff. The mountains have felt overpowering, not accessible and friendly like her familiar Adirondacks. She hasn't admitted this to E.B. who, at the beginning of the trip, promised that these mountains could make her dissatisfied with the geologically far older eastern ones. He relishes the rawness of the Rockies, mountains too vast for human habitation. Not a hardwood tree in sight – the land too rugged. The landscapes are overwhelming for her; they make her feel helpless, abandoned.

Her secret fearful reaction to this landscape makes her feel disloyal to him, just as her inability to keep her things tidy in their rooms at the hotel has made her feel small. E.B. never leaves a sock or anything else out of place. She knows by now he likes things orderly.

A sudden gush of tears threatens her. Why should she cry? This is her beautiful wedding trip, the trip she and E.B. talked about and planned so eagerly.

They would be home in a few more days. They were already in Pennsylvania. (The Alleghenies were much more friendly than the Rockies.) E.B. had promised they would go north to Schroon as soon as they found a place to live.

The car tilted alarmingly going around a long curve and she felt the force of the endless drop she now looked out upon.

She laughed at herself. Probably all brides went through this period in which they longed for home. She wished her mother had warned her, but she had probably forgotten; it was so long ago her parents had gotten married.

She had only to turn her head, and she would see the calm, handsome profile. She leaned over to him with a happy smile and kissed his neck. He didn't say, "What's all this?" but his neck went stiff, and although he hadn't moved away, it felt as though he had.

"Oh Eden B., all this grandeur is making me hungry," she said. She was thankful the winding roads didn't make her feel sick the way they would her sister. She stretched, shaking off the chill of his wariness.

She entertained herself by thinking about setting up house, and how the days would be for her while he was at work. She wondered where they would live.

She swiveled in her seat and watched him for a while. He was concentrating; she felt he was unaware of her and she could look at him at her leisure. She still had a sense of excitement, seeing him as if for the first time.

"Where would you like to live?" she asked. He didn't react. She looked over at him. Had he somehow failed to hear her?

"Eden B.?"

[144]

"Obviously I'll want to live someplace where I won't have too long a ride to work."

"But you know where you're working so we can talk about actual places."

"I won't be going back to your father's bank, Connie."

She had no idea what he was talking about. She thought he was refusing to work for her father, that he felt slighted by something her father had done or said. For an awful moment she thought it might be because her grandparents hadn't come to the wedding. She couldn't make sense of it. "I don't understand," she said apologetically.

"There's nothing to understand." His voice was toneless, bottomless. "Someone slandered me and your father questioned my character, said for the good of the bank he'd have to fire me. So I resigned. I don't need his bank. I have other plans. You must accept what I've said and not try to meddle in something that's between myself and your father."

She wanted to reach over and touch him; she wanted to dispel the distance between them. How could she overcome his formal manner? How could she get him to let her in, where he was struggling in pain?

"Let's face this together," she said. "Please tell me what on earth has happened." She couldn't imagine her father doing anything to hurt him, to hurt them both. "Please tell me," she repeated, not pleading but inviting.

"He's accepted the word of some other men at the bank against mine. I'm not at liberty to divulge the nature of the incident. He's told me that this is for the good of the bank, that it's not personal, but simply something that must be done." He continued to face straight ahead, eyes on the road. His jaw was set.

Connie was afraid of angering him, but she couldn't bear to be shut out, as if she were a stranger. "Oh Eden B.," she said. She was filled with love for him. "You know my first and deepest loyalty is to you, my dearest and most cherished husband." She didn't waver. "Please tell me what's happened."

"I cannot discuss this. You must accept what I've said." He turned to her then. "And I must ask you, please, to stop calling me Eden B."

That frightened her. She felt the weight of it settle in her chest, occupying the space she needed to breathe. What dreams she had had of becoming ever closer to this man with whom she had pledged to share her life. She begged herself not to make a dreadful scene.

Could she speak? "I must—" her voice came out thin, but steady. "I'll do whatever you say."

She sneaked a quick glance at his face. It was composed and still, as if they had been discussing the passing scenery, and then she knew she would have to be on the alert. Changing moods. Hidden swings. She hadn't allowed herself to see them, or fear them, before. It was her silent prayer to be the very wife this man she loved so much needed, and to be the wife who would help him find his way to trusting her with his troubles.

I can almost feel what my mother must have felt as she was hearing that news. And yet I also know how my father would have reacted to her prying into something he absolutely couldn't speak about.

Mother remembered the entire scene in vivid detail. She said her heart was in her throat on that drive along the serpentine road crumbling along the edges as it wormed its way around the contours of the mountains in Pennsylvania. At that point, passing a car from the other direction made her stomach lurch. She could see tiny dots of people far below, fishing. It had been a wet spring and in many places the river had overflowed its banks. She said she had a vision of herself and Daddy, first moving easily and swiftly, without a care in the world, headed with the current southward. Abruptly, with Daddy's news, she felt herself struggling against the fast-running current, making almost no headway, about to be flung back, to crash against the Pennsylvania rocks hundreds of feet below her.

I asked her what she had said when he told her, and she got flustered. "I don't remember exactly what I said. I started to ask how it happened. I wanted to be sympathetic. But he exploded. I just clammed up. I did ask if he couldn't change his mind, apologize, ask Father for a second chance. He looked right through me. I felt his eyes boring a hole into my forehead. Then he turned and started muttering under his breath."

"But you must have asked him something," I insisted, feeling impatient with her, angry that she hadn't acted more adult, hadn't pried the answer out of him.

She hesitated. "He did say, 'It was Floyd Evans. He never liked me, called me old Mr. Harris's errand boy.'" She told me she had been afraid of Daddy's temper, afraid he might kill Floyd Evans – or her if she criticized him at all. She said she had never been able to understand why he hadn't told her before their wedding trip.

But she wasn't one to brood. She got up. "Time to shake down the furnace. Going down to zero tonight." She got moving. "Don't dwell on it. We just got off on the wrong road. Should have had a marriage Blue Book."

I TRIED FOR YEARS to screw up the courage and ask my father why he got fired from Grandpa's bank. I never did. I imagined various noble reasons why he had kept this jolting piece of news from his bride. Maybe he had uncovered some fiscal wrongdoing and kept his mouth shut rather than put the bank out of business; or he had been threatened by the jealous and evil Floyd Evans, bully and thief; or he had uncovered his father-in-law in some shady deal and wouldn't betray him. After a while I tried to forget I had ever heard the story at all.

Years later I was doing research for a project on early New York families. Ours wasn't an old family in the city – our people had moved east after several generations in Ohio as farmers and storekeepers. While I was looking for information on Harrises, I also looked for anything about Thirkields. Up popped the name of my unselfish, hard-working maiden aunt, Jeannette, known as Henrietta at that time. It was a short piece, about fraud at a small law firm in midsummer of 1917. (My parents had met that spring.)

Henrietta Thirkield had been arrested for embezzlement. She had been working as secretary/receptionist/file clerk and she had been caught embezzling four thousand dollars during the previous year. (I'm sure that because of the crime, Henrietta had to become Jeannette. Right here in my office, up on a high shelf, sits the vanity case she had for years and years, and on it are her initials: H.B.T.)

My mother was still alive at the time I found the article. I asked her about the car Daddy and Jeannette had driven up to Schroon Lake that summer of the year they met, 1917. I had heard a lot about that car. It was part of family legend, a Marmon 34. It was an expensive, sporty car. E.B. was working at that point as a salesman for a soap company. I have a letter stating that he was being paid eighteen dollars per week, good pay in those days.

I asked Mother how he could afford such a fancy car. She said, "I never thought about it. I had a well-to-do father, I just assumed."

I showed her the newspaper article about Jeannette. She got pale. I was thinking, how strange it must be for her, to have the beginnings of an answer to something she's never understood. But then she told me her brother had told her about it at the time; she had never mentioned it to E.B., but she knew from her brother that even though Netsie had never been indicted for the crime, it was because of the accusation that E.B. had been asked to resign from her father's bank.

Jeannette stole from her law firm – at the suggestion of her brother? Surely not, too horrible to think of. I preferred to believe Aunt Netsie had the initiative and the guts to do it on her own, out of sisterly loyalty to her one and only brother, who had met the lovely daughter of a wealthy banker. She would make it possible for herself and E.B. to arrive in style and she would gradually pay it back. E.B. would make a great match and they would all live happily ever after. Their mother had recently died, leaving behind her the debts left by their kind dreamer of a father, twice bankrupted. And Daddy never wanted to reveal his sister's crime. He couldn't tell, not even his poor bewildered bride. Wrong road, indeed.

EVERY THING is redolent, for me. Every item is part of a romance or of a secret. Not for Dwight. He slammed around the place that whole week, denying himself sadness.

I was upstairs one morning working on a bureau drawer. I heard his angry sounds coming from the back porch and went downstairs to find out what he was up to. He was bent over the huge black trunk that used to sit at the rear on Daddy's '34 Pierce Arrow. The trunk had been in the woodshed for years, as long as I could remember. Dwight had a screwdriver wedged between the front of the trunk and its rusted lock, and was about to deal it a blow with a hammer. I wished he didn't have to break the lock, but I knew better than to say so.

He waved the hammer at me without looking up. "I've wanted to know what was in this blasted thing for years," he said, and he brought the hammer down on the screwdriver. The lock gave way with a metallic squeal.

"You remember this old trunk?" He set down his tools and rubbed his hands together as if he were an evil magician about to reveal horrors. I reached over and wiped the dust away from the place beneath the lock where I knew Daddy's initials were painted in red. There they were: E.B.T.

"That Pierce Arrow was Daddy's favorite car," I said.

"Must've been gone by the time I was old enough to know anything," he grunted. I was surprised; Dwight had loved cars as soon as he knew anything at all.

"It's the one he drove to Texas and back," I said. "It was around for a while after that."

He was working on the trunk lid, trying to pry it loose. "I kept asking him why not open the damned thing but he'd just shake his head no. Talk about stubborn." He got the heavy lid ajar and raised it unceremoniously.

A smell of long-disintegrated mothballs rose from layers of clothing wrapped in tissue paper, lying beneath leather trays for delicate clothing. Without looking I remembered the lining of cornflower-blue paper with stripes of tiny white fleurs-de-lis. I remembered shorts and halters, Dwight's rompers, itchy woolen bathing suits, rubber wading shoes, sneakers, Oxfords and patent leathers, white summer sweaters and white balls of socks. On top, fluttering now in the breeze, were two pale blue dotted-swiss church and Sunday-dinner dresses for me and Maya.

Before we started living year round at the lake we lived on and off with Aunt Charlotte, on the New Jersey shore. Daddy took the car to Heidt's garage every year for its spring tune-up, but the trunk didn't go to the garage, it was brought into the house to be packed. Daddy got Frank, Aunt Charlotte's yard man, to help him unclamp it and lift it off its heavy chrome platform at the rear of the car just over the bumper, and carry it into the house.

"Do you remember Spring Lake?" I asked Dwight. "The Jersey coast?" He was only three when we moved to Schroon Lake. I leaned over the open trunk, breathed in the dank smell, trying to find other old smells in it. I started lifting out clothes from inside the trays, things my sister and I must have outgrown by the time we moved to Schroon Lake for good. Mother had layered everything with tissue, keeping our things separate, similar types of clothes tied together with ribbons. I felt protective of these wrapped packets with her block printing on them. Dwight only wanted to cast things away.

"I remember very little," he said. He reached out and picked up a bundle labeled "Dwight's baby clothes," didn't open it but handled it as if he might know its contents by feeling them. I waited for him to toss the bundle into the trash pile with a sneer, but he stood there holding it.

"Tell me about Aunt Charlotte's," he said. "I like your stories. But let's not stop. Talk and work."

"I'll tell you about the *Morro Castle*, a cruise ship that burned off the beach near their house. First official public news I can remember. Nana read me headlines the next day."

Dwight had opened the bundle of baby clothes. They were moth-eaten and discolored with damp. He tossed them lightly into the grocery carton we were using for trash.

"Tell me," he said, and I realized I had been standing there watching him. He grabbed another tissue paper packet and ripped it open. Those clothes, too, were all moth-eaten and moldy. He started grabbing the packets by the handful.

I worked at a less frantic pace, pushing his hands aside if he got close to something I was about to pick up. I was determined to savor Mother and fragments of the past in this small way.

"I used to get up first," I said, "sneak downstairs so nobody'd hear me. There was an old horsehair sofa in front of a big window that looked out on the ocean across the street. The sofa was covered in gold velvet, and the horsehairs poked out into my knees as I knelt watching the water. I'd look at the horizon. I didn't see how it could be so straight if the ocean was all waves." We had emptied the top tray, and he lifted it out and we unsnapped the straps on the next one.

"I wanted to see if I could find a boat just becoming visible a little at a time so you'd know the earth was a ball," I went on. "Never could." I remembered this vividly, and I was pleased to have an audience. "This one time I saw black smoke going up from the horizon. The boat was invisible, but somehow I knew the smoke must come from one. I ran to wake everybody to see the bonfire on the ocean."

"And they read you the headlines?"

I nodded. "The fire had started in the middle of the night. It was a cruise ship on its way home from Cuba. A lot of people burned up or jumped overboard, got drowned."

"Why'd they tell you about such a disaster? Was that another one of their gruesome horror stories with a moral? Don't play with match-es or you'll burn up the whole house?"

"Oh Dwight, you think the worst every time. I was the one who spotted the thing burning, after all. I'll never forget the way the smoke blackened the whole sky as the day went on."

"They could've played it down, told you they got the fire out. Why scare little kids with something like that? 'Don't do this or something terrible will happen,' over and over."

"You're determined to remember our parents in the worst possible light." I kept myself from shouting at him. "Well, you're way off base this time. You can't hide bad stuff from kids. And anyway, Maya could read it for herself. Should they have hidden the papers? Besides, the boat burned out there in front of our eyes."

Dwight was slinging everything into the grocery carton at the other end of the porch as I talked, condemning each garment as he threw it, talking under me. "Moth holes. Too worn out. Old-fash-ioned. Needs mending." When I finished he turned to me.

"Seems to me they liked stories of disaster," he said coldly. "All of them. The aunts and the parents, too. That whole generation. It meant they could keep preaching. And if we didn't mend our naughty ways it'd be our own fault."

"The *Morro Castle*'s different, Dwight – if you want to hear it."

"So tell me. Then let's decide what to do with this stuff. I need a break." He went back to throwing.

He had taken the fun out of telling it. I kept quiet, calming myself by sorting. I had everything I had gone through in piles on the floor, rather than throwing things around. After a few minutes he reached a foot over and toppled one of my piles. I looked up ready to fight him but he was grinning and we both laughed.

"So tell me," he said again.

"Daddy was a hero," I said. "He and Mother knew people on the ship. So did friends of theirs."

"Sure, he wanted to show his friends how brave he was."

"Oh, come on, Dwight. He saved whoever he could; crew members, anybody who needed help. He didn't ask for ID, for God's sake." I had heard the story lots of times; I had always been proud to hear it. He rescued people all that day, all night, into the next morning till the Coast Guard called off the search. It was all in the newspapers. He wasn't that young either. Forty-two.

Dwight seemed to have lost interest. "I'm going to get his truck," he said, heading out the back door, "take a load of stuff to the dump." He took the back steps two at a time. "Okay, Sis," he called back to me. "If you want to believe he was some sort of hero, it's fine with me." And he disappeared around the house, out of earshot.

He made me mad. What right did he have telling me he knew better? And that was exactly what he meant.

I started putting stuff into bags for the dump. The trunk was empty. There had been no treasures, nothing unexpected, just the sight and feel of the past. That blue liner paper, and the broken hasp.

He was mellower when he got back from the barn with the truck, and I went along with him, acted as though everything was fine. He was there in the present. I arrived there in the present with him.

"Okay," he called out cheerfully, as he backed the truck up to the porch. "Let's get this show on the road."

I was poking around in the four cartons and several shopping bags we had managed to fill with the clothes, taking a farewell look. He was out of the truck and standing over me before I knew it. He wagged a finger at me.

"Don't you dare look at anything twice," he said. "This is all going out the door – now." He grabbed a carton and took it out to the truck. "You and I are breaking the saving mania once and for all," he said, coming back for another carton.

When I didn't move, he stopped, too. "I wish I had better childhood memories," he said with a shrug. "All I want is to clean things out once and for all and move on." He spread his arms, bent and swept up a pale pile of ancient tissue paper. He collapsed it into a rustling ball as if he could compress the past into nothingness. When he looked up at me, his eyes were wet.

"God damn. You'll make me get sappy and sentimental. I do remember running around in the middle of this stuff, with Mother chasing me." He squeezed and squashed as hard as he could.

Mothball smell brought it back. Mother after Dwight racing through a blizzard of tissue, all of us laughing and shrieking, those empty compartmented trays piled on beds in the maid's room, tissue paper flying. One good memory for Dwight, I thought. I swept up some of the tissue paper that was left and threw it into the air and we laughed together as it fluttered back down between us.

The sun made long shadows as we loaded the truck with the rest of the bags and boxes we had accumulated over the days we had been working. Still the summer twilight lingered. The drive up the Charlie Hill Road revealed vistas of the lake unfolding exactly as I remembered them from those early days of my life. From far away, it all looked the same. That was a comfort.

Grandpa's place, which had gone to Aunt Rae, had been all but obliterated over the years. Aunt Rae had sold the place suddenly over one weekend, years ago now. She had taken the first buyer with ready cash – a pittance really. Uncle Joe needed twenty-four-hour nursing care at that point, and the cost of maintaining the place made it too much of a burden for her.

Near the road, a motel jazzed up to look modern filled the former sheep pasture. The Big House had been stripped of its comfortable porches, places for lounging and reading that epitomized languid summer afternoons. The brown-stained shingles had been painted bright yellow, the dark green shutters were now swimming-pool aqua. Grandma's gardens had been bulldozed to extinction, and the earth-leveling machine was parked permanently in Harris Fort, site once upon a time of family photos, Grandma's English garden.

[153]

Mother never let change bother her. She said, "I had a wonderful childhood but let's not dwell on the past," and became a good neighbor to the new owners. Her brusque dismissal irritated me at the time, but now I use it myself whenever I feel myself bristling, and it helps ease me.

As Dwight and I started unloading our stuff at the dump, Mrs. Vanderlindt, the dump mother, as we always called her, waved from the far side of the lot, where she was raking. The dump mother was not paid a salary; the town allowed her to live on the dump grounds, and in return she kept an eye on the fire that smoldered continuously, burning away the town's leavings. She salvaged anything usable or salable, and she separated what the animals would eat from the burnable trash. It was a well-run dump.

She didn't break the rhythm of her raking. I watched her for a moment. After every few pulls, she moved her arm in a sowing motion, probably scattering seeds.

We carried the bags and boxes to the lean-to.

The dump mother's tiny figure approached. She moved at an amazingly rapid pace. She was dressed in a bright flowered cotton skirt that fell halfway down her heavy grey-green man's Hood rubber boots; a man's business shirt hung outside her skirt, cinched at the waist with a tasseled gold curtain cord; a red bandana covered her head, came down almost to her eyebrows. Tanned face and forearms, snapping black eyes, face weather-beaten, not wrinkled.

"Miss your ma," she said. "Nice lady. Said she'd have lots of stuff soon." She nodded at our lined-up bags and cartons.

"Mother said you have fifteen grandchildren," I said.

"Twenty-three great," she said. She held her rake without leaning on it. "Your dad and mother got me a pension. I can stay. Sorry she's gone now too. Good woman." She gave a little wave-salute. "Bear out tonight. Leave your lights off. So long." She didn't wait for us to go, but turned and began raking behind the lean-to.

Dwight cut the engine as soon as we were back on the Charlie Hill Road, and we coasted slowly down and around the first curve, our eyes well adjusted to the darkness. Just past the curve, a bear paused, staring, his bulk dark against the paleness of the dirt road. He turned slowly away as if we weren't worth his attention, loped ahead a few paces, down into the ditch, and disappeared into the blackness of the woods.

NEXT DAY we were at it again. As soon as we had finished breakfast Dwight got up and started washing the dishes. I picked up a dish towel but he took it from my hands. "Together, we'll talk," he said, "waste time." He shooed me out. "Get cracking," he said.

I went to Mother's room. Went right to her massive bureau and put my hands to the ornate pulls of the bottom drawer. With a squeaky groan it opened halfway. I stared into jumbled depths, many strata of tumbled, twisted clothes. The drawer looked as though someone had ransacked it; it was completely unlike the neatly packed trunk and the boxes we had found over the last days. Had Mother been looking for something, gone through the drawer in a hurry, maybe that last morning while I scraped the frost off her windshield? What could she have been looking for?

I pulled out the middle drawer. It, too, was a jumble of old, moth-eaten clothes, mostly undergarments. What had she used, then, as a bureau, while she was here those summers, once she was living with me in New York? It made me sad, seeing this mess where I had been expecting to find her. I plunged my hand into the drawer and pushed things around, and came up with a small bathing suit. Swimming-pool green, I used to call it. It had a pattern of green squares, with a circle in the center of each square like a bull's-eye. I held it up to the light; I could see daylight through the moth holes. I rubbed it against my cheek and felt the scratchiness I remembered. Itchiest article of clothing I ever wore. Lumpy wool. I learned to swim in it. It felt better wet, drooping and sagging, dripping water down my thighs.

Daddy taught me to swim.

This was the day. What a triumph.

"Don't drink the water, girls," he warned us. He walked into the lake. His white legs looked fatter through the water. He did a surface dive, came out far ahead swimming with smooth, strong strokes, breathing each time he turned his head. He headed straight out from where we were.

Mother swam close to shore, kept an eye on Dwight and me digging at the edge of the water. Where was Maya? Mother patrolled back and forth, doing a steady, strong dog paddle, her mouth always just above the water line. What she lacked in style she made up in stamina. And she didn't splash at all. When she was finished swimming she walked out of the water, came and sat with us where the wavelets lapped the shore. She looked out, shielding her eyes from the sun.

I followed where she was looking. I could barely see Daddy's head, moving through the water. He swam silently, his feet barely breaking the surface. He kept going.

"E.B.," Mother called. "Don't swim out so far."

I watched Daddy swim on and on, so far he was a tiny speck. All of us children, even the big cousins, were told never to swim alone, not to go beyond our limit. What was Daddy's limit?

Mother stood, called louder. "E.B., look at the sky. We're going to have a storm. Come back." The tone of her voice frightened me. He had told me he could swim all the way across the lake. But what if he got a cramp? Mother kept calling. I wanted him to come back so he could teach me to swim.

I ran out onto the dock, jumped up and down to make him see me. "Daddy, you promised to teach me to swim," I yelled. "Come back, come back."

He stopped. He floated on his back for a long time. Then he swam slowly, slowly back, doing the breast stroke, making hardly a ripple. When he was close, he stood up and walked toward shore.

I ran into his arms. He held me. He put me on his shoulders, my legs hanging down against his chest. He walked back into the water, holding my calves tight with one arm. I held onto his chin. The water rose higher and higher, black and deep, up and over my feet and almost to my knees. He lifted me above his head, swung me down into the water, his hand under my stomach.

"You can touch here," he said. "Put your toe to the bottom." He let me hold his arm. It was like steel. I stretched my toes. I was afraid of what was down there but I didn't want to act like a baby. I stretched farther. Finally I felt mucky bottom. The water was over my chin, running in and out of my mouth. I rested on his arm.

"Cup your hands and move your arms one at a time," he told me.

"I showed you on the grass. Don't swallow water. Kick your legs. Kick hard." He spoke calmly, in a firm voice.

I forgot his arm, moved my arms back and forth, in and out of the water. I kicked my legs harder and harder. I started moving away from him. I was swimming.

He grabbed me, hugged me hard. He lifted me up, smiling at me. His neck was wet and salty when I kissed him. He hugged me again, lifted me back up over his head, and settled me on his shoulders again, and walked partway back to shore.

"Tomorrow I'll teach you the crawl," he said. His voice was filled with pride. He squeezed my feet as they bumped against his chest. I was so happy I could have burst. "You can make it from here," he said, and he lifted me off, launched me into the water. I swam all the way back to shore, Daddy swimming beside me. We climbed out of the water together.

My teeth were chattering. My legs were covered with goose bumps. Someone wrapped me in a towel – Maya, I think. My fingers were wrinkled.

A chilly wind blew. My suit was dripping a cold stream down my legs. Waves rolled up onto the beach, curling and breaking. The lake was no longer blue. The sky was dark and unfriendly. Mother was right, a storm was coming. Heavy dark clouds raced by, just above the tops of big pines at the edge of the lake.

Somebody said you could smell rain coming, the end of the heat wave; we needed rain. I didn't want rain. I wanted to learn the crawl tomorrow. Everybody bustled and hurried, brushing off hands and bottoms, tugging at suits, tying straps, gathering bathing caps, sun oil, straw bags, putting towels or sweaters around their shoulders.

Daddy said we must all go to the house, get there before the storm and close windows. He walked ahead, carrying Dwight on his shoulders. He walked slowly, steadily up the hill, Dwight's yellow head bobbing up and down against black clouds. Daddy never changed his stride. He was far ahead, up the hill at the steepest part. I ran as fast as I could, throat hot, a stitch in my side, heart pounding. I stopped to catch my breath, looked downhill. Maya was walking slowly with Mother, holding her hand. She couldn't run because of her asthma.

Lightning streaked across a black cloud. Thunder rumbled. The wind was cold blowing across my wet suit. I ran again to catch up with Daddy and Dwight. I reached the top of the hill where the lawn stretched in all directions. Gray boulders crouched on the grass. Daddy was still ahead, near the big elm, its branches twisting in the wind. He lifted Dwight to the ground, watched him run ahead. I watched too, Dwight's diaper slipping low around his knees. Not so steep now; it was easier to run fast. Lightning flashed again. Finally, I was close enough. I grabbed Daddy's hand.

He looked down at me. "Now count between lightning and thunder," he said. "One one thousand, two one thousand, three one thousand. You can tell how far away the storm is." Another flash. He counted and I counted with him. The storm was closer. "Let's get a wiggle on," he said. He walked faster. I had to run to keep hold of his hand.

"Now just listen," he said. "You'll hear things most people miss with too much chatter. Be still. Listen to the storm coming."

I listened. I heard wind rustling the poplars high above the pines. The pines started to move, sighing. I heard a bugle from the camp next door. More and brighter lightning flashes, louder booms of thunder.

Daddy squeezed my hand. "Here's the rain," he said. "It'll be a flash in the pan. Heat wave's not over, mark my words."

I felt fat drops on my face, on my scalp, the backs of my legs.

"Run ahead," he told me. "Watch Dwight. Don't let him near the road. I'll get the windows."

He looked down the long lawn and so did I. Maya and Mother were hurrying now, catching up. Daddy started to run smoothly. He did it just the way he had taught me, keeping his feet pointed straight, like an Indian – no wasted motion.

Maya and Mother just made it. The screen door slammed. Rain thundered on the porch roof.

After a little while it stopped, and a hazed sun came full out, low in the sky, lit up every blade of grass. The air was sticky, still, thunder rumbling far off.

Later, after supper, we heard more thunder rumbling. I stayed up late; the air was too heavy for sleep. Maya and I took turns swinging, cooling off in the rush of air. Our shadows stretched long, making grotesque, ghostly shapes. We played shadow tag; easy for me to catch Maya's longer shadow.

Fireflies came out. Long beams of gold light blazed low through black pines across the road behind the barn. Black clouds piled up, cloud on cloud, edged in pink gold. Thunder rumbled louder. We chased fireflies until our legs were limp.

"Time for bed, girls," Daddy called out to us. Later, when I was in bed, I heard him downstairs. "Mark my words, another storm's coming. It'll be a humdinger." He came in to say good night. "Front'll move through, be clear tomorrow," he told Maya and me. He tapped my foot. "I'll teach you the crawl," were the last words I heard before I fell asleep.

Pitch dark. I was suddenly awake, heart pounding. The storm was back, as Daddy had said it would be. Lightning and thunder came almost together: flash ... crack. The storm was on top of us, one lightning streak after another, instant ear-splitting thunder. I was more afraid of the flashes than of the cracks; that unearthly gray they turned the room – it made me think of mummies, graves, ghosts. I was terrified of looking into the room lit in those seconds, afraid of that cold light. I closed my eyes. The flash was so bright it penetrated my eyelids. I called out.

Daddy was there. He lifted me out of bed and I held tight to his neck. He talked to me quietly, explaining lightning.

He laid me back on the bed, lay down beside me, and we watched for another flash, counted how many seconds before the boom.

"Thunder's a reaction of air – air heated fast by lightning," he said. I listened to his low, calm voice. "The air gets intensely hot, then cools instantaneously, makes a vacuum. When air rushes back into that empty pocket – BOOM. Thunder." He talked more, about controlled explosions, gas engines, pistons. I was too sleepy to listen. His voice was quiet; he was in control, above the thunder. Flashes came farther apart. I looked at the room in those seconds of flash. It was only our room, in gray, pale light.

After that I no longer awoke in terror in thunderstorms. Over sixty years ago now, and when there's lightning and thunder I feel his presence, his patience, making me understand.

AT THE END of the morning of clearing out Mother's bureau and closet, I carried bags downstairs for the dump, looking for Dwight. He was sitting on the back steps, oiling and polishing a lineup of Daddy's tools, his hands moving with that same deftness I remembered from his model-plane building days. Quick squeeze of the Three-in-One oil can – exactly the right amount so it didn't drip – then a slow turning of the working end of an awl or a bit or a series of graduated wrenches or screwdrivers to allow the oil to slide seductively where he wanted it. Finally, slow, patient massage with fine-grained sandpaper to rub away years of tarnish.

"Our father had a beautiful collection of tools," he said. "Took care of 'em too. Only a few'll need penetrating oil. Must've been a leak in the corner of his tool shed – see these?" He pointed his short right index finger toward a set of chisels orange with rust.

"I'm going to make some peanut butter sandwiches," I said. "Want jelly? First these go in the truck." I started down the back steps.

"Give me the works," he called after me. "What'ya got there?"

"A bunch of stuff from Mother's bureau, too good to throw away."

He eyed my packing job. "Wouldn't it go faster without all that folding?"

"Maybe, but Mother wanted things to look attractive." Here he was, carefully cleaning and oiling Daddy's old tools. Wouldn't it go faster if he packed them as they were and oiled them when he got them home? I continued down the steps. "She always said if she folded them nicely Mrs. Vanderlindt would know there was still good in them."

"Lady Bountiful to the core," he remarked, going back to his tools.

I kept walking. No point in answering him. I put the bags in the back of the truck and came back onto the porch.

"You know even when plastic garbage bags came out after the war Mother refused to put old clothes in them, said they were ugly, made it look like we thought the clothes were garbage."

"Our father, too," Dwight said. "He was ahead of the times. I remember him saying people should be shot for throwing plastic into the woods or the lake. Creatures would choke on that stuff, he said. Ought to be banned."

"Speaking of shooting, Dwight, do you know where he stored his guns? Those are yours."

He looked up from his sandpapering, pulled a key out of his jeans pocket. "Mother sent me this a few months before she died." A small tag dangled from the key. "E.B.'S GUNS" was written on the tag in Mother's block printing. "That got to me," he said. "Meant to tell you."

I MADE SANDWICHES, thinking about Daddy's guns. I remembered them in the downstairs attic, above my head now, over the kitchen, stored on a rack behind the kitchen stove chimney. He had insisted we know how to take his rifle apart, clean it, load it, and most important, fire it as accurately as possible. "Women should know how to handle a gun," he would say to me. (For some reason Maya was never in on these sessions.) "They had to on the prairie. World's still a dangerous place, don't kid yourself." Dwight and I had our gun lessons sitting on those same back porch steps.

Two simple parts: a beautiful satin-smooth reddish-gold piece of wood, the stock; and a barrel, silver blue and cold, the killing part. I imagined the feel of the warm wood against my cheek. I imagined it felt like Daddy's huge biceps when he flexed them for me. The solid metal barrel was too heavy for me to hold absolutely balanced and still, in one hand, in those days.

Daddy would lift the barrel with both hands, place the inner end gently against my right eye. The gun oil penetrated my nostrils. If I closed one eye, squinted my aiming eye, and looked through the barrel the way I had watched him do many times, I could see faint circles going down the inside of the barrel – if I looked just right. It was like looking into a narrow, round mirror; rifling marks spiraled down the barrel and out toward the target.

Behind a hidden slot in the rifle's stock there were two long metal rods, which he would screw together. At one end there was an eye like the eye of a needle but a lot bigger. He let me thread the eye with a long strip of soft old undershirt, and when I had done this he wrapped the cloth as far along the rod as it would reach, and dipped the wrapped end into the small amber-colored bottle of gun oil.

I see him. His lips are set straight; he's concentrating. Gently, with the precision of a surgeon, he inserts the rod into the barrel, sliding it in only as far as it is wrapped. He pulls it out, pushes it in, pulls it out again, then replaces the strip with a clean one and repeats the operation.

Three times he would do this, entering from both ends of the barrel, always making sure only the cloth touched the inside of the barrel. Finally, he would hold the barrel up to my eye again for an inspection.

I can still look across the road toward the woods, even though the woods aren't the same; those majestic pines are gone. And I can still smell that gun oil.

He never took me hunting. I would have been good at it. I knew how to listen with all my senses. Still do it.

Ten

WE WERE going out for a walk in the woods; it was early in December, our first winter in the Adirondacks. I was seven. Dwight's legs were shorter than mine but he was wiry and determined. Three years old. I almost wanted him to be able to keep up, but not quite. He was allowed to come into the near woods to get the feel of it in this first snowstorm. But Daddy insisted it was to be a walk, not a romp. Only I knew, because Daddy had told me, that our mission was to find fallen trees that might have hit the power line from a late Thanksgiving ice storm. He knew I was old enough to go on this mission of inspection with him. He had told me exactly that. I also knew it was mainly just to walk in the silence and to watch the snow fall in the woods.

"It's imperative we be still, if you want to see a deer or a snowshoe rabbit," he said. We nodded. I knew he liked silent walking. His stern "Be still" always meant we would see something if we were quick enough.

He closed the storm door firmly behind us. We paused at the edge of the porch while he tilted his face upward, snowflakes melting the instant they touched his skin. I knew the drips were running down into his collar but he ignored them.

"This is your first true snowstorm, children," he said. "You sure you're ready for it?" He glanced down at each of us in turn, and each of us answered, "Yes, Daddy," nodding our heads for emphasis.

We stepped off the lower step and walked between Grandpa's two square stone towers to the edge of the road. The stone wall was disappearing under flakes falling faster and faster, the air a mass of tiny drifting whiteness. The standing stones embedded in the top of the wall had slouching dunce caps of piled white powder.

Daddy held firm to my arm, and to Dwight's on the other side of him. He was wearing his gauntlets, as he called them, huge bear-fur gloves that reached almost to his elbows. The fur was dark brown sprinkled with a few black and white hairs, which gave the gloves a grizzled appearance. He seldom wore gloves, so I knew we were in for a long walk with a real purpose. I hoped Dwight could stay quiet enough so he wouldn't have to be scolded and spoil things.

When we were across the road Daddy let go of our arms and we charged ahead of him, up the driveway toward the barn, scuffing up snow as high as we could. Dwight took off at an angle, climbed the pile of shoveled snow along the border of the driveway. He flung himself down onto his back and made a snow angel. I was about to race after him, do my own bigger and better angel, but I turned back and caught Daddy's eye.

"Dwight, you'll only get wet," Daddy called out. "Get up. Let's brush you off." His voice had the sound of disapproval, not quite scolding. I ran to Dwight and pulled him to his feet, slapping snow off his back and front, harder than I knew was needed.

"Let's see who can make the biggest running leaps," I shouted, demonstrating with two or three lurches in the direct path toward the wood. Dwight copied me. I heard Daddy call after me, "Atta girl." I was thrilled, proud.

Once we were past the shoveled driveway, the snow was up to our knees, and it was exhausting to run in it. We slowed to a walk, and fell in with Daddy, who hadn't altered his pace. He stepped firmly with his high-laced boots, keeping us moving.

At the edge of the woods, he gave us instructions. No one unfamiliar with these deep woods could have found the way. Daddy spoke softly. "I'll break the trail," he said. "You follow in my path, Dwight." He looked at me. "Scout, you bring up the rear." I knew this was the more responsible position. "And keep your eyes and ears open," he added. Then he turned and walked in.

He led us among the silent pines caught with snow, their branches sifting it, making the going less difficult than through the open field. These woods, that had always been familiar in summers, now seemed forbidding and unknown.

The going got harder on my legs, even with Daddy breaking the trail for us. Dwight kept at it, ahead of me, pushing himself hard. Daddy glanced back every now and then to make sure we were close behind. He caught my eye, showing his approval, giving me renewed strength.

Thick brambled bushes clustered under the bare maples. Daddy had to hold the elastic branches back to protect our eyes. We trudged along. I tried to look everywhere. I wanted to be able to tell him things I had seen, later. I knew he liked the fact that I was always looking around, noticing things.

Suddenly he stopped. He pointed his hairy bear-gloved finger straight ahead. "Look," he said in a heavy whisper. "A snowshoe rabbit."

"Where, Daddy?" Dwight's voice piped loud, in the deep silence.

I wanted to punch him. He would scare away the rabbit and make Daddy mad.

"You missed him," Daddy said. Again, the sound of dissatisfaction in his voice. I felt disappointed for him – for Daddy – and for myself even more.

"How'd you like a ride?" he said to Dwight, and before Dwight could answer, he lifted him up onto his shoulders in one smooth motion. Now we could move faster. We got past the brambles and into another, more open, white pine grove. Daddy's strides lengthened. I forced my legs to keep up.

Pretty soon we came out into the open field far beyond the barn. I had hoped we would have taken Dwight home before we got to the real woods, but I said nothing, matching Daddy's steps as closely as I could, right behind him. We got to the power line and all was well.

Daddy carried Dwight on his shoulders all the way back. We crossed the road silently and at the steps of the porch he swung Dwight down. "Here, Skeezix, let's get you dry," he said. "Now find your mother." He opened the storm door and nudged Dwight inside. "You did well," he said after him. Then he looked down at me and said, "You and I will close up the barn."

These were my magic words, my cue. I was out the door, Daddy close behind me. We recrossed the road, silent together, the way we knew how to be. He didn't take my arm and I matched him, stride for stride.

WAS I MANIPULATIVE? I was. I liked being the chosen child. I wasn't nice to my siblings; I always felt I understood something they apparently didn't. In a way I thought of them as dolts, since they didn't seem to be able to make themselves part of the family. And on the other hand, I seem to have needed to prove myself over and over again to each of my parents, but most particularly to my father.

As I've said, E.B. was not easy to please, and not loose and fun and down to earth; I tried extra hard to be someone to him. When I did get his loving approval, and I was in the privileged position, there was something overwhelming in his attention. Although I basked in the public glory of it, privately it could be a burden, not a reward. It was something for which there was a price. I had signed the contract without knowing there would be a contract; I was bound to play fair, act on my honor.

THIS IS the way it would happen:

E.B. comes home from one of his many trips to Albany, or New York, or a political convention. He finds Connie out, little Dwight busy with his pals in the woods, Maya studying – or, eventually, away at school. His sisters (Netsie and Charlotte) don't count because they're living in his (but really Connie's) house – and they're not there at his invitation. (Connie invited them.) I'm there, at home, about to run off and play with Antzie next door, or later, with Elisabeth, when my father asks me if I would like to go for a drive.

He has just gotten home. But he hasn't let anyone know exactly which day he was arriving so he shouldn't be miffed if no one's waiting with open arms. But he's somewhat hurt, I can tell. I really want to go play with Antzie – I've even told her I'm coming – but then I sense my father's deep disappointment after he realizes I may not go and do this errand with him. So I say I'd love to go, and I secretly phone Antzie to tell her I can't come up and play, my mother wants me to do chores.

I lie to my friend to be able to be with my father. It's a secret.

We go to get some part for the car, or a tool he needs, or a replacement for something broken on the single-cylinder engine that runs the saw because he wants to cut wood over the weekend. I know I should be interested in what it is he has to do. I ask the right questions. I know that Dwight is often not interested in asking anything of Daddy, I've observed this, and I know it upsets him; he feels

Dwight ignores him. It's true, too. And Dwight is also afraid of Daddy. I know how to be someone. Dwight and Maya don't.

So we go on this fairly long drive to Ti or maybe North Creek. Daddy loves to take the long way around to see the view, and that's when he tells me a lot of the lore of the Adirondacks — what it was like in the old days, the lumbering, the Indians. I'm interested, I truly am, and I know he loves my intellectual curiosity. So I ask all kinds of questions: questions about glaciers, and the stars and what is the aurora borealis and why do the leaves turn red in the fall and what did your ancestors do in the Civil War. That's far enough off in the past.

I know that with Daddy you can't talk when there's silence, and I know there are secrets, and with him I know when the silence has to be broken into, when it's not real silence but need. Though it doesn't always work.

I DON'T LIKE the way E.B. came off before; too cold, by far. He was there, but always on his own terms. That mysterious person who was my father, so remote and yet so much there to love. He had a tough time connecting, even to me as a child. By instinct, I knew how to get through to him. My birthright.

I have some feelings of guilt. I would like to be able to shift Dwight's opinion so he's not so judgmental. And now that I've written those words, I have to admit that I know there's not one iota of change I could effect in his perception of our parents. It's over and done with.

I did occupy a favored position. It was based on my good luck, nothing that I angled for or shoved anyone aside to grab, to begin with. I believe it was mine for the taking. Certain personalities mesh better with other personalities and that can include one's own children, whether one wants to admit it or not.

I was the mediator, but not necessarily because I was the middle child. I think I was the mediator in a larger sense, between my father and other members of the family, since I felt compelled to look after him or be nice to him. I think I took on a role as the one who understood him or got along with him, and the rest of the family metaphorically groaned about him or rolled their eyes, or braced themselves for whatever mood he chose.

One big aspect of the drama of the family was my father's sensitive nature. From an early age I felt in some way responsible for his happiness. Or maybe that's putting it too baldly. I know I've said this before, but I keep trying to get at it. I think I felt he needed something, needed attention. I don't know if anyone else in the family saw this need in him. My mother must have. I don't think my brother and sister did, though they must have known it instinctively. Maybe they saw it and each responded in his/her own way, just as I did in mine. Or maybe somehow he scared them away.

There would be other things to take into consideration, too. The way Mother seemed to make me her ally, talking to me about things I really didn't want to know and didn't want to spend time on, when Daddy was away. I used to wonder, while she was talking to me, what she wanted from me during those talks. I didn't know enough to be able to say anything useful or comforting, but she kept doing it. She would talk to me about the unfortunate decision on her part to hand over all her inheritance to him and how he was spending principal and how she had hoped he'd get a regular salary-paying job. And she'd tell me things he had said to her, hurtful things, over the years, like "I'm all over that love stuff."

"I just want to keep him as happy as possible, not add to his worries," she would say to me. "Poor Daddy, I know he's been so disappointed in his life." And another lament: "I wish he could have more fun, get a kick out of silly things and not be so serious."

She would talk about him out there all alone; during the winter when we didn't hear from him for so long, she talked to me about how inconsiderate his silence was. I tried not to take it in. I was afraid something terrible had happened to him. Mother said she was worried about that, too, but I could tell she was more irritated than worried. I could too easily have agreed with her and it would have ruined the glory of my father. My loyalty was based on him in his pure state. I used to try very hard to ignore what she was saying, but the alliance between her and me was not entirely possible to resist. And I saw her side too, and felt sad for her. What she told me made me feel that my father was alien to me and to us all.

[168]

WHAT MADE ME different from Maya and Dwight? What was expected of me? I was there. I was sensible. I wouldn't go and blab anything to anyone, particularly not E.B.'s sisters – the aunts. Or to Mother, either.

I've been trying to think about his bottled-up nature. Bottled up was my mother's term for how closed in he was. Apparent reasons were old parents, the financial disasters, atmosphere of doom and gloom, the much older sisters, the huge contrast between his family background and Connie's – light vs. dark, straightforward vs. constrained. Sad story.

One day I asked him, "Don't you love Grandpa's new flower bed?" It was a special flower bed Grandpa had had put in as a surprise for Grandma.

Daddy answered that Grandpa had put the flower bed in the wrong place. And then he went on to explain to me that Grandpa didn't take care of his property the way he, Daddy, would do it. "Why mow that beautiful field? It should be growing wild flowers," he said. "If he'd just hay it once or twice each summer. So much more natural and beautiful and not so manicured." Or he would criticize Grandpa for being extravagant by having a more expensive car than he – Daddy – felt he needed, but he would always do this as if he were teaching me about how to live wisely, which meant frugally.

His conversation about my grandfather always had an edge to it. I could sense it and I knew he didn't really like Grandpa. I heard this from my mother, too.

"My father always said he couldn't talk to E.B.," she told me. "He was so closed in on himself, Father couldn't discuss anything with him. So, he came to avoid trying."

The closest I ever came to asking my father outright about what he thought of my grandfather brought the answer, "Oh, I can never do anything right."

DADDY'S VERSION of why we moved up to Schroon Lake year-round was always the same, no matter how I approached the question. "Your mother wouldn't live anyplace else."

I knew my mother would have liked him to get some kind of reg-

[169]

ular job, but as long as we lived in Schroon Lake, that was pretty much impossible. Mother said, "If he'd only get a job with the telephone company, with some insurance company, with any reputable business, and work his way up, get a regular salary, so we wouldn't be spending principal." If I heard this once, I heard it a thousand times from my mother when I was growing up. And she didn't resist adding, "And it should have been as soon as I inherited the money from Grandfather." She would scold herself, in my presence, for turning over all that money to Daddy, and call herself "dumb and stupid" for doing it. If Daddy had gotten a regular job, she believed, we could have lived in a little house in some regular town, wherever the job was. But she would quickly tell me how impossible it was to bring this subject up with him. "He'd fly off the handle."

I certainly never had the nerve to ask him. Now I wish I had, but it would have ended my good relationship with him. I would have felt I was taking Mother's side against him.

No one told me why we were staying on in Schroon Lake after the summer of 1938 ended.

Now I know that the Texas visit was pivotal, that it brought to a head E.B.'s inability ever to feel he could communicate with my grandfather and vice versa. I think it was after this visit that my grandfather gave up, although he continued to help us by sending generous birthday checks, promising to pay tuition for us children, and giving Connie small sums of money to put aside (those also got spent as the original inheritance dwindled away).

E.B. wanted to stay in Texas; Connie wanted to go back. There's the statement, clear. I wrote that and for the first time I had an idea of the way Mother might have felt, down there in Texas. My husband and I lived in what seemed to me the other side of the moon, in the depressing suburb of South San Francisco, for the first six months of our married life. I had had a miscarriage, my husband was away all day at work, and I was terribly homesick for the look of something familiar, green, soft, and not dusty; some color in the fall. And I felt I couldn't complain. It's ancient history, but I remember it keenly.

I've always thought of my parents as having decided to live in

Schroon Lake because they couldn't afford anywhere else, and then characteristically turning that into a virtue. My father had known life on a farm, and he liked the idea of owning one, and Grandpa's land included what had once been a farm, run by someone else, which Daddy might have imagined himself managing. Living in Schroon might have looked like a good compromise between a farm and the one place in the world Connie wanted to be.

I've also always thought E.B. really did not want to live in Schroon Lake. Not that he didn't love the woods and the rural way of life, but that it was Connie's father's place, even if he had given it to them. It was Connie's place, more than his. I've thought that might be part of the reason he went away so much, though he might also have gone away because he was uncomfortable with the expectations that living as a member of the family thrust on him.

When my grandfather first acquired all the land for his summer place, he himself had liked the idea of owning a working farm. The tenant farmer lived in the farmhouse my grandfather gave to Connie and E.B. There wasn't much of a farm by that time, and Grandpa gave the caretaker/farmer the down payment for a small house on property that the caretaker developed into tourist cabins. My mother and we three children went back north by train from San Antonio, and E.B. drove – by way of California, where he had some business leads.

According to my mother, her father must have been thinking about dividing up his property for some time; it's not the kind of thing he would have acted on overnight. So he must have been thinking about it long before he and Grandma came for the Texas visit. This was a good thing, because it meant Mother and Grandpa didn't seem to be in cahoots. Because Mother wanted very much to go back home, and this was a chance to do that, she was particularly anxious that it not look like a hasty plan to cajole E.B. into moving back up north, get him to forget about his dreams of living on a ranch in Texas.

E.B.'s REAL SKILLS were as a behind-the-scenes analyst of the stock market. If he'd become a broker, as Connie had hoped he'd do with part of her inheritance from her grandfather, he might have done well. But as she often said, he was determined to make it on his own. He wasn't a joiner, and that meant he was not going to become a broker. He invested for himself. He probably didn't want to be responsible for other people's money. No one has ever mentioned the amount Connie inherited at her grandfather's death in 1926, which she handed over to E.B., but it was the proverbial nest egg and according to Mother, it was fairly substantial – certainly enough to supplement a steady income handsomely. And while the market was still booming, through the twenties, it was hard to make a mistake, no matter what one bought.

All might still have been well, even after the crash, if Mother's brother hadn't been so heavily overextended. Nobody in the family knew about that until it was too late. My grandfather bailed him out, which in turn left my grandfather with greatly diminished capital, so that when he died, in 1941, there was no large sum of money to be passed along. I heard this story in various forms from various people my whole life. I never once heard any actual figures. That was the way it was in my family, and I suspect in many families where there was an expectation of means. You learned that you weren't supposed to spend capital, you heard about unfortunate reverses, and you never knew what anyone had. It was all hidden. Money was secret. It was a shameful thing to talk about, as shameful as the intimacies of the body.

And about the ranch: not only did E.B. want to carry through with that plan, he felt he would look stupid to the bank – who owned the mortgage and from whom he was going to buy the place – if he pulled out. One thing that would have saved him, in his own eyes, was that (with Connie's money, of course) the well had been dug, which would enhance the property by supplying good water. So the falling in of the deal was not a complete bust for the bank. The banker who brought him in on the deal was someone with whom he had been doing business the whole time we'd been in Texas.

The portion of the Schroon Lake property Grandpa gave to Connie and E.B. had the only year-round house. It also had a boathouse; The Lounge, down by the lake; maybe ten acres on the lake side of the road; and about one hundred fifty acres of woods. The woods were important because they meant a good supply for heating, and an additional source of income through timbering.

DID I KNOW we weren't leaving Schroon that fall? It had always been my dream to stay, and I was sad when the time came each September to go back to wherever we were spending the winter. But I never knew how different it would be, without the rest of the family and the house guests who always overran the place, summers. I must have known we were staying, because we moved into the farmhouse before Grandpa and Grandma left.

I remember the morning Aunt Ann and Uncle Dwight left with Bill and Mary, being told we were staying. Their Air-Flow Chrysler was crammed ceiling high, and there were suitcases strapped to the roof, as they left early in the morning to make Philadelphia in one day. We three children waved till they were out of sight over the crest of the hill, rear bumper dipping low. When Aunt Rae and Uncle Joe left, their car was nearly empty because Aunt Rae shipped things by Railway Express; plenty of room for Snooks, their dog, to loll across the back seat. Muriel was already off at college, her first year. Uncle Joe, tall in the passenger seat, tipped his straw hat to us as they pulled out of the driveway, cigar smoke trailing from his window.

Grandpa and Grandma drove off in their high old Pierce Arrow, with James following in the Ford woody V-8 station wagon packed with their luggage. They took two weeks to get to Florida in those pre-World War II days. Bridget and Etta, the maids, went by sleeping car straight there so they could open the winter place for Grandpa and Grandma's arrival.

As soon as they had gone, Harold, Grandpa's gardener, started closing down Almanole.

Next door, the boys' camp emptied out. I remember watching the cabins stripped of canvas flaps by bronze-armed counselors, and saggy mattresses piled high on a truck. I went over to the camp after everyone had left it and found naked iron cots scattered every which way on worn wood floors, bureaus crammed into one corner, with overturned black metal wastebaskets on top of them like squat, pointy-headed dwarfs crouched together.

Harold looked after things at The Place all winter. He didn't want to go to Florida. "Heat's too much for my Indian blood," he would say. The very day my grandparents disappeared down the road, the green-

and-beige-striped awnings were taken off the porches of Almanole, along with the porch furniture, the rattan rugs, and the swinging couches. Harold piled things high in the back of the truck, rolled the rugs and loaded them on top. I sat on these thrilling thrones of familiar objects, helping to anchor down each jouncing load on many trips to the barn. Unloaded, how small and forlorn the things looked waiting outside to be stored away in darkness, with only chipmunks for company.

The boats were hauled out of the water into the rollercoaster boathouse by a mechanized windlass attached to a trolley cart. The canoe and the rowboat filled the cart for one load; then Grandpa's fishing launch (his big motor boat wintered alone in its own boathouse); and finally the Adirondack furniture, carried from its place at the water's edge where grownups had sat and talked endlessly all summer while we children raced in and out of the water with our cousins. Now the doors of the boathouse were brought together and the flat padlock was fitted into its place and snapped closed. Grandpa's unfriendly sign above the boathouse doors warned: Private Property! Keep Off! Trespassers Prosecuted! I thought it said "persecuted," felt it sounded threatening and mean. I wondered if any teachers or kids in the school I was going to in a few weeks would have seen this sign.

Finally the green docks themselves were hauled out of the water, with the help of extra men from the village. The men sloshed into the water wearing high wading boots, lifted the docks off the pilings and stacked them in pairs on their sides under the deep eaves of the boathouse, each pair covered tightly with a canvas tarp. I watched everything, staying out of the way but ready to rush in whenever I could. Harold called me Scout, just as my father sometimes did.

With September came the fall equinox, shorter days, the first frost. The air changed. The light looked sad and pale. Even at noon the sun's warmth was fleeting. No sun came in the kitchen window now to the east while we were having breakfast. Mornings we needed a daybreak fire in the kitchen range.

The lake no longer beckoned with seductive power. Often at dawn heavy fog blotted out the water, silencing any birds not yet departed. A mysterious quiet settled over the woods. I was an Indian scout seeking out friendly settlers. I would work my way through a shroud of mist, down to the water. I saw the first leaves change: patches here and there at the tip ends of certain branches of maples, brilliant red, wild and unexpected as flames.

The scout was dragged away to shop for back-to-school clothes. Mother took Maya and me to Glens Falls, the nearest town with a department store, and we had to spend hours trying on clothes and shoes in the overheated, stuffy store. Another day, Mother took Maya and me to the school to register. I was curious to see what a real school would be like. I had only gone to kindergarten, and that had been two years ago, in Florida. All we did was play. During the year just past, Maya and Mother had taught me to read from one of Mother's childhood McGuffey's Readers that had no-nonsense black line drawings I liked of old-fashioned children. And not many pictures at that, only every other page.

The school building was new, finished that summer. It looked too big, stuck up too high out of the ground, which had tiny shoots of new grass, even though it wasn't the growing season.

"Why so big?" Grandpa had fussed, at the last Sunday dinner. "A one-room schoolhouse was plenty for me. Who needs granite floors, brass doorknobs, that enormous gymnasium? No wonder local taxes went sky high."

"Think of your granddaughters, Father Harris," Uncle Joe teased, softening Grandpa as only he could.

Grandpa glanced at me and Maya. "At least you girls'll get the benefit," he agreed. "Now work hard, girls." He gave us a serious look, patted our heads.

Now Mother took our hands and we went into the school and down a long empty corridor, our footsteps echoing. I remember watching my new oxfords sliding on the gleaming, hard surface – black squares and gray squares. Was this the granite floor Grandpa hated? I hoped he hadn't talked to anyone at the school. I was relieved my last name wasn't Harris.

Mother stopped outside the principal's office and knocked on the door. A man's voice called, "Come in."

The principal got up when we came in, bent his head forward, pressed his hands onto his desk. There was a smell of furniture polish in the room. He shook hands with Mother. His hair was gray and stiff, combed flat. Mother answered questions about Maya and what grades she had been through in school. Then they were talking about me. They talked as if I weren't in the room.

I felt a knot in my stomach when I heard the principal say something about my having to start back in first grade even though I was already seven and a half and could read.

"She reads well," Mother said. She sounded firm. "She can do second-grade work." More talk, about what books I could read. I was thinking, I can read any book you give me. I was thinking, if they would just talk to me he would see I could go right into second grade.

Finally he looked at me. "Let's keep an eye on her," he said. "See how she does."

I didn't understand what he had decided, but Mother seemed pleased. He told her how to get to our classrooms, which door was Maya's classroom, sixth grade, and which was mine, Miss Crowe's. "Your little girl's class," he said. I wanted to kick him in the shins. Mother took us to see our classrooms, even though no one was there. When we got to mine I read the card stuck onto the door. Miss Crowe, Grade 2. The knot in my stomach eased.

Now that I was going to go to school, and Maya would be in the sixth grade, the gap in our ages felt bigger than it had ever felt. Not that we spent much time together anymore. Her asthma kept her from running around. When we were together, she talked about movie stars and how she thought she might be in love with this one or that one. I thought she was silly. I only wanted boys as pals, not heartthrobs, as she called them. But I was secretly very glad she would be going to school with me.

ALL MY LIFE I've been drawn to people who knew something I didn't know. Maya was the first. Daddy was more important than Maya and I took up with him after my earliest years. Once I came upon Antzie, I think a slight gap must have opened up between me and who I was to my father. To call it an estrangement would make it too solid, or obvious. I think that once I began to know things I couldn't tell him, I began to have to adjust myself in order to fit back in with him. Antzie didn't replace him, but she knew things about the world, and ways to negotiate life, and my year or two of being inseparable from her set me up outside the world of my family and apart from anything Daddy and Mother would have approved of if they had known.

Also, she saved me.

First day of school; my new clothes were scratchy, hot, unfamiliar. It was hard to eat anything at breakfast. I waited at the front door with Dwight next to me pressing his nose and forehead against the screen. I didn't want to wait with him, I wanted to stand on my own, but he looked up at me and his forehead and nose were checked with tiny squares. I felt sorry for him being left home. The bus came, huge, yellow, strange now that I was going to get on it. Dwight and Mother stood back, let me and Maya out the door. I left them. The screen door slammed. I followed Maya; I didn't look back. Maya waved, blew kisses. Then she turned to me, offered her hand. I pretended I didn't see, concentrated on lifting my foot up onto the high first step, another step, the bus door slapped shut. From the dim aisle inside I saw Dwight's face pressed against the screen, Mother shadowy behind him. They waved. I didn't.

Maya tried to sit. The boy in the other half of the seat turned away, didn't move. "Girls don't set here," he mumbled. He had a curtain of white-blond hair. I saw his eyes looking sideways but I could see he was trying not to. Fingers with bitten nails, black moons of dirt under each nail, grabbed onto the seat in front of him. Legs in baggy brown corduroy knickers, spread wide.

The bus didn't move. We had to sit down first. I followed Maya. Some heads turned; some eyes sneaked looks at us. Nobody made room. There were only boys for three or four rows, sitting as close as they could to the aisle edge of the seat without falling off. Maya walked to the first empty seat and slid in, and I slipped in next to her. The bus lurched forward and slowly picked up speed.

A finger poked my shoulder. "Hey! You live next door." A burst of laughter, like a machine gun.

I twisted around, looked into gray-green eyes under black bangs. A pink sweet-smelling bubble grew from her mouth. It popped. She sucked in pink film, laughed another short burst.

"I'm Antzie," she said. "Want some gum?" She held out a stubby chunk of bubble gum. I had never chewed bubble gum. I was only allowed Pepsin or Dentyne.

I put the bubble gum into my mouth and started working on it with my teeth. I loved the sweetness, the size of the gum. It filled my mouth. Maya said under her breath, "You can't chew gum in school." I chewed softly.

Behind me I heard, "Antzie, you'll catch hell. Spit it out." I looked around again. A boy two rows back — same black hair, same massed freckles, but much older — held out his hand. "Spit."

"Shut up and mind your own beeswax," Antzie said. Another burst of laughter.

The boy leaned over the back of her seat. "You're too fresh for your own good, Annabellie," he said into her ear.

"Says who?" She blew another bubble. "That's my know-it-all brother, Ray," she said to me, and pointed at two other seats. "And those are my brothers Bill and Bobby, Mike and Timmy. We're the Herlihys up the hill. Come after school. Pop's building a garage." She blew an enormous pink bubble that hid her face.

"Annabellie, you'll catch hell from Miss Crowe if you chew in school." This from one of her biggest brothers, who looked as if he shaved.

The bubble got bigger, paler. It popped. Thin pink skin filmed her eyebrows, eyelashes, even her black bangs. She pulled out her huge wad of gum and rubbed it around her face, vacuuming away the pink film, then stuffed the ball back into her mouth and laughed another staccato burst.

"The hell you say. Phooey on Miss Crowe. She's a battle-axe and I hate her."

I had never heard anyone say "hell" except in church, and I had never heard a child call a grownup a battle-axe. I felt a stab of excitement. Here was danger. And a friend who lived next door with all these brothers. I wanted school to be over fast so I could go up the hill to Antzie's house.

She poked me again. "What grade're you in?"

"Miss Crowe's. Are you scared of her?"

"Naw. Just keep your trap shut. Don't let her catch you. She's mean. We'll stick together."

I wondered if Antzie knew that our farmhouse went with Almanole. I was afraid she would think I was stuck-up if she knew I was Mr. Harris's granddaughter.

More kids crowded in. The bus got noisier and noisier. When we got to the school Antzie poked me again. "Follow me when we get off."

Kids thundered down the metal bus steps. I got separated from Maya and from Antzie in the flow of rushing bodies. I got carried along and pushed through the doorway but it wasn't the same door as before. I didn't know where I was, and no one even noticed me.

Then Maya was there. She had waited for me. "I know where you go," she said, and she took me by the hand. I didn't want to look like a baby. I pulled my hand away. She put her arm around me and I felt mean not to want it there. The Subabeeba days were gone. Then we were at Miss Crowe's room. I kissed Maya fast, then quickly opened the door and slipped inside.

I KNEW I was an outsider, a strange kid who came from someplace else, had parents who weren't like their parents, had a different background. I didn't know anyone who went to the school because we didn't know local people. Daddy always emphasized proper speech, and Mother and the aunts had standards of behavior and dress. At school, my proper speech set me apart, and my behavior, which would have been called manners by my family, didn't help me in the classroom, where it looked like apple polishing; or on the playground, where I had to learn to push right back. I remember that these kids even smelled different from what I was used to. I remember the smell of kerosene in that classroom, sweaty feet, coal-tar soap, body sweat. I wanted to fit in, not be noticed as the new girl and especially not as a rich summer kid, granddaughter of Mr. Harris (the man with unfriendly signs all over his property who said terrible things about the money spent on this school).

I remember Miss Crowe as a taskmaster. I would have fallen in love with any teacher who opened knowledge to me, and as I made my way through the various schools that constituted my formal education I was lucky enough to find one or two like that and I did fall in love with them. But Miss Crowe was interested in discipline, and she used humiliation to achieve it. That was how Antzie came to have such a saving role. She knew the ropes. I didn't even know there were ropes.

One day, early that first fall, Miss Crowe asked me to tell the class where I had gone to school the year before. I was silent. I had not gone to school the year before. I had never gone to first grade at all. I remember Miss Crowe bearing down on me. Maybe she even said, "Cat got your tongue?" and "Don't you know where you went to school?" but if not, it was something like that. I didn't want to lie, so I kept quiet and tried not to let her make me cry.

A loud crash broke the silence and everybody turned to see what it was. Two boys in the back of the room had tipped over their desks. They were punching each other. Miss Crowe lunged, yelling. She grabbed each boy by an arm, dragged them to the front of the room, made them stand in the corners.

Later, when we had all written the alphabet in cursive, she sent the two boys down the aisles to pick up our papers.

Emerson came down my row. When he was next to me he pulled back his lips, made his face skull-like, opening his eyes as wide as he could. He stood close, hissed fish breath at me as I handed him my paper. "Earl 'n' me'll gitcha at recess."

There was no way to get out of recess.

Miss Crowe was writing on the blackboard and heard nothing. I was lost, done for.

Then, a "psssst" beside me. Antzie was squatting next to my desk. She beckoned me to lean toward her, and she put her mouth right at my ear and said, "Don't listen to that lummox. See you at recess. My brothers'll sock 'im." Then she was back in her seat two desks behind me, just as Miss Crowe turned to give us our next instructions.

When it came time for recess I hurled myself out into the yard, running fast, trying to keep up with Antzie. She ran hard, legs pumping, skirt flying up showing her underpants. Emerson disappeared in a knot of boys. He never even looked my way.

I got a hard push from behind but before I could be angry I heard the loud staccato laugh.

"You're it," Antzie shouted. And as if I were one of them, I became part of the game. Antzie was fast but I didn't give up and finally I caught her. Eventually we become leaders of a pack of tougher girls who grabbed the boys' ball, taunted them to catch us if they could. I realized Emerson wasn't going to bother me once he saw I was friends with Antzie. She had those five older brothers.

Antzie didn't consider herself a local. She told me the first day, "Watch out for Miss Crowe. She always picks on new kids, especially if you're a summer person like you and me." Her family had moved the year before from Flatbush, in Brooklyn. She called Schroon Lake a hick town. You can see how she rescued me. And that's the way our friendship stayed. She rescued me from ignorance, from innocence.

One day, when the bus got to my stop, Antzie told me again to come up the hill and play. I ran in and told Mother, and would have run back out but Mother wouldn't let me go on foot; she said it was too dangerous because of cars coming full-speed over the hill. If Daddy had been home he would have walked me up there. She drove me up in the car, made me look like a sissy. At the top of the hill, I got out of the car and ran. Antzie was waiting at her driveway, where the new garage was going up. The raw new lumber was pale yellow and fresh-looking.

Antzie's father and some of her brothers were pounding nails. Sometimes the hammer blows went together, sometimes just off like jerky music. Her father had his back to me. When he turned I saw nails coming out of his mouth. "Who's your new friend, Antz?" he mumbled.

She introduced me and he took the nails out of his mouth and tucked them into a pocket of his carpenter's apron. He wore round steel-rimmed glasses, his brown eyes almost filling the lenses. I thought of my father, who would never hold nails in his mouth like that because you might swallow them by accident.

"Pleased to make your acquaintance, Miss," Antzie's father said. "I know your Uncle Joe Early. See him at Mass. Here's the newest addition to the Herlihy estate." He waved his arms to encompass the nearly finished garage. "If you and your fresh friend behave I might let you paint in half an hour or so."

With a smooth motion, Mr. Herlihy lifted the short stump of his left leg off the handles of a pair of crutches I hadn't noticed until that moment. He fitted the crutches under his arms and before I realized it, he was across the bright yellow, brand-new wood floor and over on the far side of the garage. "Keep those nails in line, Ray," he said in a friendly way. Ray was nailing shingles to the roof. "We don't want this looking like Paddy's outhouse. Mr. Harris next door wouldn't like it." I felt myself blushing. Then I saw Mr. Herlihy wink at me, and it was okay.

"Race you to the lake," Antzie shouted, and she was off. We ran downhill on a rutted path through the Herlihys' woods, more wild than Grandpa's next door, more exciting and unknown. At the lake she told me how her father had lost his leg. She had a rapid-fire delivery; she never paused as she hurled stone after stone and we watched them skip – skip – skip – skip – before they sank. She told me her father had been left for dead in a shell hole overnight. When they found him somebody had started to put a dead tag on his only foot. He said, "Hold it. I'm not dead yet." The Red Cross guys almost dropped him, thought he was a ghost. "And his stump stunk," she said.

He must have told her that. I can remember the frisson it caused in me, to hear her talk about these things. "I'll show you the telegram that says he's dead," she said. "It's on our wall. Last one up the hill's a rotten egg."

We ran back to the house. Antzie's mother was fixing dinner. She opened cans of fruit cocktail, dumped them in a big blue-and-white-striped bowl. A pyramid of hot dogs sat on the kitchen table. More hot dogs sizzled in a frying pan; baked beans bubbled in the oven.

"You have to start early to feed this mob," Mrs. Herlihy said. "Where are your manners, Miss? How about introducing your new friend?"

Antzie introduced me and I said, "How do you do?" but I didn't curtsy as Grandma had taught me to do.

"Maybe Mr. Harris's granddaughter can teach this hooligan some etiquette," Mrs. Herlihy said. She aimed a spank at Antzie's behind. Then she winked at me, just as Mr. Herlihy had.

"We're going to paint for Pop," Antzie told her, and then she was out the door, with me trying to keep up. When I caught up with her she punched my arm, not hard. "You're okay," she said. "I thought you'd be stuck-up, coming from next door. Race you to the garage." She was off like a shot.

Mr. Herlihy had started painting. "Wood's so dry it sucks up paint like a sponge," he said. "Now girls, watch what I do and you can finish the bottom there." He dipped the brush, drained out most of the liquid against the sides of the paint pail, and stroked slowly up and down, overlapping his brush strokes. "See if you can do it without making a mess," he said, and he handed the paintbrush to Antzie.

She followed his instructions to the letter. When she had put on several brushfuls she handed the brush to me, and her father checked her work. Nobody had ever asked me to do a serious job before. I dipped the brush into the thick white paint only so far. I pushed the bristles against the rim of the pail on both sides until all the big drips had fallen back in and disappeared. I watched where I was walking so I didn't tip over the paint bucket. Then slowly and carefully I stroked on a big band of white, up and down.

"So far, so good, girls. If you help with the rest of this fine garage I'll give the two of you a quarter. Now I'll milk that cow for Mrs. Herlihy." He swung down the rough path on his crutches, faster than most men could walk.

We painted until it was too dark to see. When we went outside it was starting to rain and we ran down to the house. Mrs. Herlihy insisted I stay for dinner, not make my mother come out in the downpour. My mouth watered as I thought about those forbidden hot dogs.

It was the first of many meals with the Herlihys. The table was crowded, arms reached for more hot dogs, more rolls, mustard, relish, catsup, coleslaw, potato chips, and endless helpings of baked beans. At the Herlihys', brothers were coming and going throughout the meal, getting more to eat, feeding tidbits to Rootie the dog and Tootie the cat, giving each other the odd punch. They all waited on their father, called him Pop. Now and then he would raise his voice above the hubbub, shout to bring the noise down. "The gangrene couldn't get me but your noise'll do me in. Enough of this. Blixoudi. I'll put an Irish hex on the lot o'ya." If he wanted he would get off a thick Irish brogue.

Everybody talked at once. Nobody told anyone to lower their

voice, to close their mouth, not to reach. They laughed a lot; they were loud and boisterous. They counted how many hot dogs disappeared down the current champion's gullet.

At one point Mrs. Herlihy clapped her hands for quiet.

"Jesus, Mary, and Joseph," she shouted. "You'll frighten our neighbors down the hill. Tone it down to a dull roar." I had never heard such a statement before. And it wasn't a rebuke, it was more a shout to loved friends.

Mrs. Herlihys' resonant voice could be heard above any din. I remember hearing her singing "Ave Maria" and "Oh, Holy Night" at St. Ursula's, times I went with Uncle Joe and Aunt Rae. Her voice soared, warbling a bit on the high notes. It used to give me chills. At the table she would get everybody quiet with a roar of "Silence, you hooligans." And then you could hear a pin drop.

I spent a lot of time up the hill with Antzie and her family. Mrs. Herlihy was the disciplinarian. Antzie could get away with murder around Pop; she was the apple of his eye and Mrs. Herlihy was harder on her because she was the only daughter and she was such a favorite.

One day I was coming toward their house and I heard Antzie yell "Bitch" at her mother, and then Antzie came running from the house. I heard that and felt as if I had been punched in the stomach. How could she dare? But she had. Her mother's voice echoed after her. "And don'tcha go blubbering to your father neither, you little hussy." I remember being habitually shocked by Antzie's behavior toward her mother; it was far beyond anything I myself would have thought of, let alone done or said to my mother. I was in awe of Antzie.

Why did my parents let me play with her? They must have known she wasn't the kind of girl who would improve me, as they might have put it. I think I kept that whole side of myself hidden from my family. I would go over to the Herlihys' and I would come back, but I never talked about what I did there, or about any of them, to my family. And I was careful not to show by my behavior either that anything about me was different.

But it was. Different. Antzie introduced me to things that were exciting, forbidden. They were the kinds of things that made my stomach drop into space – diving off the high board; jumping off the roof of Grandpa's porch into snow banks; leaping with a huge splash from a bent pine tree canted at an angle above the water. And sex.

When we were in fourth grade she taught me the meaning of the word I had seen scrawled on one of the concrete supports underneath the boardwalk, when we were staying at Aunt Charlotte's in New Jersey. I had never said the word, but I knew how to spell it. When I asked her what it meant, I spelled it.

"Fuck," she said, right out. We both got off the bus at her house. We had on all our snow things, leggings, too. Antzie had bought bubble gum, and a pack of Luckies for her brother. She had to lie. We went down into the woods.

Her brothers were still at school sports or working at after-school jobs or at the family store. We were alone, snow coming down so fast no one could have seen us from more than a few yards away. We knelt under a thick spruce, so the sheltering branches could keep our cigarettes dry enough to light.

"You show me you can smoke," Antzie challenged me. "I don't believe you. Then I'll tell you about your word." She carefully tore the blue New York State tax seal, then tapped out one cigarette for herself, grabbed it with her lips and pulled it out of the pack. She lit it, puffed a few times, and when she had the cigarette going she handed me the pack.

I imitated what she had done, and drew in hard. The smoke filled my mouth; some spilled out and went into my eyes. I tried not to cough but it was hard not to.

"Take it easy," she said. "You're doin' okay."

Her praise thrilled me. I took a smaller puff and tried pulling a little bit of smoke down into my lungs. It made me dizzy instantly. My head felt woozy but I blew out the smoke, slowly, easing it out. This time I didn't cough. I thought of cowboys, smoking as they rode, as they lassoed. It had looked so easy. I narrowed my eyes, reached over toward Antzie and handed her the pack. I managed to blow a little smoke from my nostrils. She whistled.

We smoked our cigarettes down to small stubs, and dropped the glowing butts into the snow. They hissed, and disappeared. We stood

[185]

and stomped our boots on the tiny holes in the snow to make sure we destroyed the evidence.

"We've gotta chew gum to kill the smell fer sure," Antzie declared, and popped one of her big bubble-gum balls into her mouth. I was fighting nausea, but I copied her, and chewed hard, determined not to show it. I was still waiting for her to get to the taboo subject.

"Let's siddown," she said, and we sat side by side, leaning up against the rough trunk of the spruce. I shivered in expectation. I felt her arm move against my side as she pulled a long, sagging strand of bright pink bubble gum out as far as she could reach. My hood acted as a blinder, and I had to turn my whole body in order to see her. I watched as she retracted the gum quickly into her mouth by winding her long tongue around and around the fine pink string. Sweet bubble-gum smell wafted into the air between us.

Now she was doing something different. She wet her fingers and took the entire glistening pink wad out of her mouth. Rolling the gum and wetting it with more spit from her tongue, she started making it into a cylinder, fat at one end, pointed at the other. It was about the size of a new art-gum eraser, but pink and exciting. She squeezed the fatter end into two ball-shaped lumps. When she had done that she immediately plunged the pink shape into the snow and pulled it out again. Chilled, it maintained its oddly fascinating shape. She rolled sideways to her knees and turned to face me, so close that the sides of our hoods met. I got to my knees too. Our hoods created a dark cave; I could just make out her mouth and white teeth.

"Okay, here's the word – watch," and she moved the pointed end of the gum shape slowly toward her mouth, now rounded into a tight little O. She slid it into and out of her mouth several times. "You know what your brother's thing looks like," she said. "Well, it gets hard and then boys stick it into a girl's thing." And she pointed to the space where my legs came together, what Mother always referred to as down between your legs.

I was having trouble sorting out this information, wondering where exactly that thing could fit.

"Not in your mouth, dummy," she said. I must have looked blank because she sounded disgusted. "Don't you know anything?" She had put her mittens back on and she stood up and brushed the snow off the seat of her pants, banged her hands together to warm them. She punched my arm, grabbed my hand and pulled me out from under the branches.

She stuck her face inside my hood, put her lips to my ear. "It goes in where the baby comes out and that's what makes babies," she hissed. "Now we have to go clean my room. You smoked pretty good."

When we got back to the house it was full of boys – taking off boots, helping their mother move the table out from the wall for dinner, filling the woodbox, getting a fire going in the fireplace at the far end of the kitchen. Mrs. Herlihy was stirring and beating at the stove, strands of curling red hair escaping from her knot and the combs just behind her ears.

"Your mother'll be here in the car for you in half an hour," she said. "Too much snow coming down for you to walk. Timmy'll see you up the hill to the road. Now you go help Antzie get a start cleaning her room, or no Santa for her." She waved us off.

We passed Mr. Herlihy coming in. He hopped over the threshold neatly on his crutches. His boot was covered in snow almost to the top. As he passed Mrs. Herlihy, he patted her behind, then winked when he caught me looking. I was embarrassed, but I couldn't help watching everything that happened in that household.

He perched on a stool, held the toe of his right boot with a crutch, anchored the heel with his other crutch, and lifted his sock-covered foot free and clear. He looked over at me and smiled.

"Only one foot to warm up," he said as if it were an asset. "How're you doing on this lovely winter's day? Antzie and you staying out of trouble?"

I felt a guilty jolt in my stomach, an unwanted flash of him and his wife in bed together, doing it. I could feel a blush rising.

"You've got nice pink cheeks from the cold," he said. "Now run along, you and Antzie."

Antzie had already gone to her room, a separate one just for her. The boys all slept in a dormlike arrangement up on the second floor, bunk beds along one wall, card tables for studying opposite.

When I got to her room Antzie was delving into her closet, sling-

[187]

ing things out of its depths. She acted as if there were no further secrets to divulge. I felt a terrible letdown. But then she made a running leap onto her bed and stretched out, one socked foot resting on the other scab-covered knee.

"Okay, go to it," she commanded. "Pick up my old stuff and throw it in those bags." She pointed to three grocery bags – one for toys, one for clothes, one for shoes. I moved clumsily, still wearing my snow pants to save time when I had to go home. "Carry 'em to the back porch," Antzie said, and I realized she would only dole out further information if I gave in to her demands as she went along. I knew I should try to act as if I didn't care, but I did everything she ordered me to do.

When I got back from carrying the bags down we had a warning call from her mother that dinner was almost ready and I had to be up the hill by the road in ten minutes.

Like a shot Antzie was off the bed. "Don't tell or I'll beat you up," she said under her breath. "Come on," and she dragged me into her closet – empty now except for dust fuzzies and dog and cat hairs from Rootie and Tootie. She pushed me down. "Pull down your snow pants," she whispered.

I followed her directions in a trance of shyness and excitement, pushing at the tight elastic around my waist. Antzie's hand had disappeared inside her underpants to that never named area. I copied her motion, scared witless, unable to do otherwise. What exactly did she say? Maybe nothing. At some moment, some flash point of revelation, I knew what she was trying to show me – the spot connected with f-u-c-k, the place where babies came out.

Timmy's voice yelled at the door. "Antzie, get outta there. Yer friend's gotta go."

Terror. We scrambled. Somehow I snapped my snowpants up in place, and we burst out of the closet and tumbled together on the floor. Timmy was standing in the doorway waiting for us.

"Come on," he shouted, and he turned and charged down the hall, with me after him pulling on my snowsuit jacket. I had to stop at the door to pull on my boots and he waited. Then I was tearing after him again, winding my scarf around my neck, trying to zip up my jacket as I went. Walking fast up to the road, snow brushing my face, I was glad to be out of that closet; I felt cleansed, almost ready to see my mother.

The car advanced up the hill slowly in first gear, Mother's head barely above the steering wheel. It was almost dark out. Her headlights picked up millions of flakes in their golden light, the woods on the far side of the road closing down, mysterious and secret, the shoulders of the trees sloping under their white burdens. Tim gave arm signals to guide Mother turning around on the apron in front of the new garage.

He opened the car door for me and I climbed up onto the running board and he closed the door as I settled onto the seat next to Mother. She pushed the huge gear shift into first and we moved slowly down the hill, the headlights boring a tunnel into swirling flakes.

She asked me if I had had a nice time. Her voice sounded so normal. Of course I said yes.

The ride down the hill to our house took minutes but I felt it as a long journey. I came home another person, with a secret. I looked back from that moment with terribly mixed feelings. I felt not only awe for Antzie but fear, fear she would tell. I knew I had given her power over me. There was no going back.

Antzie rescued me from ignorance, time and time again. No one ever rescued Mother, or Daddy. Though maybe not for lack of trying.

IN THE BOTTOM of a drawer, one of those last days at Schroon with Dwight, I found some old Christmas cards from the grandparents. I sat on the floor and looked through the packet of cards, each with a handwritten note mentioning a little something extra from your own private Santa. I came across a photo that must have been taken around the time I was three, still the baby. Mother was leaning toward Daddy and they were actually touching. His head was bent toward hers and they were both smiling lovingly. I was straining to pull away from the circle of Mother's arm. I looked as if I were about to run out of the picture. Maya perched like a good girl on Daddy's left knee, her head a mass of golden, Shirley Temple curls, her smile angelic. Right there, for all to see, our father's right arm was around our mother's shoulders, his hand reaching halfway down her reaching arm.

So, I thought, there had been better times. And I did have a bigger portion of happy family memories than Dwight did because of the four-year difference in our ages. Things had been different in the early years. What had happened to turn things sour? It must have been about when I was eight, when Daddy started coming and going.

It must have been about then that he realized he was not going to live the way his parents had lived before the bankruptcy; he was not going to live up to the wealth and position he had been born and raised to recapture. (He and Mother had been married for almost twenty years by then.) Around the time the Johnstones came to Schroon Lake, and the war began in Europe, everything changed. I see this now, but not until now. It's because of Dwight that I'm putting together the fragments I always kept as if in tins like pieces of broken china that could be glued together but could never be used again.

Eleven

I'M LYING on my side on the bed, my head resting on two sloping pillows, another pillow pressed to the other side of my head. Mother comes out of the room across the hall buttoning a long navy sweater around her hips, continuing up the front to her neck.

"It's bitter cold," she says. "Around fifteen. You have to wear your snowsuit. That heater doesn't do much."

I roll onto my back and let her pull heavy wool snow pants up my legs and fasten them around my waist. I reach one arm, then the other, into my snowsuit jacket.

"Daddy's got the car ready," she says. "He's coming up."

I hear his slow steps moving up the bare wooden staircase. Then his big body, encased in a long black overcoat, fills the narrow doorway. Little drops of melting snow trickle slowly down his forehead, onto his ruddy cheeks.

"Ready, Scout?"

I can feel some of the cold from outdoors like a halo around his bulk.

"Be careful of her head going through that door," Mother says.

He says nothing. He reaches down and easily lifts me off the bed and high into his arms. I inhale his strength, pushing my nose deep into the warmth of his neck where it meets his collar. With one arm I pull myself as close and snug to his chest as I can. "Please don't bounce on the stairs," I whisper into his collar, "it'll hurt my ears more."

He goes down the stairs as if he were walking on delicate glass that might shatter under too firm a step. "Where's her hat?"

Mother is two steps behind him. "I didn't want her to be too sweaty when you got her outside," she says gently. "Here, I'll put it on."

Daddy stops at the bottom of the stairs. I wince as Mother pulls the wool cap well below my ears. I feel her pull on galoshes and buckle them, four buckles on each boot. I hear her rooting around in the small chest near the door.

"Here," she says, and then she's winding a scarf around my neck, tucking it into the collar of my coat.

"We've got to go, Connie." Daddy speaks with a controlled sense of urgency as if he's been waiting longer than anyone should ever be expected to wait. "The car windows will all have to be cleaned off again if we don't go now."

He carries me out the door, down the porch steps, to the car, and lays me in one motion on the back seat. He tucks me in under a bear rug, two soft pillows under my head. I lie as still as possible. Bumps make a stab of pain in my ears.

I'M SMALL in the full-sized bed (I'm in the grownups' ward). The top sheet is folded over the white seersucker blanket cover. I play my fingers slowly up one column of seersucker bumps and hollows and down the next.

Winter evening is closing in on the window, but I, coming to a hollow in the fabric, am walking into a dip in the summer lawn, my feet sliding silently through dewed grass, feet pleasantly cooled by the dampness, small strips of mowed grass sticking to my feet. I try not to notice the path of the sun as it dips lower outside my window.

I know Daddy can't come; he has to be in Albany with Uncle Joe. I'm waiting for Mother, but I imagine seeing Daddy in the doorway. Then she's there, taking off her gloves, opening her coat. She stamps her feet, leans down and undoes the buckles on her galoshes. I sit up in bed and reach my arms straight out in front of me and she crosses the room in two big steps and envelops me.

I remember the smell of her; it was balm to me.

I bury my face deep in her neck and hold on, even though I know I have to let go. I want to hear her voice, too, have her tell me what's been happening at home, maybe have her read to me for a little while. These visits were not long. Dwight was sick at home, and Maya's asthma was always worse in the cold weather. And the drive was slow, with the roads slick; it could be two hours or more.

She sits on the bed, but she hasn't taken off her hat, so I know she won't be here long. We ask each other questions. I ask about my sister and brother; she asks if I've had a fever and whether I'm eating. And she asks if there has been any more discharge from my ears. I'm able to tell her only a little but at least the stabbing pains have stopped.

She fluffs my pillows and I lie back to listen to her read. I used to listen to her voice more than to the story, which I usually knew by heart. I settle back into the pillows and float on her voice into sleep, even though I don't mean to miss one moment of her visit.

She doesn't go away. She's still there when the nurse wheels through the door with my dinner. I come to with a jolt.

The nurse cranks me up and sets my tray on the rolling table over my knees. She yanks off the metal covers. "Now don't leave a single pea," she says, and she's gone.

Mother comes to the side of the bed. She says, "Let me give you a few bites. Maybe I can make it taste better." She cuts the meatloaf into bite-sized pieces; she stirs a pat of butter into the mashed potatoes and sprinkles them with pepper, and the peas, too, with salt and pepper both.

And then she feeds me. I haven't been fed since I was very small. I always hated being fed. But now I pretend to myself that each mouthful is delicious, transformed. One thing I remember about Mother is that she was never in a hurry. I don't remember her ever making me feel as if she was too busy for me. This meal is an exquisite example.

Soon enough, she has to leave. I watch her work her galoshes over her low-heeled tie shoes. She stands and pulls on her heavy coat and tucks her scarf in around her neck. She squares her hat, glancing into the tiny mirror over the sink in the corner. I know she's coming over now to hug me and then she'll be gone. I don't want to cry. I never wanted to cry. I was determined to be the good soldier for which I was habitually commended by my father. In order to keep the tears from jumping into my eyes now, I hold myself away from her hug. She envelops me again in her arms, and I secretly clench my throat muscles and hold my breath until the hug is finished.

She knew. Mother knew me well, though I didn't understand it for many years – not till she came to live with us at the end of her life. I used to worry afterward that I had hurt her, but she never let me see it, if I had.

That scene or something like it played itself over and over again during the six weeks I was in the hospital surviving and recovering from mastoiditis in the days before antibiotics.

WHEN IT WAS TIME to go home, Mother came to get me out. I remember her packing my things while I rolled myself around the room in a high-wheeled wooden wheelchair.

I roll over to the small closet, jump out of the chair, pull my heavy winter coat off its sagging wire hanger, and fling it onto the bed.

"I don't have to wear this now, do I?" I say.

She's busy rolling a pair of socks together. I watch her tuck them into a corner of the suitcase to fill a gap. "It's still chilly," she says. She looks out the window. "Your father said all the forsythia was in full bloom down there," she tells me, her tone matter-of-fact. "They had big bunches all over the house." She's talking about Brooklyn, where Daddy went for Grandma and Grandpa Harris's fiftieth anniversary party, to Aunt Rae and Uncle Joe's.

"Give me those books and games, Weezie. There's enough room for a few more things in here."

I jump back into the chair and roll over to the window seat, which is piled with green-backed Bobbsey Twins books, a tin board of Chinese checkers with marbles in place, a regular checkerboard with frayed edges, a Parcheesi board. I pile several books on my lap and lift all the game boards together and place them carefully on top of the pile. I roll over to the bed and stop, fast, next to Mother. The games slide onto the floor, marbles, checker pieces, Parcheesi cups and dice rolling far and wide.

"Why couldn't you be more careful?" She stamps her foot in exasperation.

I shoot out of the chair and fall to my hands and knees, scooping up game pieces as fast as I can. "I'm sorry," I say, stung that she has scolded me. I work silently and quickly, crawling into all areas of the room including the closet, where there are still a few things to be packed. In there I find a bright white Best and Co. box. I pull out the box and lug it to the bed.

Mother has gone back to her folding. "That's for you, from Aunt Rae," she says. "Daddy brought it back with him. Rae thought a surprise would perk up your spirits. Go ahead, open it."

I open the box, pull away crisp layers of white tissue paper, and lift out a navy blue coat, darker navy velvet collar, two rows of gray-white pearl buttons marching up the front. I immediately love this coat. I undo the buttons and slowly push my arms into the smooth, satin-lined sleeves. The coat fits perfectly, and it's not too long. A brand-new coat, all my own and not one my sister has already worn for two years. I marvel that Aunt Rae would know I would like to have a present like this.

I go back to the bed and start picking up the spilled froth of tissue paper and push it back inside the box. Underneath the tissue, face down on the bed, I find a large card, which I pick up and turn over thinking it must be for me from Aunt Rae. It's the invitation to the party I missed, the golden anniversary. Raised gold lettering. Paper-clipped to the invitation is a photograph of the entire family group, grandma and grandpa seated in the middle of the aunts and uncles and cousins, and my sister and brother. The ladies and girls are wearing long dresses; the men are in dark business suits, white shirts, vests, ties. Very formal. Even the cousins are wearing their most formal clothes.

All those family faces look out at me, most of them smiling big happy smiles – though my father has his usual stern face on. How handsome he looks, I think, as I hand the picture to Mother. She holds it up, examining it as I have just done, and I see, in Aunt Rae's handwriting on the back, a brief message: "We all missed you terribly, Connie. It's never the same without you. But we're thankful Weezie is getting well and we send our love. Rae and Joe."

My mother reaches over and takes my grimy hand in hers and gently pulls me toward her. My head is at her waist. I'll be eight the next week, and I've been glad I'm going to be home for my birthday, not in the hospital. But right now I know I've been childish, I've only been counting up my own losses, and I've counted as compensation having Mother stay here with me while the others went to Brooklyn. Why did I not think about her missing her parents' fiftieth wedding-anniversary party?

I feel sad, heavy and ashamed. I reach around her waist and bury my face in her stomach. She should have been in that picture. I wish I could have the magic power to turn back the clock, to have said, "Go, you must be there too. I'm fine here, please go."

[195]

We stand together – one of the rare times I sought this kind of comfort, from her or anyone – holding each other close, comforting each other.

Twelve

ONE HOT afternoon when Dwight and I had been working solo in different parts of the house we decided to do something together. The woodshed would be dark and cool, a welcome change of scene. We left our lunch dishes in the sink for once and went out of the kitchen through the small back vestibule that led directly into the woodshed. The vestibule had been built for an old fashioned true icebox that had later been replaced with a humming, electric model, still there and still humming. Across the threshold from the vestibule was the platform, well above the deep floor of the shed, where Daddy always left a small pile of wood for the kitchen stove at the ready so the women didn't have to descend all the way into the woodshed.

We stood together on the platform. The place was full of Daddy, whom neither of us had been able to know. His work pants hung on the wall on a nail right next to my shoulder, high rubber boots on the floor below them. Clothing. Empty and silent these many years. I brushed against the rough pants; their woody fragrance stirred me.

I caught Dwight looking at me. I let go of the old pants and stepped away, but I had remembered something.

Dwight and I made a scarecrow out of Daddy's clothes, stuffing them with newspapers. We seated him by the front door, and called Netsie – a terrible thing to do. The furor, the guilt, the turmoil immediately after Netsie saw the specter, was huge.

"Who is that?" The sound of fear in her voice. "What are you doing here? GET OUT." Then real fear, alarm. In hiding, I realize it's not funny. Netsie shrieks, "GET OUT OF HERE." She runs to hide. I know I've got to reveal our trick. I'm scared silly. I think Dwight will run into the front room with me and say, "Boo! It's only Daddy's clothes. We did it," or something like that. At that moment Mother, Charlotte, Virginia, and Nana get home from Glens Falls. As soon as the door is opened, Netsie sees the truth.

Mother turns on the light. Netsie is ashen, clearly unsettled, frightened. "What have you done?" Mother says, turning on me. Dwight has disappeared. "Why would you do such a thing? I'm surprised at you." Shame is heaped on my head. I know I've played a mean trick; Netsie might have had a heart attack. Did I think of this myself or did Mother throw these terrible words at me making me feel more guilty, cruel, vicious. And where was my bratty brother? But I had been the brains behind this mean prank.

Mother had no patience at that moment. She had had a long day: Charlotte had to look in three stores for exactly the right color thread; Virginia had been fussy for the last five miles. "You're old enough to know better," she said to me, truly angry. "Why can't I count on you?"

When I said, "Dwight helped me," she only got madder. She stamped her foot.

"It's all your doing, Lueza, and you know it. You apologize. This minute."

I was choking on tears of rage at being blamed for everything. I got out the words, "I'm sorry, Aunt Jeannette," then I ran from the front room, out to the kitchen, out the back door with black hatred in my heart. I was out to find that brat and make him sorry he had run out on me.

But I remember Charlotte, too, standing in the doorway saying, "That nasty little boy, how could he? He needs a good paddling." She was making sympathetic sounds, giving her sister support and comfort. "I'm going to tell E.B. when he comes home; he should know about this and punish that child."

"You'll do nothing of the sort," Mother said, and Charlotte must have known she had better keep her mouth shut.

Mother remembered the horrible ending to that day. When she first got in the front door, the afternoon light fading, the lamp not yet turned on, she saw the slumped figure. Of course it was E.B., she knew those clothes so well. She was hit by the horror that it was E.B., slumped in despair. Could he be drunk? He spoke of drinking, at times, after work, with Joe, the other reporters. Or was he dead? Had he shot himself? That lifeless-looking form – it could only mean he had given up; he had spoken of being at the end of his rope, how he wanted to leave them all, just disappear.

When the light went on, she realized her foolishness, that it was a vicious trick.

There is a time, growing up, when a child begins to realize that actions have consequences and that growing up involves being able to foresee the consequences, to some extent, and to take responsibility for one's actions. That afternoon, excited by the hurried creation of this lifelike figure, I was proud of our stranger at the door. Looking at him from the living room, I found him truly frightening. I knew it was only Daddy's empty clothing stuffed with balled-up newspapers. Anybody would know that in a second. But the light was dim. And Netsie's eyes weren't so good. (How many times had she asked me to thread her needle, and said how lucky I was to have such sharp eyes.) When our trick turned out as it did, I knew there was no excuse for what we had done. I knew then that I knew better, just as my mother said I did. And whether I admitted it to myself or not, I also knew that Dwight was too young to think of consequences, but I was no longer too young. That horrible incident was my fault.

Now, with Dwight there steadily sorting through things and seeming to pay no attention to their meaning, I shook off the flash of unwelcome memory.

"Mother'd love to be here," I said. "We used to laugh."

"Finally getting rid of stuff," he said. "She kept everything the same."

Daddy had been gone fifteen years. Mother had kept everything the same not because she was a maker of shrines; she was too busy living to spend time sorting over the past.

"We all had so much fun," she would say, matter-of-fact, holding out some ancient garment or piece of sporting equipment when she did try to weed things out. "Can you believe I ever wore this old number?" And she would send whatever it was hurtling across the room into a give-away box. "Let's not dwell on the past. Time for a swim."

Dwight pulled the old pants off their hook and tossed them into one of the cartons we had brought in with us. The heavy rubber boots followed. "Let's get to it," he said abruptly.

[199]

The woodshed was Daddy, emotionally charged by him; his aura loomed here. He had designed it to act as buffer for the north-facing side of the house, provide simpler access to the wood supply for the kitchen stove, which had a fire going in it night and day between early October and mid-June. He and two men from the village built the woodshed – thick stone walls about four and a half feet up, then the rest plaster-covered cement block (a popular and inexpensive building material available right after the war), and an aluminum roof. Snow slid off by itself, piling up on the ground through the winter till Dwight and I could step easily onto the roof – which was forbidden. It was a great spot for spying on each other's comings and goings.

The woodshed had a dirt floor dug down to a level well below the frost line, which made for more space between floor and ceiling, and created almost a churchlike atmosphere of muffled silence. Even the biggest trucks, shifting gears to get up the hill to the south, sounded faint and far away from inside here. Several cords of wood, enough to get Mother and Daddy from March to June – I knew the number once upon a time – were still stacked in even rows along the walls and into the middle of the fragrant-smelling space. One of the last things Daddy said was, "I put in enough wood to last us till the birds fly north." He was gone before then.

Dwight was looking down at the chip-covered floor below, Daddy's chopping stump hollowed in the middle into a bowl-like depression from the splitting of thousands of logs. The even rows of now thoroughly seasoned hardwood were beautiful to look at – some of the final physical labor Daddy was able to perform in the eightieth year of his life.

"Tomorrow I'm calling my old friend Jimmy Sanchelle," Dwight said. "I know he could use all this wood. He's got a family. They'll haul it away."

I had been frozen in my tracks just looking at the wood. I liked the idea of giving it to someone Dwight knew. "Just think of Daddy doing all this," I said.

"He wanted to take everything out on wood."

It was true. He had expended his energies on wood, cutting down trees, trimming and sawing them up to movable size, hauling them from the woods to the barn via tractor and cart, further sawing and splitting and hauling and stacking in the new woodshed. He had given in to an oil furnace at the end of the war. But there had always been a need for wood for the fireplace, a vital part of the heating system.

Dwight had started taking the gardening and farming tools down off the nails and hooks along the wall. We marched them through the outside door, as many as each of us could carry at a time, and put them in the back of the waiting truck. Mrs. Vanderlindt would be glad to have them.

When the last nail was empty I felt relieved. Dwight was grinning. He had a smudge of dirt down his forehead and across his left eye.

"Feel better?" I asked him. I wanted to wipe away the smudge.

"Time to get on with it," he said, dusting his hands on his pants legs. He pointed over my head. I turned. Hanging within reach were the picnic baskets of childhood, plump, double-partitioned baskets nicknamed buttocks baskets. Part of Daddy's golden Ohio boyhood. He used to tell us stories about family gatherings along the Olentangee River – always idyllic, as if picnics were perfect back then, with never a bug bite and never a cross word between his sainted mother and his gentle father. His family had grown more saintly the further his memory had to stretch.

"Let's save these baskets," I said. I couldn't bear the thought of letting them go. So beautiful. And they were useful too. Dwight was already out the door.

"Take 'em," he called back. "Too chilly for picnics in the Straits of San Juan de Fuca. What the hell will you do with 'em in New York City?"

He was right. I left them for the auctioneer. But I felt an annoying stab of disloyalty.

When he came back in he went up the ladder to the platform where picnic and kitchen equipment was stored. He started handing things down to me and I set them aside, keeping myself aloof from them until a worn leather plate carrier came into my hands. Blue-bordered white enamel plates – I didn't even have to open the carrier; I knew them inside there – thermoses, picnic silver. He handed down nested picnic platters too chipped for the table but fine for a meal on the ground, wooden tubs for ice, assorted bowls wrapped in newspapers with World War II banner headlines.

Then another item that stopped me. Aunt Charlotte's fly-proof celluloid salad cover and the plate with the picture on it of a stream winding into the distance, overhung with weeping willows. I used to think the stream must be the Old Antangee River. The salad cover was complete with clamps guaranteed to keep out the most persistent pests. Dwight and I laughed at the same instant, though probably for different reasons. Remembering the picnics. Remembering the aunts, those looming factors in the tense atmosphere of the house when I was growing up. The aunts had their personalities, which became part of the way everyone in the household behaved. They rose to their most magnificent in the preparations for picnics.

Picnics began the night before, when Aunt Netsie would boil two or three chickens in broth with onions, celery, carrots, parsley, plenty of salt and pepper. No excuse for tasteless chicken, Aunt Netsie's motto. When the chickens were cooked she heaved the heavy pot into a shaded, breezy spot on the back porch, settling it into a battered washtub full of lake ice clear as crystal. "Let the old birds stew in their own juice," she would say.

Next day I would help pull legs, wings, breasts out of the gelatinous chicken broth, then the meat off the bones, the one cooking chore I liked. I remember pushing my fingers in, separating chunks of chicken from bone and gristle. Aunt Netsie cut the chicken into just the right-size pieces. How many times did I hear Aunt Charlotte say, in her older sister way, "Not too small, Nettie, not too big. You know how I like my chicken salad. Tidy, even bites."

Aunt Charlotte would appear in the kitchen the moment the chicken pieces were ready. She was the one who mixed in the mayonnaise Aunt Netsie made, the chopped celery, finally the green grapes and walnuts Aunt Netsie prepared, and the seasonings. On top, she put carrot curls and radish flowerettes.

Once she appeared, Aunt Netsie switched her attentions to covering her yellow layer cake with near-fudge icing. Aunt Charlotte had made her angel cake the day before, with its snow-white frosting in swirls, peaks, and valleys. "Angel cake takes an even dozen, like

Mother said," she told me each time she made it. I would wait for the slithering clear whites to pile up into glistening mounds, like snowy peaks, in Aunt Charlotte's special green-striped brown bowl. (One day when Dwight and I had dragged the bowl out of the closet and were using it in the yard for making mud pies, Aunt Charlotte, sweeping around the corner of the house, snatched it away from us with the scolding words, "You know I can't cook without Mother's bowl. Your father will hear about this." I know I waited days for Daddy's punishing roar, but it miraculously never came.)

Mother would make brownies, Toll House cookies, deviled eggs. She cooked the eggs at dawn, chilled them on chunks of lake ice. Her special egg holder had little hollows to keep the eggs from sliding around, messing each other up. She made sandwiches, packed potato chips, plenty of fruit. Everything was piled into the buttocks baskets. Thermoses were filled with lemonade and iced tea.

Stowing these odd-shaped and potentially messy substances in the car was Daddy's job. Maya, Dwight, and I ferried everything to the car, where Daddy put almost everything into the trunk strapped onto its platform over the back bumper. The last two things to go in – at Aunt Charlotte's insistence – were always Aunt Charlotte's chicken salad (no one ever explained why, but it was always considered to be Aunt Charlotte's) in its fly-proof celluloid salad cover, and her angel cake, safely encased in her mother's Franklin cake carrier. The cake was so fragile, even in its carrier it had to be wedged in a corner of the back seat or held on someone's lap. The chicken salad had its own ice-filled wooden tub. And Aunt Charlotte didn't trust anyone else to move her chicken salad. "Don't touch it. I'm responsible and I'll bring it out at the last minute," we all heard her say on many occasions. "You know how I love my chicken salad."

I remember one picnic above all others. Daddy had put all the food and accoutrements in the car and I carried the delicate angel cake out and handed it to Aunt Charlotte, settled already in the back seat.

I rode in Grandpa's open touring car. The woody station wagon was ready too, piled high with tablecloths, napkins, sandwich carrying case, with thermoses and plates, blankets, cushions, toys, inner tubes, bathing suits, hats, a parasol for Aunt Charlotte. For these all-family picnics with Grandpa and Grandma and their house guests – Aunt Rae, Uncle Joe, Muriel and Snooks, Uncle Dwight, Aunt Ann, Mary and Bill – at least five cars were used, maybe six. (When I saw *Citizen Kane* I realized our family picnic convoys were slightly smaller versions of Charles Kane's, winding its way along the California beach below San Simeon.)

The caravan kept a steady, sensible pace, slow to prevent spillage and breakage as well as to infuriate all drivers for miles behind us. But we didn't stay on the main road for long. Our goal was one of many favorite picnic locations: some rushing stream where Grandpa and the men could cast for trout or a pasture with a vista of the high peaks.

On this particular day we pulled into the chosen spot, a meadow stretching out, a backdrop of mountains, a brook gurgling from rock to rock. (Those rocks were great as stepping stones.) An ideal day, billowing summer clouds to cool us, rolling by in an endless blue sky; a breeze that would keep bugs at bay.

As always, we kids scrambled out and ran to explore, the moment we got there. You'd look back at some point and see plates and platters and bowls, thermoses and baskets all set out on steamer blankets. Nobody had to call us. We raced for the feast.

"E.B.," Aunt Charlotte called out, on this particular occasion, ready with serving spoon in hand to dispense her specialty. "Why didn't you put out my chicken salad?"

I saw Daddy, leaning against a tree, eyes closed, cap slanted across his face, big hands laced over his chest.

"Why, Lottie," he said, his voice solemn and steady. "I didn't see your chicken salad. I thought maybe you hadn't made it this time."

For Daddy to say he thought Aunt Charlotte had not made her chicken salad was as if he had said the sun wouldn't set that night. No one spoke. Aunt Charlotte made long strides over to the LaSalle, the main food car. She leaned over, peered down into the trunk, her arm reaching this way and that. She turned, faced us all.

"Well, someone must have stolen my chicken salad. I put it on the side porch and someone passing by must simply have walked into our yard and stolen it. I would never have forgotten it."

I waited for Daddy to walk over to the car and pull the chicken salad out of its hiding place. He was so calm, so quiet, I thought he must know where the chicken salad was, and he wanted his sister to get a good dose before he let her off.

But when he moved it was to go over to the picnic spread and hold his plate out for potato salad, for a sandwich, and then the picnic proceeded as if nothing had happened.

Late in the afternoon, when we got home, low rays of sun were reflecting off the celluloid top covering the stolen chicken salad, just where Aunt Charlotte had said she put it – on the side porch, sitting in its wooden tub, melted ice water lapping at the edge of the plate. No one said a word about it.

WHEN THE SUN had slid behind the pines at the back of the barn, Daddy led Maya, Dwight, and me in solemn procession to offer up Aunt Charlotte's chicken salad to the raccoons and possums, maybe a few skunks. It was all gone the next morning, every last shred of chicken, chopped celery, green grape, wrinkled walnut, and limp green rag of lettuce.

Thirteen

DWIGHT WROTE:

> I remember riding from somewhere with him. We were headed toward home. He got to ranting and raving about Aunt Jeannette, Aunt Charlotte, Virginia and Nana. How he had to take care of all of them (as if he ever earned much money at all living on Mother's inheritance, or actually provided for them or any of us). We were passing by the Loon Lake Colony Club (I think it was called, where Route 9 turned left to go to Chestertown or right to go to Riparius) and he said, "Sometimes I'd like to tell Charlotte, Jeannette, Virginia and Nana to all go fuck themselves." It got so I dreaded to go anywhere with him.

I was pushing the swing, almost dozing, with Dwight next to me leafing through an old magazine as if he couldn't rest.

"I was jealous you didn't have to help in any way I could make out," I told him. "Were you expected to help Daddy with the wood?"

He put down his magazine, stretched his legs out straight, his arms high over his head. "Don't ask me about that. As they say today, I'd rather not go there." He jumped up from the swing. "Let's get the stuff over to the dump." He headed out to the truck.

He might as well have said let's get rid of the evidence. In a different way, I felt that too. I felt we had committed a sacrilege as we hauled those old picnic things out of Daddy's woodshed: those tools, his old dusty clothes, the leather gloves still curled into the shape of his axe-holding hands, his old woodsman's pants still full of rosin smell. He always smelled of that smell. It was piquant in my nostrils, a delicious smell. And his ancient battered fedora. I hated throwing it away even with the chewed tiny semicircles along the brim where some rodent had worked on it. Dwight hadn't looked at the stuff; he just wanted to toss it. I had handled the hat, looked inside, at the band 7 7/8. Daddy's head really commanded attention.

I had gotten some kind of vibration from Dwight when we looked at each other over that hat. I had a weird feeling when he held open the garbage bag, as if we were committing a hideous sacrilege. Ridiculous. After all those years. But we both knew that to disturb his stuff was to risk rousing his terrible wrath; although we had never talked about this as kids. I knew it in my bones. And here we were finally disturbing stuff Daddy had left not to be disturbed. We had put his clothes — that hat of his — into the bag, a garbage bag, and pulled the yellow seal-up strip tight. His tools, the Thirkield family's sacred picnic things, even his cords of wood would be disturbed before this day was over, and they would be gone forever.

When we finally headed for the dump I knew we had crossed some kind of Rubicon. Once we had left today's bags and bundles with Mrs. Vanderlindt, I would feel lighter, a huge burden cast aside.

WHEN WE GOT BACK from the dump and were settled on the swing with a couple of beers, I started thinking about Netsie's old stuffing tub, the last item Dwight had reached down to me — final sacred item to be cast out. It was an enormous galvanized footed tub from the old homestead, the circumference of my adult encircling arms.

"I can't believe you don't remember that old stuffing tub," I said now.

"I knew I'd only get in trouble in their kitchen." He took a long swallow of beer from the bottle. "I can't understand why Mother didn't lock the aunts out of her kitchen. All they did was give her grief."

"They were cooking up a storm when she was still in diapers," I said. "Don't think they didn't tell her that about ten times per day. Not in words, maybe, but in looks." I listened to him swallow more beer. "Maybe she liked having somebody else do the cooking, Dwight. Besides, she hated confrontation and you know, they did a lot of the cooking, especially Netsie."

As a child I had watched Netsie fill the seemingly bottomless tub crumb by tiny crumb. She sat slightly askew on the old kitchen stool, one knee crossed over the other leg, the heel of one black Enna Jettick lace-up shoe hooked onto the lowest rung of the stool. Somehow she balanced the massive tub on her lopsided lap, while she quietly picked apart a mountain of leftover homemade loaves of bread until she had filled the tub. She never spilled a crumb.

"Mother said you can't make a decent stuffing out of store bread," she told me every November, with a ladylike wrinkling of her strong, aristocratic nose. She needed glasses to read, especially her *New York Times* and her *Tribune*, but she cooked bare-eyed. And she measured by instinct. When I would ask her how much of this or that ingredient was required, she would indicate the amount in pantomime – holding out her thumb with its beautifully (home) manicured nail, gesturing above the nail with her left forefinger the amount of butter or cream or whatever other ingredient happened to be part of her recipe. When I would ask about her pie crust – flaky, tender, floating-in-your-mouth – she would make the fingers of both her hands go in a gentle kneading motion, thumbs rubbing against fingertips. "It's all in the feel," she said.

When I think about it now, I actually have to look for my mother in the kitchen. She had learned to be in the women's territory of the house, most especially in the kitchen, by easing herself between the two aunts quietly, only insistent when she felt directly challenged. Cooking, and the aura surrounding family recipes and the right way of doing things as opposed to the wrong way – meaning someone else's way – so hemmed in the preparing and serving of meals, nay, even the saving of the leftovers, that I grew up with a dread of never being able to master these secrets. I avoided the aunts and the kitchen rather than invoke their disapproval.

Mother's awareness of her sisters-in-law as guardians of the family cooking lore made the kitchen a setting of potential booby traps. No two women could have been less willing than the aunts were to part with the sacred cooking secrets, and the fact that they were a generation older than Mother gave them an even loftier status in the womanly hierarchy. As must have been true in many households in those days, and maybe still is today, the kitchen was the battleground; the stove, the icebox, the sink, the storage cellar were all settings for skirmishes in the war.

Dwight wasn't welcome. I heard Aunt Charlotte say, more than once, "Little boys don't belong in the kitchen. Shoo!" He couldn't know much about the sniping and the territorial challenges that took place on that field of battle. A truce went into effect when it was time to sit down at the table, say grace, eat the sacred meal; but the cudgels were once again taken up the moment chairs were pushed out, plates removed, and the post-meal tidy-up was underway.

It was always the two sisters against the sister-in-law, but Aunt Charlotte and Aunt Netsie also vied with each other. I used to sit and watch it all, worried for Mother and silently taking sides with Aunt Netsie against Aunt Charlotte.

One story will stand for many. It's Thanksgiving time. I see Aunt Charlotte looking around the kitchen in her imperious way.

"Where on earth did you put that bird, Jeannette?" she says in an accusing tone. The bird she's looking for is yesterday's Thanksgiving turkey. "You know Mother always said it shouldn't be chilled to death or we might as well be eating sawdust," she goes on. She wraps a wool scarf around her head, opens the door to the back porch and sticks her head out. Cold air blasts into the kitchen. "I hate cold weather," she says severely. "Only one hundred and sixteen days till the first day of spring."

"Oh, that bracing air feels good," Aunt Netsie sings out from where she's standing at the stove. She turns her face toward the door, sniffs the cold air.

Evidently Aunt Charlotte saw no turkey; she slammed the door shut.

Aunt Netsie stirred whatever she was cooking in the double boiler. Steam oozed from the joint between the lower pot and the one above. Short curling tendrils of her white hair had escaped from tortoise-shell hairpins at the nape of her neck. Her free hand lifted the slipping apron shoulder strap back onto her stirring shoulder.

Mother was at the opposite end of the stove. "I've read it's not a good idea to leave the bird out too long," she said in her quiet voice. "Something about spoiling faster after it's stuffed." She said this into the opening of the stove's firebox, holding up the stove lid, looking down at the flame. She added a stick of wood, then shook down the ashes. "Bucket's full," she said. "I'll call E.B."

Almost before the words were out of her mouth, Aunt Netsie had licked her stirring spoon, dropped it into the sink, and grabbed the scuttle, which was piled high with powdery gray ash. She headed toward the door, opened it, and Aunt Charlotte let out a moan. "I hate the cold." Aunt Netsie came in with her line, "I love it," opened the door wider, ashes swirling back into the kitchen on currents of icy air.

Mother headed for the door, tried to grab the coal scuttle from Aunt Netsie's grip of iron. "I'll take that out, Jeannette." But Aunt Netsie's stride was too long. She was out the door, down the steps, and off to the side to dump the day's accumulation.

"Where is that bird?" Aunt Charlotte opened the door to the chilly vestibule where the new electric refrigerator hummed along.

Before she could head out that door, Mother turned and faced her, looking like a naughty schoolgirl. "I did it with my little hatchet, Charlotte. I made room for the turkey in the refrigerator last night. Don't want to take chances."

Aunt Charlotte huffed. "Well, if it's tough and dry . . . We always left our turkey on our porch and it was perfect the next day. Nobody got sick." She pulled off her scarf with a sharp snap, flung it onto the kitchen stool.

Aunt Netsie was back. She shut the door behind her. "Snow in the air. I can smell it."

"No you can't, Nettie," Aunt Charlotte said, "and don't talk about snow. You know I hate winter." She was standing at the sink, running hot water over her hands. She shivered her shoulders up and down.

"I hope we get plenty of snow for Christmas," Aunt Netsie said.

Mother's voice came in from behind the turkey. "This turkey's so juicy I can't imagine a little cold air hurts one bit. Would've frozen on the porch. Only twenty-five when I came down this morning." At this moment I was triumphant. Mother had gotten the last word.

Without even turning around, she said to me, "Go ask Daddy to please come and carve."

"Did you make enough gravy this year, Nettie?" Aunt Charlotte chimed in. "You know I'd rather have gravy and stuffing, especially if the turkey's all dried out."

The turkey was not dried out. I had had some for lunch. But I kept my mouth shut and went to get Daddy.

When Daddy and I came back into the kitchen, Aunt Charlotte was still running hot water over her hands. Daddy stood in the narrow doorway, filling the space. I could see him monitoring the precious hot water running down the drain.

"Lottie, you know it takes half a cord of wood to heat that water tank," he said in an even tone to his oldest sister. "If you're cold, there's a good fire in the fireplace."

Aunt Charlotte turned off the water, shook her hands dramatically over the long sink. "If I can't have a little water to get the chill out of these old hands . . ." she said to the shelf above the sink. She rattled the roller towel loudly to a dry area and carefully wiped her hands; her engagement ring, set in an old-fashioned gold basket setting, caught the light. She turned her hand in the air, showing off the ring. "My Walter gave me this exquisite ring while we walked in the June twilight on the banks of the Little Miami River," she said (for the thousandth time). She pronounced it Miamuh, the same way she said Cincinnatuh and Ohiuh. "And then we went in and he asked Father for my hand in marriage." She swept out of the kitchen.

Daddy was rummaging around in one of the crowded drawers. "Where's my sharp knife, Connie?" he asked pointedly. "I've asked you a thousand times to wrap that good knife in a napkin." More softly he added, "That was fifty years ago, Lottie," as she got out of earshot, heading for the fireplace.

"Here it is," Mother said, "in that lovely knife holder Rae gave us."

Daddy looked at the knife holder as if it were a bomb about to go off.

Aunt Netsie came over and stood next to her brother. "You will slice it across the grain, E.B.," she said. "Doesn't taste the same if you don't and you know that's the way Father always did it. I'll do it if you're tired." She reached toward him.

"I'm fresh as a daisy, Nettie. Let me get at that bird. Connie, where's my wet towel?" He insisted on setting the turkey platter on a slightly damp towel to keep it from slewing around, skidding away from his accurate, slow-moving weapon. Once the platter was settled, he pulled off sheet after sheet of tucked-in waxed paper, crumpling each sheet into a ball. Finally the bird was naked, bare to the bone on one side.

He carved in silence. Aunt Charlotte flounced back into the kitchen, cheeks flushed from her warm-up near the living-room fireplace, and she and Mother and Aunt Netsie moved in complete silence around the kitchen. One stirred and served at the stove, distributing turkey dinner leftovers from heating casseroles – sweet and white mashed potatoes, creamed onions, sweet and red cabbage, stuffing; one added sticks to the stove, shook down the ashes again; one bent over the open oven door, pulled out the huge bean pot, stirred the slow-cooking homemade baked beans to be set aside for tomorrow night's supper, then stirred milky rice pudding, to the brim in a dark brown casserole dish, to be served tonight still warm, with whipped cream.

I was silent, too. I set the table in the breakfast room – once upon a time the milk room, where cans of milk would rest on a wooden counter till the cream rose to the top to be skimmed, ladled into separate crocks. Before my time.

When everything was arranged on the table, platters and bowls of steaming food, Aunt Charlotte broke the silence.

"Why E.B.," she said as if she was hurt, "you've put the dark meat together with the white meat. You know I prefer the white meat separate from the dark. It's my allergy. You know I can't eat dark meat." Her small pince-nez wiggled on the bridge of her nose as she faced him. He stepped away from the skeletal bird.

Bang. He slammed down his favorite knife onto the porcelain table top. His voice, soft but angry: "Nobody in his right mind could claim to be able to eat white turkey meat and be allergic to dark turkey meat. Now let's eat." He took his place at the head of the table. Aunt Charlotte flounced out of the room.

Chairs scraped, bodies lowered themselves onto seats, heads bowed, grace was said. Aunt Charlotte's door slammed just off the living room.

"I do believe this is the finest bird we've ever had in this house," Daddy announced as we all lifted forks to our mouths.

Fourteen

I THINK E.B. was always in some sense in competition with everyone in the family. I have an idea that the women who brought him up never let him do anything around the house, but that he was expected to do whatever would have been man's work. I have a strong sense of those women – my aunts and their mother – being exquisitely competent, or at least believing they were. E.B., so much younger than anyone else in the family and the only man (his father was in a morass once the bankruptcy occurred), would have been expected to be as competent; but I can't help imagining how undermining those sisters and mother might have been, since they believed they knew how to do everything and how to behave, and so forth. From my own experience I know a paragon is difficult to live with; it causes one to be constrained. I have a feeling E.B. was as constrained as he was constraining. He affected Connie and us children, and then when his sisters moved in with us, I imagine they affected him again firsthand. Think of the pressures in that household.

As for me, I must have figured out very early in life how to survive in a family where there were different messages coming in from all sides. Or do I make this too dramatic?

E.B. passed along the pressure in his insistence on helping Connie in her chores – always doing them better, faster, and making her feel at the same time that she could never be as competent, as quick as he was. Connie was slow in the kitchen but she always came through, and being looked upon as incapable irritated the hell out of her.

It would have been a carry-over from his upbringing to put women on a pedestal, which really meant that women were delicate. (Remember, the Victorian era was still in full sway when he was born.) I think his sisters and his mother were probably good at having it both ways. They always knew the single best way to do something or handle a situation, and they were also fragile females, proper Victorian ladies.

It's fascinating to me to think of E.B. caught in the middle of all this. Connie would surely have been unlike the women he had been brought up by and for. It's touching to think of him trying to keep up. One of the things I really want to get across is the sense of E.B. feeling, ever since Connie's serious female troubles in Texas, that he had to protect her and that she was not very strong, not able to do as much as she was ready to do around the house.

IN THOSE EARLY YEARS of Schroon Lake year-round, my mother had not made friends yet. After Labor Day the summer set were gone. Summers Mother was surrounded by family – at least till the war years. Uncle Walter was still alive, so Charlotte, Virginia, and Nana hadn't moved in with us yet. Jeannette helped the family who needed her the most. And the way I remember it, Daddy was away a lot of the time, in various places, working or looking for work.

The Johnstones blew in like a refreshing breeze the second year we were living there. They changed all our lives for the better. They arrived in Schroon from England in the fall of 1939, just as the war started. (They were halfway across the Atlantic when the German army invaded Poland. I remember her describing the ship on high alert, blacked out and zigzagging its way toward New York, trying to avoid attack by German submarines.)

I SEE MOTHER pressing on the accelerator, coaxing home the old LaSalle filled with provisions for the guests. Driving to town has given her a chance to enjoy the pleasure of remembering her much-loved roommate, gone these many years to her life in England. The last time they saw each other was when Virginia married her gorgeous RAF flyer, Douglas, handsome in uniform, an air ace and a wounded hero. He had come to train American pilots at an airfield near Oberlin. It had been love at first sight. Virginia, a stunning auburn-haired bride, wed her flyer and they headed for England the minute the Armistice was signed in 1918.

CONNIE'S SMOOTH gear shift from second to third pleases her. Then the last stretch down the hill to the house. The familiar stone wall comes out to meet her. How like Father, she said to me once, to have continued his rock wall well beyond his own groomed Almanole driveway, carrying it along the length of the old farmhouse. Nearing the driveway she brakes carefully. Little Dwight moves like lightning now.

She swung the car carefully between her father's stone posts and came to a stop. The grocery bags had shifted with that final turn, some of them slouched over, cans, jars, bottles, bags of fruit sliding across the floor in the back. She went around to open the back door of the car.

"I'll help you with that, Connie," E.B. said behind her. She hadn't heard his quiet step.

"When did you get here?" she asked. "I thought you wouldn't be here till tomorrow."

He landed a quick kiss on top of her head, then turned immediately to the task of picking up oranges and apples and putting them into bags. He reached into the back of the car and picked up two bags in each arm.

"Let's get these things inside, then we'll talk," he said. He was halfway across the yard and up the small hill at the north end of the porch. In three strides he was inside the screen door of the kitchen. He settled the bags on the table. His arms moved in a continuous motion, lifting things out and putting them in their places on shelves or in cupboards.

The kitchen door slammed. He got a pained look. He was already smoothing, creasing, and folding the brown bags. He studied the offensive just-slammed door as if to make sure it had not been broken.

"Oh E.B., I'm sorry," Connie said. She had seen his look. "I didn't have a hand free to catch the door."

"There's always your foot, Connie. It saves wear and tear, to close it quietly. I just re-hung that door last week." He stowed the bags in the space between the wall and the kitchen china cabinet next to the back door and dusted his hands together. "Looks as if you might have shopped for the winter," he observed.

She was at the sink, running the drinking water faucet. She helped herself to a tall glass, drank the entire contents. "Would you like some water?" she asked.

"I had two full tumblers just before you drove in." He stood now, his arms folded over his chest, his backside resting against the top edge of the kitchen table. "Are we expecting guests?" he asked.

I see her. She's thinking about the new arrivals. She had not been able to reach E.B. with the news of their actual arrival tomorrow. She rinses her glass. She upends it into the rack at the left end of the sink. Her back still to him, she says, "Why E.B., I must have mentioned to you that my dear friend Virginia Johnstone is coming for a visit with her three children."

E.B. cleared his throat. "I remember perfectly well," he said. "It struck me because I got the feeling Virginia was hoping to be invited to stay with us."

"We discussed it," she reminded him. Sometimes it was hard to get his attention. Douglas had wanted Virginia to get the children to America before the bombs fell. "I thought we'd agreed we'd put them up, at least for a little while." She went into the small vestibule, came back with a small basket of blueberries. She dumped them into a sieve and began rinsing them in a stream of water.

"We haven't had much rain, Connie. Go easy on the drinking water."

She poured the blueberries into a colander, shook it gently.

I hear her, the distinct tone of her voice, tossed over her shoulder.

"These are the last of the local berries. Father says it's a well that'll never run dry. I thought I'd make some blueberry muffins for supper." She turned off the faucet quickly.

E.B. crossed over to the sink and added a final twist to the faucet. The trickle stopped. "It seems to me Virginia may be trying to take advantage of you," he said.

"Oh E.B., we have room for them for a few weeks or so, until they can find a place of their own."

"It's the 'or so' I'm worried about."

He headed for the woodshed. "I know it would be companionship for you," he said over his shoulder. He was off to get wood for the kitchen range.

The phone rang. It was Western Union. Virginia and the children were arriving the next day on the 4:15 Trailways bus.

E.B. came back in with the wood. "I think I'll drive to Glens Falls and pick up a turkey," he said, already heading for the door. His voice sounded warm, not as if he was angry that Virginia was coming.

Connie was pleased. "You almost sound glad she's coming. What happened?"

"I never objected. She's an interesting woman. Opinionated but interesting, that's how I remember her. But woe betide anyone who crosses her in an argument. You'd better have your facts straight." The door made no sound as he headed across the small porch off the kitchen.

As if E.B. would ever have his facts anything but straight.

She followed him out onto the porch. At the top of the steps, he turned to face her, grasped her upper arms with his fierce grip and looked into her face.

"I don't want you to be worried by this visit," he said gently. "Don't, under any circumstances, agree that they can stay longer than a few weeks."

Of course not. Of course not. Wouldn't she be longing for him to put his arms around her, hold her close.

He let go of her, squared his shoulders. Hitched up his trousers in a way he had, girding his loins, she always thought, getting ready to go into battle. A few strides and he was in the car, starting the engine. She stood on the porch and waved.

WHAT HAPPENED between E.B. and Virginia, in the long-ago encounters when E.B. visited my mother at Oberlin, and that summer at The Place? Mother was vague on this subject. She seemed to remember the two of them, E.B. and Virginia, in a hot debate about some current issue. She had a vague feeling E.B. might even have been flirting with Virginia back then, but she laughed at herself when she said that to me. Absurd? She told me Daddy had said more than once that Virginia was too aggressive and that he didn't enjoy such an overpowering woman. But she's smart, he would say. Quick intelligence, quicker tongue. Was this praise or blame? I know he always appreciated Virginia's intellect, her grasp of world issues. But he didn't like women who – or, he didn't approve of women who wouldn't fit themselves into the social order. What would be the nice way of saying that? He believed in the old standards. He was fierce in his beliefs.

So here's Connie, light of heart. She can hardly wait to see Virginia again after all these years. She's hoping the children will like one another. She's praying E.B. and Virginia will get along.

CONNIE GOT the house ready, E.B. bought the turkey, the day dawned. She awoke at first light, the room still gray.

She was down the narrow stairs, well into the middle of the living room, before she heard sounds from the kitchen. She had meant to be up first today, to wrestle with the bird – a cumbersome, plump-breasted Tom carried in triumphantly by E.B. after dark the evening before. "We'll give those English children a Yankee feast," he had crowed. "I found yams and cranberry jelly too." She was touched. In spite of his concerns about Virginia's arrival he had driven ninety miles, down and back, to find a bird big enough to feed a crowd for several days.

This morning, she watched him for a moment through the doorway. He was standing at the sink, water flowing in the back end of the bird and out through the craw. It was the only time he ever let the water run for any length of time. She was seeing him from behind. He stood straight as a ramrod even as he performed this menial task.

"Good morning, Connie," he said without turning. "You're up betimes. Mother always said how important it is to cleanse the bird thoroughly from inside out." With that, he shut the cold faucet off, no drip, ever. He held the bird high and shook away the last drops of water.

He had spread the oldest and softest dish towels across the entire kitchen table, two deep. He already had a towel at the sink, and was patting the cavity dry. "No need to drip water all over the floor," he would say. With a swift motion, he pulled the bird up by its yellowed knobby ankle bones at the ends of the drumsticks. Two big steps and he was rolling and patting its body with the dish towels.

"I found day-old bread at the Italian market. The dressing's all made, out on the back porch."

She was grateful. He had done the tasks that were onerous to her, the endless picking at stale bread, the chopping of celery and parsley, not to mention the eye-pricking job of slicing and dicing the onions, the delicate task of adjusting the seasonings to please a family steeped in a tradition which it would be considered deviant to change. She still dreaded living up to the time-honored method of properly roasting a Tom turkey. And here was E.B., the sun not even up yet, ready to stuff the bird and slide it into the oven – which, she knew, must already be at the desired temperature. Another worry thrust itself into her mind.

"How will we ever fit everyone around this table?"

"I know just how we'll do it," he said. "I'll put one leaf in the table and we'll put two to a side, with Dwight on the kitchen stool."

She heard the concern in his voice. But he didn't need to be worried about her doing too much. If Virginia was anything she was resourceful. And she was decisive. She'd find a house within a week – or two, at the most.

E.B. brought the tub of stuffing in from the porch. As soon as he set it down, he rolled a ball of the stuffing and popped it into his mouth. "Mother always said you've got to taste to know it's right. No adjusting those seasonings once it's inside the bird." He rolled another ball and gave it to her. It was well seasoned and just moist enough. She couldn't quite control her thoughts. They went back to that empty bed beside her this morning. It made her sad.

He must have slept out on the back porch, a favorite place of his. She had never spoken to him about their odd sleeping arrangement. Better not to think about it. She hoped Virginia wouldn't catch on. She reached for the knobbed ends of the bird's drumsticks, grasped them and pulled the cavity open, and E.B. stuffed the bird with huge handfuls of the old family recipe – first the back end, then the craw. He trussed up the bird and set it in the roasting pan. Connie opened the oven, E.B. pushed the bird inside.

He positioned the kitchen chair near the oven door so that he could open it and baste the bird without reaching far. Connie began to clean up. After about twenty minutes, he opened the oven door, pulled the bird out, and wielded his long-handled spoon skillfully along the length of both sides.

"And now," he said, "you can do me a great favor." He wanted her to drive to town and get the morning newspapers. He said he would hold the fort, feed the children if they got up before she was back. "Car's all warmed up," he said. "I brought it over from the barn before I started with the bird."

She put on her heavy black and red flannel shirt. She hated to leave that fragrant kitchen. She reached over to pat his shoulder as she passed by him perched on his chair. He caught her hand and held it. His grip was frightening. "Careful of that hot oven," he said. "I'll have a quick snooze while you're gone." She headed for the door. He would sleep in the chair. That was E.B.

It was almost seven o'clock. Cold out. The car started at the first push of the starter button, no need even to use the choke. E.B. had also run the heater. He was thoughtful; she never stepped into a frigid car. She concentrated as she began to pull out into the road. He had backed into their driveway, making it easy for her.

She loved taking the wheel. Was E.B. watching her from the kitchen window? She had only a quick glimpse, too quick to be sure. She hadn't lost her touch driving, she knew that. Time alone. Driving, she was by herself.

In town she collected the two newspapers, said a few hellos to other early risers, and headed home. A few cars kept her waiting to make the turn into the driveway. She shifted down and navigated the turn slowly, in first gear, sure E.B. would be aware of her approach. She didn't want to give him cause. He had been insistent. He had a notion that driving might injure a woman's female organs. And he was not an easy man to convince. It had already been over four years since Dwight was born. Why make such an issue about her driving any longer? She had to smile when she thought of the previous winter's driving, E.B. away weeks at a time. She had had to drive and she did. But when he was home, it was as if she were some helpless flower. Didn't make sense.

She opened the heavy car door. E.B. was already there, holding up his hand to give her an assist to the ground. "You made awfully good time, Connie. I hope you didn't speed. You know I've a while to wait by that turkey. I've basted it a dozen times already."

E.B. HAD A QUIET, unstoppable efficiency in every task he performed.

I remember him sitting within reach of the oven door, potholders, kitchen tools at the ready to baste a chicken or a turkey. I've watched him work his way methodically through two newspapers from front to back, stopping every few pages for his culinary chore. The kitchen would be filled with the fragrance of roasting turkey. He basted breast, drumsticks, stirred around the cut-up vegetables, then tested the progress of the cooking by moving the drumstick up and down gently. I can see him slide the pan back into the heat. "Another half hour, that should do it for you," he might say under his breath, as he shut the oven door with finality.

I liked coming in and out between other things I was supposed to be doing. I can see myself standing in the kitchen doorway. He cocks his head and listens to my mother's footsteps overhead. He takes his gold watch out of his vest pocket, looks at it and looks at me. "I want to surprise her," he says, "have the gravy ready by the time she gets down here." How many times I saw him neatly and carefully fold the newspaper he had finished reading. He took quiet satisfaction in leaving the pages lying as flat and smooth as they had been when Mother brought it in from Herlihys'.

When it was time to take the turkey out of the oven he would begin to move around the kitchen, efficiently and quietly tending to the preparations. He settled the bird onto a well-heated platter, covered it with Turkish towels so it would stay warm, reposing; he moved the giblets away from the hottest part of the stove; he washed up his basting spoon and wiped the kitchen table. After a few more minutes he strained the broth from the giblets and set that pot out on the back porch. And I remember the knife, so sharp the meat seemed to fall away in its wake as he sliced the bird, carving thin, elegant pieces of white meat, the drumstick separated deftly from the second joint, the sections left to cool. There was an intensity about him while he had the knife in his hands, a kind of wizardry. He didn't make it look easy; he made it look enviable.

And now I hear him almost purring when he says, as if for my personal benefit, "And now to the gravy."

The elegant Gravy Dance. The fire in the firebox was hot enough but not too hot for the transformation of raw flour and hot turkey grease into a smooth dark brown roux that formed the essential element of a truly succulent gravy. I had a sense even when I was a small child of how much pleasure this dance gave him. I think he must have felt his hands moving in the same motions he had observed as a small boy – my age – maybe, when he was old enough to keep the fire going but not yet old enough to master the tricky combination of moves that measured, scraped, stirred, blended, to create the desired velvet-smooth perfect gravy. His mother's gravy was a legend in the household. We children used to make faces behind his back when he started talking about it, how perfect it had always been, better than any turkey gravy he had ever eaten, anywhere, in his life.

HERE'S WHAT I know. As Connie drove downtown to get E.B.'s paper, she would certainly be thinking a little resentfully about his superior attitude toward her efforts in the kitchen. But her annoyance would have been tempered by her feelings of appreciation for what he had done, and her relief that he wasn't all that opposed to Virginia's arrival. The two of them – her fiancé and her dear friend and roommate, Virginia – had crossed swords over something when they were both in Schroon back in the days before Virginia went off to England with Douglas. But Connie had never known what the subject of their hostility was. Maybe she had only been jealous but who could blame her? Virginia was a stunner, no question about it.

We had room in the farmhouse, those first two years in Schroon, before the aunts moved in with us. There were two unused bedrooms downstairs in those days, and another one upstairs that was to become Jeannette's. The Johnstones filled the house and we got to know them right away, all of us eating together, sometimes in shifts. We were like one big happy family and I loved it.

VIRGINIA HAD SENT a recent photo. She was standing on a shingle beach with her three children, their hair stirred by a sea breeze. Connie thought, we could have a child David's age. He must be eighteen by now. No wonder Virginia was running from England, with a son eligible to be drafted and another war just beginning.

On her way outside to pick some apples, she passed through the kitchen.

"Don't carry too many at once," E.B. said, not losing his place in his paper.

"I'll be sensible," she called back, quoting one of his phrases back at him. She was irritated at having him think her weak. "You know you said we should collect the windfalls. I'll have enough for applesauce and pie too." She ran down the back porch steps getting herself out of earshot as fast as she could, walked with quick steps out through her mother's cutting garden, across the driveway, between the spirea bushes toward the upper lawn and its billiard-table smooth croquet court. Such a glorious fall day. She could hardly wait for Virginia to arrive. She felt grateful that she was coming. She would have a friend.

She told me years later, when I was asking her about the Johnstones, how filled she was with uneasiness as the time drew closer to their arrival and the invasion of our small household. It had been so many years, their lives so different. She hoped Virginia wouldn't be too forceful with E.B., remembering how much she liked to argue, to win her point.

She stopped by the piano to straighten the piles of music. She wished she could sit down for five minutes to play. Why was she worried? Virginia had always had a casual attitude toward the housekeeping expected in their dormitory every week. She'd say dusting was the last thing she cared about. It had been refreshing to share a room with her, someone who hadn't been forced to live up to the strict standards of neatness Connie's parents had laid down.

She put down her dust rag, sat down, and for a few minutes exercised her fingers with scales, then some arpeggios up and down the keys. The house was ready enough. Why fuss?

Out of the corner of her eye she saw the yellow school bus, and then the two girls came bursting in full of questions. Where are they? When will they be here? What will they be like? Dwight didn't understand all the excitement.

Mother told us to change to our play clothes, and then we were out the door, keeping our eyes open for the bus.

Time to relieve E.B. in the kitchen. He of course had had the vegetables ready hours ago. She would much have preferred to get them ready closer to dinnertime, not allowing them to get so over-cooked. But she didn't say anything. She loved to have the kitchen all to herself. She could do much better without his supervision.

He offered to get the ice cream. "Anything else we need?"

She tried to put her hands on his shoulders, give him a quick kiss of thanks on the cheek. "You've done yeoman service today," she said as he moved away, too quick for her, turning toward the woodshed.

"We need wood first," he said sternly. "Don't worry. I'll be back in time for their arrival." Then he was out the door.

She didn't know how to thank him. It was so hard to thank him for anything.

The next time she looked at the clock it was close to four. Now where was E.B.? He could certainly be here when Virginia arrived, no matter how he really felt about her coming. She curbed her impatience, went to the back door to check on the children. They should clean up but surely Virginia would not be fussy, not after her twelve-hour bus ride. Finally she ran upstairs to put cold water on her face, change her blouse, comb her hair.

A sound of heavy brakes squealing. She had to run down the stairs to be at the door as they got off the bus. She saw them emerge, one after another. Elisabeth, long-legged, very tall for twelve, dark hair, like her dashing father. She looked young, shy, as she stepped from the huge bus. Gerald, redheaded, an awkward teenager, tripped slightly and jumped to the ground. Then David. An Adonis. White-blond hair, tanned face and arms. He turned and gallantly offered his hand to his mother.

Virginia. Barely changed from college days. Regal carriage, carrying her height with distinction. Her posture always seemed to be saying, I'm glad to be here, I'm going to enjoy myself enormously, and I'm not afraid to look anyone straight in the eye.

Virginia crossed the short distance between them and Connie was enveloped in her embrace. It made her feel small and girl-like, as if she were back in those college days, when she had no worries except preparing for her senior piano recital.

What did they say to each other in those first excited minutes of reunion? Surely the usual things. "You haven't changed a bit!" "I can't believe we have all these children!" Interrupting, echoing, trying to give the lie to the years that had rolled over their heads, to the weight, the gray hairs, the traces on face, hands, and body.

"Connie, I'm a complete wreck. I pray I never have to ride twelve hours straight in any vehicle ever again." She looked around. "And where's that handsome husband of yours?"

That moment the car pulled into the driveway. E.B. hopped out and ran across the lawn in three or four long strides. He took Virginia's outstretched hands, looked her up and down, then leaned over to kiss both her cheeks. "A great big welcome to you, Toots, and to your children," he said. "I hope you remember your nickname after all these years."

"I hope you're ready for some serious discussions about what's going on in this world," she bantered. "I'm thankful you've got FDR in charge. He'll stick by England."

There was a first pause. Connie didn't miss seeing E.B. set his jaw. But he let the remark slide by. She felt like hugging him. It was a little gift to her, his silence.

There would be time enough for discussion. Well, why not call it argument. It made her uneasy.

"I want to know all about Douglas," Connie said, jumping into the breach. "How is he doing? We wish he could have come over too."

"Absolutely no question of him leaving England." Her tone was bland, but there was something left unsaid. She moved quickly to another subject. "And what about your children?"

We children were standing close to the house, hesitant but curious. Mother called us over and introduced us, and there was more silence.

"Mary Belle dear," Virginia said, "I think the young ones should walk to the lake. You lead the way." (David stayed behind, too old to join children.) Before we were out of sight we had all broken into a run. The ice was broken.

MOTHER REMEMBERED Virginia purposely stimulating heated discussions, sometimes taking an opposite position simply to inject excitement. Sparks flew when Virginia was around. That first day, that reunion, after the long ride, Virginia seemed content for the most part to listen, but Connie had the feeling she was filing away points for future use.

THE JOHNSTONES stayed with us until the cold weather set in, well into October. Having them there changed our lives. From that moment, my life fell into two periods: before Elisabeth came, and after Elisabeth came. I now had a built-in pal, and this continued after they moved to their own small house in town. My mother's wish for Maya and Elisabeth to become friends didn't come true. Maya was thinking about boyfriends, and her hair, and what clothes to wear to school. Elisabeth was too shy, not accustomed to boys, coming as she did from an all-girls school back in England. And she did have a powerful mother.

Elizabeth and I were drawn together immediately. We found in each other an imaginative and eager outdoor pal. We were busy every day in our own world. We roamed The Place together, wandering into every corner of Grandpa's acres, exploring every building, finding secret hideouts where we played many roles: partisans fighting the Nazis, spies sent behind the lines to undermine the enemy, escaped prisoners working their way toward freedom. My loyalty to Antzie was eroded, seduced as I was by this older girl who came from a much farther-away place than the Bronx. I knew I was mean to ignore my former best friend. I was shocked by myself when I told my lies. I whispered to Antzie I had to sit on the bus with the new girl. I could feel myself make the false words sound believable, sighing and pulling down my mouth at the corners as I passed Antzie's half-empty seat. I tried to forget her disappointment. I told myself she wouldn't mind; she wouldn't know I had left her behind; she would believe my falsehoods.

It was too tempting. Having the right seatmate, a subtle but important mark of school-bus cachet, I had learned only too well from Antzie the year before. Someone older – tall enough to swing her books high onto the shelf overhead with a casual flip, the books secured by an English-looking, smart leather strap – impressed anyone who was looking. Elisabeth had the mysterious air of a shy girl who could seem above the childishly noisy by-play of the bus ride. Her English reserve, her way of speaking, her elegant bearing, so like her mother's, impressed these children who, in those years, had seen so little of the world outside of the North Country.

This unusual family from across the Atlantic, who had appeared out of the blue, commanded respect and curiosity in Schroon Lake. There was whispering behind hands that they were stuck-up and snooty, that they thought they were better than anyone else. I knew

Elisabeth was not any of these things. I loved the way they spoke. It made me feel as if I were in a play. Elisabeth expanded my world way beyond this mountain village. I read the books she read, and I was now allowed free range all over The Place. I was not expected to tend Dwight as much, no longer lumped together with him as the little ones, which had always insulted my feelings. Elisabeth and I became blood sisters in a private and gory ritual of wrist-pricking. I could hardly wait to wake up each morning to join her. Just stepping up into the bus with her made me feel mature and confident.

All of our lives were affected as if by a tonic. Mother seemed care-free, full of life. I could feel her good spirits. As she walked beside me when we all went to the lake to view the changing leaves, I had a harder time keeping up with her. Her initial worries of Virginia's challenging personality clashing head on with E.B.'s sensitive feelings seemed ungrounded. Her relief made her smile and laugh. They had reestablished their old friendship seamlessly.

She told me later she was delighted when she saw how E.B. took the lead in finding a house for Virginia and her children. Virginia teased him, said, "You're trying to get rid of us." He was not accustomed to anyone questioning his motives. He tried to convince her that that was not his intention. "How could you even suggest such a thing, Toots? I hope I don't find you a house too soon." I noticed him redden, wondered if perhaps Virginia was right. I hoped it would take all winter.

Something I hadn't realized until I was writing, just now, about the preparations for the Johnstones' visit was that sense of E.B.'s constant watching presence in Connie's mind that I'm sure was a great deal of the conditioning under which she lived. That sense that whenever she was near the house, coming or going, he could have caught sight of her, and would have been looking out for her. I believe he would have been watching. I think he would have seen it as his business to be watching. Strange, she was such a free spirit and yet she was trapped by him. I think he couldn't help it; it was just him protecting her.

Dwight and I were standing over the back porch table, a deep cardboard carton open wide in front of us, and we were pulling out of it assorted items – gypsy skirts and deeply fringed shawls, high black pirate boots, satin sashes, Harlequin masks, spangled gloves, old-fashioned men's and ladies' hats.

"You have no memories at all of Mother having fun, playing The Game?"

Dwight shook his head no, as he tossed one item and then another into a black garbage bag we had set up to hang open between two chairbacks. "Quit trying to make a case," he said good-humoredly.

I said nothing. I settled an admiral's hat on my head and kept going through the costumes. A long silky skirt came forth in Dwight's hands and I grabbed it from him.

"Oh Dwight, don't you remember this?" I held the skirt up to my waist and the plum-colored folds emitted a musty smell as they rippled down my legs. "Maybe they made you go to bed before the games began." He had only been four and a half that fall. Elisabeth and I used to run away from him and hide. "They still treated you like a baby."

"You were just as bad," he said. "And you thought you were too good for the local kids."

It was true, I had thought that in some ways.

"Well I didn't," he continued. "I actually envied those kids who lived downtown and had little back yards where they played kick the can after school. And had fathers who worked at real jobs, on the road or running a store."

He gave me a look. "It was just you and Elisabeth," he said, "from the minute they arrived."

I had been flattered that Elisabeth wanted to play with me.

I was still holding the skirt. I tucked it into the elastic at the top of my shorts and moved to make it shimmer and subtly change color in the morning sunlight. I kicked off my moccasins and minced along the porch. "Mother acted out *The Birth of a Nation* in this skirt. I'll never forget it," I said, and I grabbed a puffy pillow from the porch glider and stuffed it up under the skirt. Then I flopped down on the floor and started moaning and writhing, every now and then grunting with the bearing-down pains of childbirth.

"What the hell are you doing?" Dwight shouted over my noise. I stopped and propped myself up on my elbows, eyeing him over my bulging belly.

We had great fun with Aunt Virginia and those kids. After they moved into their own house, they still came for dinner on Saturday evenings. Then we'd play games, especially what we called The Game, our version of Charades, in which we would act out titles. Where had all these glad rags come from? Our forebears must have worn them.

Dwight frowned briefly. "I have some vague memory of Elisabeth acting as if she were crazy," he said. "Scary. With her hair messed up, hanging around her face."

I jumped up. "Ophelia in her mad scene," I exclaimed. "Then she drowned herself in a lake of blue pillows." I tossed the skirt into the garbage bag. I remembered Mother laughing so hard she couldn't stop, and saying, "Oh Elisabeth, stop, my sides ache." The best part had been that Daddy was home more that winter. He used to have fun when Aunt Virginia was around. I suddenly heard him call her Toots again, with a kind of ironic tone to his voice.

Mother had been so happy when she got Virginia's telegram that they were coming. She clapped her hands and said, "Oh goody, goody. Virginia's more fun than a barrel of monkeys."

Virginia was bold, fearless. She had a loud, hearty laugh, and she was independent. She would tell Daddy off without thinking twice about it. And I sensed he liked it.

SHE WAS Virginia Smith Johnstone, formerly of Richmond, Virginia. The Smiths were a plantation family descended from old Hamptonshire stock, the American branch figuring prominently in the War Between the States. She had married this English pilot who had come over to train American fliers after he got shot down over France. He had a smashed leg that had been stuck back together with pieces of silver.

Douglas Johnstone had matinee-idol looks until the day he died. In his RAF days he had looked like a recruiting poster – strong jaw, just the right amount of moustache to make him dashing, his expression serious and restrained, coolly British. When I finally met him I had to look away from this tall, lean veteran; he reminded me with a jolt of that difficult time, that long war that had lived inside me day by day as we all followed its battles and campaigns. He had stayed on and worked as an air raid warden in London all through the Blitz. I was fourteen by the time the war was over and he was finally able to leave England. One summer day he rowed me and his daughter across the lake, and I saw the deep purple-red hollow like a trench alongside his shinbone where he had taken the German shrapnel.

I WAS SWEPT AWAY by Aunt Virginia's daring, the way she would face Daddy, or the schemes she got up. I loved the way she looked, her red hair in a dramatic pile on her head, a comb inevitably slipping into her collar. She was tall, with a commanding presence, able to hold her own with anyone on any subject. Thoroughly American and yet with a subtle air of English elegance and formality: the combination was captivating

I remember one evening when the grownups had set up for bridge, and they were one person short. I had learned the suits, something about bidding – the most basic stuff about how the game is played. So I said sure, I can play, if you're short.

Aunt Virginia drew herself up and became her imperious self, straightening her shoulders, making her bosom even more impressive than it was. (Like a ship under full sail, said Daddy, after they had gone home.)

She stared down at me. "How can you possibly know how to play bridge?" she said. "It takes years of playing. It's not a game for children."

I withered. Mother was at the table, shuffling, dealing, organizing her hand. "Weezie, you be my partner for this hand," she said quietly. "Now let's see. Two no trump."

My eyes had blurred but I recovered enough to answer my mother's strong opening bid. I answered with three of my strongest suit.

"Four no trump," said Mother, sure of her partner.

WHAT WERE THEY DOING in Schroon in the first place? Didn't she have family in Virginia? I asked Mother that, and she told me they had gone to Richmond first, Virginia's family were so poor they had fed them hominy grits for dinner. And they had only one kerosene lamp for the four of them.

I WANT TO EMPHASIZE the seismic shift the Johnstones caused in our lives. Virginia helped Mother recover, finally, from the years in Texas, which had so dampened her spirit. That first year in Schroon had been tough; the cold was severe, we children had been sick a lot, and she had been alone more than she had ever been before. E.B. was away in Albany or New York. And Mother didn't have friends in Schroon.

One might have said about Virginia, back then (using an expression that today we see as an ignorant remark), she thinks like a man. E.B. didn't like pushy women but I know he admired a strong woman. I know he liked having a woman around to challenge him intellectually. He intimidated Connie and she didn't challenge him in anything. No one intimidated Virginia.

E.B. found Virginia a house, helped her with financial issues, and was ready and able to give her advice. (Connie always said he picked stocks well, he just wasn't tough enough to hold his good choices long enough.)

FOR ME, it meant a friend of my own ilk. I had to stretch myself to be friends with Elisabeth, because she was older. Nothing I liked better. I was used to stretching myself to be friends with my father (though I wouldn't have thought of it that way, then).

Elisabeth was a good student, read a lot, had had a strict and proper English education in a girls' school, so she was a tutor for me, formally and informally. In one of our games we would be back in colonial days, with Elisabeth as the teacher in the one-room school. I was required to have a proper copybook in which to take dictation and practice my letters, and I was put through old-fashioned drills like the recitation of the auxiliary verbs, or the multiplication tables. These games helped me in school a lot. She made math drill fun.

THE JOHNSTONE children stuck out, in Schroon Lake. They were tall, with erect posture. They spoke with English accents and had a certain reserved dignity. David turned heads. He countered the local kids when they tried to mimic his English accent by giving them an accurate taste of their own upstate twang. The teasing stopped. I remember Elisabeth in her tartan with knee socks (no one wore knee socks then). Gerald was still in short pants, English style – gray flannels that ended at the knee. David was probably the tallest boy in the high school. Both boys went to school at first wearing a tie and jacket. Many North Country men never wore a tie or suit except to their own wedding or to a funeral. The Johnstones caused a big stir and they were our friends. It set us off from the rest of the village even more than we already were set off.

MOTHER REMEMBERED the tension between Virginia and her father the summer she came to visit when the two friends were still in college. Mother's father was very competitive and he didn't want to be beaten at croquet. He always won. Virginia came in and in a sense didn't observe the rules, took advantage of his hospitality, didn't know how to be as good a guest as he knew how to be a host; or she didn't defer enough to him. She and he competed with each other, and there was a strain between them that was unpleasant for everyone around. She was so powerful, she was treading on his toes. And she argued with him about politics.

MOTHER TOLD ME this: When Virginia saw the wickets, the perfectly level, unblemished grass of the court, cut so short it was as smooth as a billiard table, she clapped her hands, burst out, "Oh, I was the family champion down in Virginia. Let's play this afternoon."

If there was anything Connie's father loved it was enthusiasm. She could see he was charmed during lunch and when Virginia expressed her love for the game, they agreed on a match. It was made clear that this was to be a serious game. No one was allowed on the court in anything but the softest Plimsols (he had ordered enough pairs for the entire family). Virginia found a perfect fit for her feet by using one of the men's guest pairs. "I'm a tall woman, Mr. Harris," she said. "I can fill a man's shoes."

Much to Connie's surprise, her father seemed to take the forthright statement in stride. In fact, he enjoyed it enormously, slapped the table, jiggling water from the glasses.

At the playing field Virginia protested when she was handed her yellow ball and mallet with matching stripe. "Why Mr. Harris, I was hoping I'd get to play the red ball," she said in her charming way. "It always brings me luck."

Connie's father smiled back. "This is the way we do it, Miss Smith," he said. "Mrs. Harris and I play the red and the blue balls."

Connie was relieved Virginia didn't argue, and the game got under way.

Virginia whispered to Connie as they waited their turn. "At home we could have played an entire game by this time."

Connie gave her a pretend stern look. "This is Harris croquet," she said under her breath.

The game proceeded silently, each contestant lining up each shot with great care, leaving remarks of triumph, disappointment, or annoyance unspoken. Other rules were explained in a hushed voice by Connie's father as they came up in the course of the play.

Connie could see that Virginia's version of the game was more freewheeling. Every now and then, an odd partially suppressed squeal came from her, which she immediately stifled as best she could. One time she murmured, loud enough for Connie to hear, "The ball rolls too fast. Why can't we play on a regular lawn, not this billiard table?"

In spite of her complaint, she was able to shorten the distance between her ball and Connie's father's, nearing the final pair of wickets. Taking a chance, she risked all by heading downfield to tag his ball and then sending it, with a mighty blast, more than halfway to the far end of the court.

"You'd be better off to stick to your knitting, Miss Smith," Connie's father said. "I still have only two wickets and the post to go."

Virginia had a wicked gleam in her eyes. Looking straight at him, she put her finger to her lips and saucily made the sound of a loud "Shhh". No one said a word. Connie held her breath. Would her father explode?

Forever after she wondered how Virginia caught up with him so rapidly. Could she possibly have skipped one of the required wickets?

Worse, could she have moved her ball when no one was looking? Her father, the champion, was beaten. No one wanted to speak. He was gracious in defeat; she was modest in her victory.

The following morning, at breakfast, there was a small envelope at Virginia's place addressed "To the New Champion." Inside, in many layers of white tissue paper, was a five-dollar gold piece. She held it up triumphantly.

"I'm honored, Mr. Harris," she drawled. "I propose that this five-dollar gold piece be mounted on a plaque and that it shall henceforth become the Harris Croquet Series trophy, to be awarded each year to whichever player wins the most games over the course of the summer. And I challenge you to a return match tomorrow."

There were cries of "Hear, hear," thumps of approval on the table, and finally loud applause. Connie's father dinged on his glass for order. "Here's to you, Miss Smith," he proposed, holding up his glass of orange juice. "And let the series be named the Smith-Harris Croquet Series."

More cheers, thumps and applause. Breakfast proceeded with more challenges all around the table.

WHY GO on at such length about these people who spent seven years with us in Schroon Lake so many years ago? I don't know enough about what happened to know what they had to do with my parents' lives. I know something changed for the better when they came.

I know the overall effect of Virginia was a positive one. Only Aunt Rae would have disputed that. She was Virginia's rival for outspokenness. I remember Virginia in all her wonderful directness. And I remember Mother's criticisms of her. She was a Christian Scientist, and Mother thought that was taking terrible chances when children got sick, that sickness was sickness; it wasn't wrong thinking or whatever Mary Baker Eddy called it.

I remember once when Elizabeth was very sick with the flu. She had been staying with us for the weekend, and woke up with a cold sweat, chills and fever. Mother said, "But Virginia, why not take her to the doctor? The poor child is so sick she can't possibly have any wrong thoughts or any kind of thoughts. She was delirious last night.

I'll take her to the doctor and pay his fee; it isn't much." I was amazed by my mother but I felt she had done the right thing. I can't remember what happened afterward. Mother was pretty much a realist even about people she loved, and she loved Virginia.

In our small town, everyone knew everyone else's business. Word got around fast when Virginia wrote several outspoken articles attacking pro-German or anti-English attitudes. She fired off a number of letters to the one local paper we had, the *Ticonderoga Sentinel*, with articles critical of anyone she felt was not fully behind the war effort. Her remarks were pretty blunt about the Irish and their longstanding anti-English stance. She felt it was shocking for them to remain neutral when England was being bombed. She named her piece "The Thorn in England's Side." Aunt Rae's husband was Irish Catholic, and Virginia's strong words made for some tense feelings between Virginia and Uncle Joe, although he could always shrug it off with a joke of some sort.

When Mother talked to me about Virginia, in the last years of her life, she used to say she was a barrel of fun, full of enthusiasm, with a wonderful sense of humor. As we both agreed, Virginia and her children had brought a lot of joy and laughter into our lives that we all needed. We often said what would we all have done without them?

AND WHAT OF my friendship with Elisabeth? What was she like and what was it like to be with her? How did we pass our time – besides the games of school, where she taught me things? Whispering? Secrets? I don't remember anything like that. I wasn't that kind of person, I didn't open myself. Did we have projects? I remember doing chores together. I don't think we ever got into any trouble, though we were mean to Dwight.

Did we help each other in the ignorance of childhood? I don't remember it being that way. Nothing helped me in the ignorance of childhood – not even Antzie, though knowing her for that year or so had helped me. I didn't talk to anyone about the things I didn't know or couldn't figure out. I kept quiet and tried to learn.

I tended to be friends with people more the way boys traditionally are friends than girls, I think. No secrets, all activity. The exciting thing was to roam and explore, without being spotted by any grownups who might be about. We loved running away from Dwight, as he got big enough to want to play with us. And we ran away and hid from Antzie when she wanted to come down and play with me, her best friend not so long ago.

Elisabeth had certain typically English prejudices. She was anti-Catholic, especially Irish Catholic, which was one reason Antzie was not a welcome addition to our twosome. I kept my own counsel. I didn't argue and certainly didn't defend Antzie. I didn't want to lose Elisabeth. Besides, the kids of Schroon Lake and environs all had their own tight little cliques. You had to know who was related to whom.

When I moved into high school, there was a subtle shift in our relationship. I wanted to belong, and I tried out to be a cheerleader and was chosen. Elisabeth didn't try out. She wasn't interested. She got serious about her study of the bass viol. So we were separated quite a lot. Games were on weekends. This didn't spoil our friendship but it meant we spent less time together; and we were outgrowing the age when we would conjure up adventures in our imagination. The real world was getting closer and closer.

Fifteen

I GLANCED over at Dwight next to me on the porch swing, and the slight movement of my head made the rusty springs whisper. (In Daddy's day the porch swing never squeaked.)

Dwight's eyes were closed. Maybe he had dozed off; he had done all the heavy work.

I looked over at the woodshed loot piled on the north end of the porch. There was a second load for the dump, and things for the auctioneer, and there were family memorabilia still to check over before a final heave-ho. The air was close and heavy. In the woodshed I hadn't noticed the humidity; we had been protected by Daddy's thick walls. Now it weighed on me.

I held my ice-cold bottle of beer against my cheek, and then raised it in a toast.

"Here's to you, Bubba Dwightey," I said softly.

He stretched his arms high, tilted his head back. Cobwebs had turned his beard gray on the side facing me. His forehead was beaded with sweat.

"You must be exhausted from going up and down that ladder," I said.

"It was worth it. I don't want to have to go back into that woodshed."

We swung back and forth without speaking for a while. He sat with his head back, legs barely pushing. I thought he had drifted off again. Finally he spoke.

"I did find one treasure." He put his beer bottle between his feet, reached for a speckled black and white student's notebook that was lying on the floor with some old *Life* magazines, handed it to me.

I ruffled the ruled pages. They were covered with Daddy's precise, pointed script, page after page. It gave me a strange thrill to see that writing, as if Daddy had been there a moment ago.

At the top of each page he had written the name of a town at the left, the name of a town at the right, and mileage figures in between for miles covered that day. The ink was a rusty-looking black but still legible. On each page was listed the expenses and automotive events of that part of the trip. Not a comment, not a person mentioned.

"Know what this is?" Dwight asked me, taking it back and looking at it as I had done. "I almost didn't believe it had happened till I found this. It's a log of his cross-country solo drive. He delivered a car from Detroit to Azuza, California. He told me about it when he drove me to try out at the Grand Ole Oprey in Nashville."

"He drove you to Tennessee?"

He looked sheepish. "I know it sounds insane. I told him I'd take the bus. I'd rather have gone alone, but he wouldn't hear of it. Drove me all the way there and back. I heard about every mile of this run from Detroit to the West Coast – flat tires, breakdowns, cloudbursts, tornadoes, hitchhikers. I could recite it in my sleep."

I didn't know whether to ask him about the Grand Ole Oprey or Daddy's trip. "I can't believe I never heard about either one of those trips," I said. It must have been while I was away at school.

"You doubt me?" he challenged me.

I took a long swallow of beer, and started again. "Why'd he do it?" I asked. "For the money?"

"What do you think? He was always trying to get in on some scheme that would make him money. Besides, he had some idea he could make it in Hollywood. Wanted to be a script writer or a stage designer. Director. He thought big in those days."

I began to remember hearing something about Daddy going to work in the movies. I didn't quite believe it when Mother told me. And she hadn't told me he had driven. But she had told me what he had said when he got back, which I've never forgotten because it made me cringe. He told her it was like Palestine on a picnic.

"Why didn't Mother go?" I asked.

"Grandpa put his foot down. 'You're not taking my daughter west of the Rockies, not unless it's on the railroad. You'll run into renegades, rattlesnakes, even anacondas. They'll strangle a strong man. Over my dead body, E.B.'"

Sounded like Grandpa. "So who'd he deliver the car to?"

"Ah, that's the other thing. Some big silent movie star. Never heard of her – Leatrice Joy. But he was there for a few months. She had starred with John Gilbert, even married him. Our father said she played real dynamic women. Told me she made bobbed hair the fashion."

"She must've had great connections. What happened?"

He patted my arm. "Hold it, Sis. Let's get the rest of this stuff to the dump before it rains. We've got time for the stories."

"That's mean," I said.

He made a taunting face. "What happened?" he repeated my question. "It was Leatrice who got him to California. Hollywood opportunities came as a rationale."

Did he know this, or was he guessing?

He was already up and loading the truck, and I joined him, wondering what to ask.

"But what happened?" I insisted.

He shrugged irritably. "You really think he could have gotten into the movies?" he said. "She probably got tired of him and tossed him out of bed."

I started to protest but the look on Dwight's face shut off my air supply. He looked just like Daddy at his most murderous. I let it pass.

I went back and picked up the book from the floor of the porch. The dates were all written clearly and precisely, but I couldn't find a year noted anywhere in the entire book. Then I remembered Mother telling me that Daddy didn't come straight back from Texas; he drove out to California, supposedly looking for work, and she spent the summer up at Schroon with us children, fending off her parents' questions. Was that when he had met Leatrice Joy? Had he come back then and picked up her car in Detroit?

Dwight went on methodically loading the truck. I left the notebook and joined him again. "Mother said he sort of ran off for a while, when she made him let us move back north from Texas," I said. I held onto his arm for a moment to get him to respond.

I got him to pause, anyway. "You know more than I do," he said.

We headed for the Charlie Hill Road with flashes of lightning streaking across the sky to the west. When we were finished at the dump we agreed that going home to the gloomy house with a storm breaking wasn't appealing so we headed for Cecil's.

WHILE WE WERE WAITING for the food to come, we were both careful what we said. I didn't want to hear his harsh remarks and he knew it. And I knew he had no patience, after an afternoon of going through all the detritus of all those lives, for my little good girl explanations.

As we got into our second beers, and the hamburgers were served, though, he started asking me questions about our parents. He wanted me to fill in details. Mother hadn't confided in him; he had been too young and then he had begun to pull himself out of the family orbit. As soon as he was seventeen, he left home for the Air Force, and afterward settled as far away as he could get in the continental U.S. I knew by now that his opinions of Mother and Daddy hadn't changed since then. Mother was a nagging snob with no sense of humor; Daddy was harsh, judgmental, bitter. Dwight had told me he felt lucky to escape. He had come home as seldom as possible, and never with any readiness to give either of them the benefit of a doubt. Now he wanted me to tell him about them. Why should I?

"You only want your own opinions confirmed," I said. "Some proof positive that your view is accurate."

He shook his head. "I admit my curiosity is motivated, but I know I paint things too black. Nobody could have been as bad as that."

I started eating. I was suddenly incredibly hungry. "Did you know they had an adventure of a honeymoon?" I asked him between bites.

"No. Tell me about it. Glad to know they had a honeymoon."

"They drove to Chicago. It was 1920. Then took a train out to Banff, then back, picked up the car and drove back."

I looked out the windows of Cecil's, blurred now with rain blown in on an easterly wind from across the lake. Lucky we had started when we had. I wondered how to tell the story for Dwight's skeptical ears. I might not tell the whole thing.

"Come on, shoot," he said. He sat back and waited for me to launch into it.

"They got married up here, June 25th, 1920." Did Dwight know these facts? I had always taken it for granted that facts about family members were known by everyone; they were repeated so often during my childhood. The wedding was supposed to be on Grandma and Mother's joint birthday (July 1st), but Uncle Wilbur, Daddy's uncle, the Methodist Episcopal Bishop, hadn't been able to be here then. Mother was a Baptist, but Uncle Wilbur was the family celebrity on Daddy's side. President of Howard University. "They moved the wedding date," I said, "because Uncle Wilbur had to officiate at something at Howard on July first. Bad luck to change a wedding date."

Predictably, Dwight rolled his eyes. I chuckled, paused to eat another bite of hamburger.

"Grandpa gave them a Star station wagon, made by Durant Motors."

Dwight whistled. "That was one of the first station wagons ever. In 1920 it must have been almost a custom job. They didn't mass produce it for another four or five years."

"You always did know your cars, Dwight." He looked happy for a second, thinking about that car.

"Grandpa included a complete, eleven-volume set of Automobile Blue Books," I went on, "covering all roads in the entire United States and even up into Quebec. You couldn't drive without them – no road maps yet. Their plan was to drive to Chicago, meet Mother's grandparents."

"Oh yes, protecting their inheritance," he said, then made a wry face and covered his remark with something else. "Pretty gutsy for those days, driving that distance. Did Mother do any driving?" He had taken the last bite of his burger and he pushed his plate aside, as if to get closer to me. "I always suspected Mother enjoyed driving. For our father it was too serious to be any fun."

"Sure she drove. Mainly on the new macadam roads, not much on the rutted dirt ones. It was easier to shift those truck-size gears on level ground. Daddy had said they would spend their first night in Rome – Rome, New York. Nice touch." It had always amused me. Dwight shrugged.

"They had to go through every single tiny town, city, you name it. Daddy did most of the driving; she navigated from the Blue Book." I tried to quote. "Go past the white Congregational Church, turn left onto Congress Street, two blocks ... straight on the paved road out of town for 8.3 miles till you see a large red barn ... a two-lane macadam road, for the next 15.6 miles, along the old towpath of the Erie Canal."

Dwight started chuckling. "God, this sounds familiar. Is that where he got it?"

"Yep. It was like that all the way. About 800 miles to the Chicago city line. Then they used the City of Chicago Blue Book."

"You know all this stuff," he said, as if he couldn't figure why anyone would want to. But he seemed to want to hear more.

"Good thing Daddy had worked for the Chalmers car company," I said. I was wiping the burger grease off my hands with the red-checkered napkin – same napkins as always. When Dwight didn't answer I looked up.

"I heard that hard-luck story a few times," he said. "He never got over feeling sorry for himself over that one. When I was fourteen and I wanted to caddy, he told me he just wanted me to enjoy my childhood because he had had to support his family at fourteen and hadn't been able to go to school. I caddied and lied to them about doing it."

I persisted with my story, ignoring Dwight's asides. "They had about twenty-seven blowouts," I said. "Took along spare tires plus a Magic Rubber Mend tire-patching kit. Still had to replace all the tires before Toledo, Ohio."

Daddy told me some of this, but he never wanted to talk about the early days of their marriage, and particularly not about the honeymoon. I had to pump him. And Mother wasn't much better on the subject. Too much unhappiness lay waiting in any story of that trip.

"They carried extra spark plugs, motor oil, their own funnel, wrenches. Flashlights. There were no street lights in most towns, few places to stop. No motels till after World War II. They camped out a lot. Had a camp bed, pillows, blankets, a Coleman stove. Mother told me Daddy had to cook; she had never even boiled an egg."

"Ah, so she didn't know how to cook. No wonder the aunts had such leverage." He took a long swallow of beer and pulled the bottle away from his mouth with a pop. "He always sounded like a Blue Book," he said. He signaled for two more beers. He spoke sternly, slowly, imitating Daddy. "Three point seven miles, left at the

Mobilgas Station. We'll hit the main route to Schenectady."

"He loved back roads. Never asked directions, didn't use a map, never got lost."

Dwight frowned. "No, never admitted he was lost."

Absolutely typical of the way we were each bound to see Daddy. I had never thought about whether or not he was lost, just assumed that if he didn't know where he was he could certainly find his way to where he needed to go. And he did.

"He once told me," I said, "that the trip was smooth and easy compared to Mother's grandfather's inspection of him. He went over him with a fine-tooth comb."

Dwight was looking away out the window, which was still blurred by the rain. I had the feeling he was listening, had to listen, but didn't want to. When I paused he waited, then glanced at me and seemed to nod, so I continued.

"Daddy evidently asked Great-Grandfather why he and Great-Grandmother hadn't come to Schroon Lake for the wedding." I remembered the sound Daddy had made, telling me Great-Grandfather's answer – a sound like a snort. "Great-Grandfather said he'd be ashamed of such extravagance. 'I didn't found the most successful bank in Chicago to squander my hard-earned cash – or anybody else's, by jingo.'

"The grilling evidently went on for some time. Church affiliation, family origins, ancestors," I said, "his sisters, their situations, maiden names of Daddy's grandmothers, and finally, Daddy's prospects and aspirations. Mother said she gave her grandparents a bright picture of how well he had been doing in her father's bank, a New York affiliate of Great-Grandfather's, and spoke of what a great mentor and guide her father was to him. She ended by announcing that he'd probably be promoted soon after they got home."

Mother told me all this as part of the story. The taste in her mouth of the things she had said to her grandparents must have made E.B.'s news about having been fired even more shaming for her, and for him too.

Did the old man know about E.B.'s disgrace? He didn't let on, but he might have enjoyed the predicament the young folks were obviously in. The photo portrait of him presents an old gentleman with bushy white whiskers – the self-made millionaire who had had no help from anyone. He had made several fortunes, starting and building up three different businesses before he founded the bank. So when Daddy explained that he had gone to work at age fourteen for the Chalmers Automobile Company after his father had gone into bankruptcy, Great-Grandfather's tone got more sympathetic. He then told his own story, about rebelling against his father, leaving the family farm at sixteen to seek his fortune. He asked point blank why in tarnation Daddy hadn't stuck where he was, on the ground floor of this new, wide-open automobile business.

"Remember Daddy's invention, the automobile self-starter?" I asked.

"How could I forget it? I always had the impression he felt cheated of his rightful life." His tone was bemused, for some reason not sharp.

"Great-Grandfather took him to task for that. Mother told me Daddy described his hopes for that invention and complained that it had been stolen, and said that it if had not been stolen . . . Great-Grandfather interrupted, thundered at him. 'Never use the word "if" around me. Something goes wrong, make it right by doing something else. There's opportunity everywhere,' that sort of thing. He said 'if' was a woman's word."

And then I understood. Daddy must have been hoping Connie's grandfather would give him a job. Something goes wrong, make it right by doing something else. That was an adage Daddy would quote at us but he had no idea how to use it. If he had, he would have gotten that job from Great-Grandfather. The old man was independent, and ornery enough to do anything he wanted to do – and be surprised if anyone thought to do so much as make a comment.

Dwight took a swallow of beer and wiped his moustache with his handkerchief. "So that's where he got that," he said. "Great-Grandfather really yelled at him?"

I nodded. "Mother said she jumped. Great-Grandmother spoke up calmly, asked Daddy how he liked his tea, with lemon or milk. 'We always have tea at this time,' she said, and she asked Mother, 'Lemon or milk?' and then said, 'I prefer the English way, don't you?' Nothing ruffled her."

I could feel the beers making the words come faster. I wanted Dwight to know something, even if he wasn't going to change his mind. I was thinking how easy it was for me to be critical of Dwight, but what was the point? I went to the bathroom and threw cold water on my face.

Dwight was waiting for me, two more beers sitting there. "Okay," he said. "There's Daddy, trying to impress the old gentleman, going on about his self-starter – I heard that one only a million times. And Mother, bragging to you about her rich grandparents. So what?"

"You're completely determined to make everything plain ugly," I said, keeping rancor out of my voice. I ignored the slur on Mother for the moment. "Great-Grandfather did make a pile of money. Is that some kind of sin?" I snapped at him, more than I meant to, gulped down a lot of beer, angry for losing my temper.

"A good thing, too," Dwight said, a hard look in his eyes, "since our father never worked a regular job a day in his life. We had to live off someone."

Money, I thought. And then the treasonous question. If Great-Grandfather hadn't left money to Mother, wouldn't Daddy have had to go out and get a job?

Dwight sat back abruptly against the wooden wall of the booth. "Who cares?" he said. "It all happened over sixty years ago. Mother always seemed too impressed by money and background. Who gives a damn?"

"You must've heard what Jewel said about Mother, and she isn't exactly in the Social Register. Everyone in this town loved her. You haven't been around in a long time, Dwight." I heard myself, my voice thin with anger. I stopped, sat back too, took a breath. I didn't want this sour note between us. I met his eyes. "Let's go home," I said. "I've had more beer than I should. Are you okay to drive?"

He took it the right way. "Let's have coffee. Does Jewel still bake her famous pies? Then we'll go. Why'd we get so worked up? Truce?"

The old kids' expression made me smile. We hooked pinkies, pressed thumbs, shook our locked hands up and down. "Truce."

[245]

DWIGHT PUSHED me and pushed me.

He forced me to push back. All right, I'll be honest with myself. My desire to alter his view of our parents is motivated by my having been sitting in what I've called the catbird's seat.

When I look back as honestly as I can, I know there was some self-awareness on my part. I wanted to be the good child, the one who was able to stay in the good graces of a rather difficult father, and was also able to be a willing listener for my mother, even when she was criticizing my beloved father.

And why was I willing to play this chameleon role? It got me what I wanted. Why not be the amenable one, the one who could walk quietly in the woods, never making idle chatter, getting as enthusiastic as my father was when he saw things he felt were worth pointing out. I can see now that I made myself, for the needy father, exactly what he seemed to need so much: an adoring audience.

It worked the same with Mother. Listen sympathetically, agree that he could be difficult. I could see perfectly clearly that he did fly off the handle – though not at me, because I played my role right. And in this way I threaded my way through the family minefield.

But it made for more peace and harmony, for me, while I was with each parent. I could enjoy more being with them, and didn't always have to be putting up my defenses, making excuses, criticizing when it was not my (child's) business to criticize my parents. I know I'm kicking against Dwight's criticisms, saying this. I'm not going to defend myself. It worked, that's all I can say right now.

HOW MUST it have been for them?

There's my grandfather, Arthur M. Harris, the most direct man in the world, never wasted a word or beat around the bush, and then there's this son-in-law, E.B., long-winded and prone to circumlocutions. It was one of the things my mother mentioned again and again, over the years, how different they were, and the fact that they never understood each other.

I imagine the two men in my grandfather's office, when Grandfather Harris has to ask E.B. to resign from the bank. It's his bank. He started it, the New York branch of the Harris Bank and Trust. The original one, in Chicago, was one of the earliest investment banks, the invention, one could say, of my great-grandfather. It grew, was successful, and eventually merged with other banks.

Arthur M. Harris says he's had unfortunate information from an impeccable source that has convinced him E.B. has to step down, to protect the bank's reputation.

E.B. asks what kind of information, and from whom he has received such a communication. And in the next breath, E.B. is defensive, angry, and then he refuses to answer any questions. "These very questions put my honor in doubt," would be his line. "I've done nothing wrong and I would swear to that in court, but I must face my accuser."

A.M.H. says his informant is someone he has known and trusted for many years and he can't and won't tell E.B. who it is. He says he can't take a chance with his bank; his business is based on trust and this could destroy that trust and bring ruin on their many investors.

E.B. protests that he is almost a part of the family. He mentions the promises A.M.H. made to him when he asked for Connie's hand in marriage. He reminds him that he has said he feels E.B. proved himself in the hard-knocks real world, that it isn't important that E.B. didn't go to college, because he had to go out and earn a living to support his mother and father and sisters – a most honorable reason.

But Grandfather Harris is already past all this and it can't make a difference. This potential scandal could destroy the entire family, so E.B. must quietly resign. That was the way it was done in those days. Grandfather says in closing that he'll be happy to write letters of recommendation to some of his close business colleagues, let them know that E.B. has a long wedding trip coming up, and that part of the reason for its length is poor health, the reason for his resignation. It should be for health reasons in order to avoid even a hint of scandal hurting the firm.

This makes E.B. madder than anything. He's never been sick a day in his life; since the age of fourteen he never had to miss one day of work. He asks for pen and paper, leans over the old man's desk, and dashes off a letter of resignation on the spot.

"If you feel this is necessary, I'll carry out your wishes, and we won't speak of it ever again," he says. "And I won't be needing any letters of recommendation from you, sir. I'll make my way on my own." He turns on his heel and walks out.

My father has no idea of what his sister has been up to, nor does he know that she is about to be exposed because her boss has died suddenly. Jeannette has contacted Uncle Wilbur (the Bishop, President of Howard University), who has spoken to important people in the banking and legal world, and the entire thing will be hushed up as long as Jeannette leaves immediately, also for health reasons. She must say she's had a nervous collapse from overwork, something that would have been believed in those days of a young woman from a good family who was working in a law firm. (Who paid back the money? I never learned the answer to this question.)

And I think Grandpa would never have been able to believe that Netsie could pull off such a sleight of hand, maneuvering books and figures, etc. But she was very smart.

E.B.'s extreme sensitivity, his inability to take any kind of criticism, caused him to turn from the opportunity my grandfather was offering him. And it's true, it was unfair, and he would have felt unjustly accused since he didn't know what Jeannette was up to. The money she supplied would have been completely on the up-and-up as far as he was concerned. Why would he think otherwise?

Aunt Netsie was long gone by the time I found out about her crime. Not that I would have been able to approach her about it even if she had been alive.

Netsie aka Henrietta had done the embezzling without E.B. knowing she was doing it. In those days she was always talking about the fact that she was going to move up in the firm, saying how well she was doing. Once E.B. had fallen for Connie, it became important for him to look good, and everything that was important to E.B. was even more important to Henrietta, the pragmatic big sister who was ready to do anything for this brother she felt (and the whole family, including E.B. himself, felt) was surrounded in glory. He was going to do great things.

Henrietta was involved with her boss. By the time I knew her, she didn't seem like a woman who had had an affair, but she had an elegant bearing, and a comfortingly capable demeanor. In younger, more hopeful years she must have been alluring to a certain kind of man. It was the boss/lover who initiated the plan to siphon off funds, and Henrietta carried out the plan and was given lump sums. Was he in love with her, or did he wisely bind her to him by having an affair with her, which would mean she couldn't tell on him without ruining herself?

Henrietta passed along the money she got, insinuating it into E.B.'s life, telling him it was from bonuses, raises, payment for extra work, and so forth. She had the excitement and danger of a love affair, and also the thrill of being able to help her brother in a way no one else could. A high point of this power was the purchase of the new car in which she and E.B. drove up to Schroon Lake to visit Connie and meet her parents. And the purchase, too, of the proper clothes for the house party week of hiking, lake sports, croquet, and the various meals.

This would have been some time during the summer after that spring when E.B. met Connie at Oberlin. It was during that summer visit that Connie's father invited E.B. to come and work at his bank. E.B. was still working as a salesman at the time. When he returned to the city he went to the bank and they took him on, though Grandfather Harris wasn't there; he was still summering in Schroon Lake. He had written from Schroon to his partners to let them know he had offered E.B. the job. By the time E.B. had worked for them for a year, he was seeing Connie quite a bit. Eventually they got engaged, in that odd way I've mentioned. And it was sometime right before the wedding that the scandal about Henrietta broke.

Mother had thought about it a lot, of course, by the time I discovered what had happened. She told me that the way she understood it, her father was in a fix. He couldn't interfere with what she had her heart set on, and also it would have compromised her to have called off the wedding, even though it would have been E.B. who was in the wrong. Her father evidently felt he had no choice but to fire E.B. It was just a matter of how to do it. It had to be done as quickly as possible. He thought he would ease the situation: he would help E.B. get another job. He had no intention of insulting him or of making him feel small. He had no intention of dismissing him. He thought he would have a heart-to-heart talk with him and they would figure out, together, what could be done and how E.B. could smoothly move to another position at another place of business.

And another thing. E.B. might have helped cause himself to be fired by getting angry at Connie's father's insinuations about his sister and himself. I think E.B. was his own worst enemy.

HE LOSES his job at the bank, can't bear to tell Connie. Maybe he couldn't bear the idea that she would think less of him, that she would see him in a really bad light caused not by anything he had done but by his sister, whom he had trusted, and now she had betrayed him. I'm thinking that E.B. wouldn't understand himself to be at fault in this, and would see the whole thing as something that had been done to him, that he had been wronged. And he had been wronged. And he had been duped, too, because he had believed his sister about where the money was coming from. Now he's humiliated in his own eyes. He has to face the fact that he had no idea what was going on. And he's humiliated because he trusted Henrietta, he believed she was his friend and that she would do anything for him, but he didn't think it would be something wrong and dishonorable. It might be very difficult for him to imagine telling Connie any of this. Connie was from a different kind of family, all sunshine and good food and a robust father and a mother who enjoyed nature, lived in a beautiful house, had this gracious summer place, and so forth. And it had all come about because his darling Connie had an enterprising grandfather who had given her father a leg up into the banking world. So much good fortune and how far wrong it had gone, and through no fault of his, as E.B. saw it. (And the bitterest pill, that E.B.'s own grandfather had been wealthy and well-respected, too.)

So he goes through with the wedding to this beautiful, truly innocent and unsuspecting girl who has always had everything she wanted and who adores him, and then on the drive back from the honeymoon she's prattling on happily to him about what life is going to be like when they get back and he has to stop her, because although he believes he's going to do great things and live like a gentleman, he also knows that for right now he doesn't have a job and he was fired from the job she thinks he has.

So he tells her he was fired, and he refuses to tell her anything more than that, because it's too painful for him. Maybe he says he was fired for something he didn't do but that he had to take the blame for it. She tries to ask him questions and he explodes at her, says she's against him too, and he's sure she believes he's done something wrong. And then that's that, he won't talk about it. And she's afraid to ask anything more about it.

This episode made E.B. angry with Jeannette for the rest of his life. He never forgave her.

There's something else that has a bearing. There's the suicide of his father, when E.B. was fourteen.

My father grew up from a very young age feeling he had to take on the august mantle of his grandfather, also E.B. Thirkield.

Only the fuzziest information has come down to me about my grandfather on my father's side, who committed suicide when my father was a boy. I always heard he was full of despair, and I have a feeling he would have wanted to remove himself from the scene as a burden.

He would have wanted it to look like an accident. It was too much of a disgrace, to take one's own life. It was the lowest sign of weakness.

He arranged it so that he got stuck on the tracks at the railroad crossing. (He would have had to sacrifice the buggy.) There were almost no under- or overpasses in small towns back in those days, only grade crossings, so the train was right there, at ground level. The thing that gave him away was his inability to sacrifice the horse. When they caught up with the horse, they found that the buggy's harness straps had been unbuckled.

After he died it turned out he had ordered (and partially paid for) another buggy to be made, to replace the one he wrecked, so that the family wouldn't be without their everyday conveyance.

MY FATHER'S FAMILY struggled to keep up appearances, to maintain their position and their station. My father was brought up to think of himself as a gentleman. A small example of this is the way he tipped, always generously. He never saw himself as being poor, and his plans and ideas were based on a large capital backup. When his family's fortunes failed, he was an infant, so he had grown up with the pretense, rather than the wealth itself, and the sense of failure. It might have been harder for him to understand the pretense for what it really was, because he had never lived in the family in its wealthier days.

He knew his father had committed suicide, but it wasn't talked about. It would have been a shameful thing that was covered over by the family myth that the father had sacrificed himself because he couldn't bear to be a burden to his family. No matter how strongly E.B. subscribed to this idea, it must have caused him shame, and I think the shame was somehow about himself, at the same time as it was about his father.

There was a great reluctance ever to admit anything like mental illness, and along with this would have come a terrible stigma about committing suicide. My grandfather was probably depressed for years after his business failures, maybe even before them as well. His family always hid what they called his melancholia; it was considered being unmanly, not bearing up under whatever the Lord threw your way. And although I never knew my grandmother, I know she was a strong-minded woman. Today she'd be described as controlling. She tried to keep everyone in line, including that poor husband of hers, oldest son of the Big Man of Franklin, and a failure.

In those days suicide was committed only by people of weak character, just as crime of any kind was the result of a bad streak in the character, an expression of someone's evil nature. A person from a good family couldn't do something like that. So the fact that my grandfather's death was a suicide had to be kept from the rest of the family back in Ohio. It was a horrible disgrace. E.B. and Jeannette would have been ashamed that their father could have done such a thing.

Uncle Wilbur used his influence to keep the death from being recorded as a suicide, or reported as such. The death notice says merely that the buggy wheel pulled away from its hub, the buggy itself collapsed onto the tracks, Mr. George Thirkield was knocked unconscious as a result, and the train bore down on him. The newspaper reported it as a tragic accident and a cruel fate for this most kindly and honorable Christian gentleman.

With my sister and brother, on a visit to Grandpa and Grandma's, Winter Park, Florida, 1937

Three generations: Grandpa, my brother Dwight, and Uncle Dwight, Schroon, summer 1937.

Three generations: Grandpa, my brother, and E.B., Schroon, summer, 1937

Mother and the three of us, Schroon, 1937

With my sister and brother after church, Grandpa's porch steps, 1937

With my sister and our cousin Robert Malatesta, on a visit to relatives in Owl's Head, NY, September 1937

With Snooks, Schroon, 1937

Virginia Smith Johnstone with her children: David (15), Elisabeth (10), Gerald (13), England, summer 1937

For Posterity, left to right, back row: my cousin Bill Harris holding my brother, Aunt Ann and Uncle Dwight, Aunt Rae and Uncle Joe, E.B., Connie, Muriel Early perched on the arm of the bench; seated: Snooks, my cousin Mary (Bill's sister), my sister, Grandpa, Grandma, me with circus whip, August 1937

Grandpa's driveway in to Almanole; in the distance, Pharaoh, rising above Schroon Lake, 1937

The Big House (Almanole), summer 1937

With Snooks and my sister, Aunt Rae and Uncle Joe's yard, Brooklyn, spring 1938

With my sister and my cousin Mary, Harris Fort, summer 1938

55. My brother, Grandpa's lawn, summer 1938

Back of the farmhouse where we settled in to live September 1938, 1960

The Lounge at the lake, 1940

Front of the farm-
house, 1960

Grandpa and
Grandma in their
motor launch
Codwira, 1940

With Fuzzy (one of Snooks' pups), our first winter in Schroon Lake, 1938-'39

With my brother on our new Flexible
Flyer sled, the first winter 1938-'39

Aunt Charlotte (standing) and Aunt
Jeannette, in Aunt Charlotte's back
yard, Spring Lake, maybe 1938

My grandparents' Golden Wedding celebration; back row, left to right: Uncle Dwight, E.B., Uncle Joe; front row, left to right: Aunt Ann , Grandma, Grandpa, Aunt Rae (Note: Mother was with me in the Glens Falls, NY, hospital due to serious ear infections.), Aunt Rae and Uncle Joe's house, Brooklyn, April 29, 1939

E.B. on top of Grandpa's fence-post, Schroon Lake in distance left, winter '38-'39

E.B. and Connie, Northfield, Massachusetts, 1940

Grandpa and Grandma at their Winter Park, Florida home, winter, 1941

Grandpa and James, cooking a picnic feast, Sunset Cabin, in the woods across the road from our house; (James Miles worked for a number of years for Grandpa and Grandma as chauffeur, butler, general around-the-place helper), 1940.

With Aunt Charlotte, summer 1941, Schroon Lake (before she came to live with us – it might have been a visit after Uncle Walter had died, early that spring); written on the back of the photo, by Aunt Charlotte: "Mrs. Harris took this last August – by their south porch – Aren't the trees lovely – C. Please return later."

A chorus line of little girls; I'm 3rd from left, with Antzie to my left, summer of 1940 or '41

Elisabeth Johnstone, near Coral Gables, Florida, 1941 or' 42

My brother age 10 or 11, Schroon Lake, 1945 or '46

My sister after she graduated with an RN from Fitkin Memorial Hospital, Asbury Park, N. J. (She was voted "Miss Fitkin" for being all-around best nurse of her graduating class.)

My brother in a school photograph, probably taken in 1948 when he was 13

My sister, age 17, taken by Grandma,
Schroon Lake, summer, 1944

Posing reluctantly for Grandma, age 13,
summer 1944

Daddy in front of the "stockade" he
built, probably 1960

Mother in front of Daddy's "stockade,"
probably 1960

Daddy and Mother in front of Daddy's garden

With Daddy, taken at Bruce and my apartment soon after we had moved in, October 1964

Late in E.B.'s life, 1965, '66, or '67. He was bringing wood in from the woodshed. He died November 27, 1970.

Mother in her older years, taken by my brother. Mother had been playing the piano, just glanced up and my brother caught this completely natural photo of her, 1978. She died December 19, 1984.

With my sister, about a week before my wedding, end of May, 1953

With my husband Bruce right after our wedding, June 6, 1953

Sixteen

THE EXACT WORDS my father supposedly used to describe me to my parents-in-law when I was born were, She's got big hands, lots of black hair, and she looks like a Jewess. It got a lot of laughs around the family dinner table, which I can actually remember later on, so they must have repeated the joke for years.

I think I liked the fact that he said I had big hands; he had big hands, too. I also liked having dark hair. I felt it was more interesting, exciting, serious. And I liked being different from my sister. She was blond, as a child. As far as looking like a Jewess, I don't remember if I asked what my father had meant by that, but I think that to me it sounded exotic, foreign, out of the ordinary. I don't remember feeling it in a negative sense.

I can't honestly say exactly why E.B. sent that message to his in-laws. He had a need now and then to say something slightly off-putting. His unusual way of describing me (I was named for his side of the family) might have come from a need to make his parents-in-law sit up and take notice. And I gather it did. It was 1931, and they were in Europe. Mother said he wanted his birth announcement to stop them in their tracks. He sent them a cable with those words in it, and his message caused quite a stir.

While there were no obvious slurs around the Sunday after-church dinner table, there were subtle references and the occasional joke told by Uncle Joe, who was a newspaperman and who could deliver a joke with a Yiddish accent. Ugly racial talk was considered to be in poor taste, even if your golf club (on the far side of the lake, started by Grandpa and his wealthy pals) did exclude anyone who was Jewish.

Mother told me I was a baby they had wanted. I always thought it was a way of telling me they loved me. But there was another part to the story. Maya.

Maya was born seven years after Mother and Daddy got married, in 1927. The story Mother told me was that E.B. was determined not to have a family until he could support one. He refused to sleep with her. Maya was conceived one weekend when they were staying with friends whose spare room did not have twin beds.

It was only by chance, and because in the years after E.B. died and Mother lived with us and I began to know her, that I finally understood what she had meant about my being wanted. It was her way of saying they had made love, they had had good sport, to paraphrase the Bard, in my making. It must have been a moment in their lives when they believed everything would work out. Connie's inheritance from her grandfather had come through a few years earlier, and E.B. must have felt solid, with the nest egg to look after and no need, at least for the time being, to be apologetic about money with friends, family, or strangers.

Maya was four when I was born, and she never seemed like a child to me. I was a toddler when she was already going to school.

I thought she was the best possible sister when I was small. She made me the star of our adventures, and the worst situations came out right because Beeba would act in the nick of time to save us. When I was small, she was my adored guardian and teacher, my champion. She was the one who had picked my name, Lueza. Mother read her a list. She loved the sound. She was generous with everything, not only that birthday check. She practically never lost her temper. And she never treated me like a baby. She knew I would skate because she would teach me. She did the same with reading. She did it with everything. She was too good to be true. By the time I was seven, and in school, I didn't want her overpowering protection any longer.

Subabeeba games had been real to me in Texas. Later, I didn't want people to know I had once thought my dolls were alive, that they could talk. This made me terribly sad. Sometimes I slipped back into trying to be Wifeuh, but not for long. That person wasn't me. Once, Maya had been able to take Suba and Beeba anywhere in the world. When I outgrew our games I let go of her, and we lost each other.

Maya always wanted to travel, and her games were the first way she went to exotic places. She always wanted to be a missionary. Before Korea she was received into the Roman Catholic Church. Later she married in a hurry, a man who wanted to dedicate himself to mission work too. He had wanted to be a priest, had dropped out, tried to teach, had no credentials. They moved every year. And every year there was another baby. And Maya wore herself out, died at fifty-six. I never got back to her.

ONCE WE WERE growing up, she was nothing but a nuisance and a wet blanket to me.

Here we are in our small bedroom – twin beds, one desk, in the corner at the foot of the bed on the outside wall (Maya's bed) – window facing west, late afternoon sun shines into the room; very small passage between the two beds; the bureau, with drawers open, on the other wall, the one with the door going to the hall, closet; easy chair in the small space near the radiator, ancient radiator hissing and banging.

Maya is moving about. I'm silent, curled into the chair. I'm ten or eleven, but when I was younger it would have been the same, only the subject might have been different. I'm reading a book, paying no attention to her; she goes in and out of the closet, removing clothes, laying them on the bed, one after another.

"WEEZIE, I know you're reading," she said. "I have to show you this." She held out a photograph from a magazine, thrust it toward me.

I looked up, sighed. "Who's that?" I said, holding my place on the page with my finger, waiting to go back to it. I knew the photograph was of Farley Granger.

"He looks like that new boy on our bus," she said.

"So what? He's a movie star," I said "We saw him in *North Star*."

"He has such a nice face. I just know I'd like him."

I realized she was talking about the new boy. "How can you possibly like someone you don't even know?"

"I feel so sorry for him. He's new and the kids pick on him." She went to the desk, picked up the Scotch tape, pulled off several strips and taped the photograph of Farley Granger in the corner of the mirror over our bureau.

I sighed pointedly again, and turned back to my book. I had my back to her, my legs flopped over the arm of the chair. She was humming a popular song under her breath. I started to read, and forgot her.

After a few minutes, she presented herself in front of me, dressed in a different skirt and blouse. "You like this skirt with this blouse?" she asked.

I looked up even more slowly and reluctantly, glanced at her outfit. "It's very nice," I said. "I was with you when you picked it out." I held the book directly in front of my face and pretended to go on reading. But I was too angry, I couldn't concentrate. I could see her pick up another skirt, grip the waistband and hold it in front of her. She turned herself sideways, looking at her reflection in the mirror, turning her body this way and that.

"Or do you like this combination better?" she asked, inevitably, tossing away the second skirt and displaying a tweedy brown-and-white number. "I want to know which goes better with this blouse." She was wearing a lemon-yellow cotton blouse that I thought went well with the fine line of yellow woven into her previous choice of dark navy and green plaid.

I realized she had me. It was impossible to read, and she wasn't going to quit. And I refused to get up and leave. This was my room too.

"Sure," I said. "That's fine."

"Now how about these two? Do they go right together?" One more plaid skirt, with more red, and patches of white here and there.

"No, Maya, the blouse looks better with that first skirt." I would have to make a definite choice or she would keep asking me forever.

"Oh, thank you," she said, with one of her big smiles. "You're such a help."

I went back with renewed concentration to my book. I was aware of her, attaching skirts to hangers, folding blouses.

"Now, which sweater goes best?" she said, as if she hadn't noticed I had gone back to my reading. She had pulled out three cardigans. One at a time she held them up in front of her, clutching the back of the sweater in the middle, pulling the sleeve out and extending it along her arm.

They all looked fine. I decided to make a big deal of this decision. I moved my head to one side and then to the other, compressed my lips to convey concentration, hesitated a bit, and finally made my pronouncement.

"You should wear the green one. It goes well with your hair."

Then she was on top of me, hugging me, gleefully thanking me.

After that, it was quiet in the room for a few minutes while she folded the rejected sweaters and stuffed them into the drawer. I dove back almost immediately into the exciting climax of the adventure novel I was reading. The room was gone. Then it was back with the loud bang of the closet door shutting.

She was standing over me, looking down at me while I continued to pretend to read. She just stared. Right then I would have given anything to have my own room.

"Weezie," she said. "I hate to interrupt you again but I have to ask you an important question."

No, she didn't hate to interrupt me, she loved to interrupt me. "What?" I said It came out hateful.

She was unfazed. She looked down at me as sweetly as ever. "Do you think it's okay for me to ask this new boy – I think his name is Lester Smallwood – to the sock hop they're having on Valentine's Day? I just know I'll like him."

Maya was always declaring with wide-eyed, innocent insistence, "But Mother, I could fall in love and marry the dump mother's son just as easily, even more easily probably, than I could one of Aunt Ann and Uncle Dwight's kids' friends. I don't think it matters one bit what somebody's background is or even what their education has been. Love is what matters. I don't need anybody with fancy clothes or fancy manners."

I HAVE CLEAR memories of Maya her first year of high school, during the year of '41-'42, when we spent the school year on the Jersey coast because E.B. was helping his sister Charlotte with the paperwork after her husband died. Maya had to be driven to the high school in the next town. She spent a lot of time on her hair. She knew the lyrics to all the pop tunes, especially the slow romantic ones, and she used to talk to me about her big crushes. I had a crush on a boy in seventh grade (I was in fifth) but I wouldn't have told anyone about it because I was afraid I'd be teased. Maya was teased and she seemed to love it.

She went to boarding school in 1943, for the last two years of high school. She was sixteen when she went. My parents picked the school, St. Mary's in Peekskill, because some friends from our New Jersey life had sent their daughter there. Maya was determined to become a nurse, from an early age. She went to Skidmore, in Saratoga, in the practical nurses' training course and then had to leave during the period when she began compulsively washing her hands.

I remember one Thanksgiving vacation, the first year Maya was away at boarding school.

I remember Mother was playing scales in the front room when Dwight and I got off the school bus and we thundered across the porch and burst into the room. (Mother, half joking, used to call it the music room. Her baby grand piano occupied most of the floor space in that tiny front parlor. The low ceilings made for good acoustics, allowing the sound to flood up the stairs and flow freely throughout the house. When Daddy was home, he would sometimes call out his requests to her as he finished up in the kitchen. "Play the *Appassionata*, Connie" or "Another Chopin étude.")

Mother asked how our day at school had been, and reminded us that Maya's bus would be there in less than an hour.

We kissed her cheeks, raced each other through the house and into the kitchen for something to eat.

Aunt Netsie was chopping onions at the kitchen table. "We're having a beautiful pot roast tonight, one of Maya and your father's favorite dinners," she said. "Here, have a carrot." She lifted two scraped carrots from a bowl of cold water in a corner of the table. We took them with hurried thanks and ran out the back door. I wanted to watch Daddy, who was working with one of the men from the village piling extra wood for the winter behind his new woodshed.

He was in his work clothes, heavy work gloves, worn, dirty fedora, a faded plaid shirt, black with sweat under his armpits, tucked into dark gray work pants. He didn't stop his steady motion. "Why don't you watch out by the driveway," he suggested, "and when you see the bus at the top of the hill, you can let your mother and me know." He wiped his dripping forehead with his arm, never breaking the steady rhythm of handing the next stick of wood to his helper.

We raced each other to the spot from where we would see the beige-and-red bus cresting the hill to the south to begin its descent toward our house. The bus was due in the village at 4:05. We had about twenty minutes to wait. We started a contest to see which of us would be the first to spot it.

In the meantime we were playing a game, throwing pinecones at a designated target. After a while we began creeping closer and closer to the target, making it easier to score. There was a scuffle about who had started cheating first, and then there was the face of the bus looming at the top of the hill, shifting its gears to speed rapidly downward. We started shouting and running back toward the farmhouse. But the bus didn't slow down – it seemed to speed up, taking advantage of the long straight stretch of road going past our house and heading north past the boys' camp next door.

I saw Daddy round his woodshed, and head for the road, as the juggernaut roared past the house sending swirls of gravel and dead leaves in its wake. He raised his arms in a stopping gesture, crossing them over each other several times as he watched, surprise and disappointment on his face.

"What a damned fool thing to do," he said. "That bus driver must be stupid or drunk." His voice was deep with scorn. "I told your sister to alert him when they stopped in Pottersville." The drivers knew the house. "I don't understand it." He took off his heavy work gloves and banged them together, shaking off bits of bark, pine needles, and sawdust.

He went inside and we followed him. After a hurried conference with Mother, he headed for the barn to get the car while she telephoned the local restaurant – which served as the Schroon Lake bus stop – and asked them to tell Mary Belle to wait right there, they'd be down to pick her up immediately.

I went with them. Dwight was already off working on a model plane or something, and the aunts were busy with preparations for dinner.

As soon as we pulled up across the street from the restaurant, Maya called out hello to us in her sing-song that was so familiar – the first syllable spoken in a somewhat low pitch, then rising into the upper registers with the final o dropping down a third. She crossed the street and embraced us all, one by one. She was full of news of her traveling companion.

"Please meet my new friend," she said in her sweet voice, indicating a full-bosomed woman who was just catching up with her. "Her name's Anna Belle Parks and we've been riding together all the way from Peekskill." Anna Belle's size was exaggerated by a dress printed with huge cabbage roses, visible beneath a beige shorty coat. "She's got a son stationed up at Plattsburgh and I've told her she could come home with me and have a lovely family dinner with all of us," Maya finished.

I expected my parents to wince, and I waited for them to react; maybe I even felt slightly miffed when they hid their surprise.

Everyone started talking at once but Daddy's voice was the one that could be heard.

"Mary Belle, did you ask the bus driver back in Pottersville to stop at our house? You know I go back and forth all the time." He had to settle this right now. I was glad. I was betting Maya hadn't told the driver.

"Oh Daddy," Maya said in a rush, "Mrs. Parks and I were so busy talking I completely forgot about it. There are so many things we have in common." I felt like rolling my eyes as Maya rushed on, listing the things. "The same name, and she was born in February and she's a nurse. She encouraged me to keep plugging away."

"But Mary Belle," Daddy said in his low, reasoning voice, "wouldn't Mrs. Parks prefer to get to her son as fast as possible? This is the last bus of the day."

Mrs. Parks put her hand on Maya's arm. "I've been trying to tell Mary here that she shouldn't spoil her first evening home," she said. Her New York accent made me feel embarrassed, knowing how both my parents hated the sound of any localized pronunciation. But no one seemed to be paying attention to this embarrassing detail, even though Mrs. Parks went on talking. "I'd love to join you but I hear you have a pretty full house already," she finished up.

Daddy's mouth was set in a firm line. I knew it was not a good idea to talk to strangers about our unusual household. "Just keep your own counsel," he would say. "It's nobody's business." I could tell he was not pleased.

[276]

Mother said nothing, but I knew she wouldn't want to share Maya her first night home after almost three months. When the hubbub of voices subsided, Mother spoke up.

"Why, of course we'd love to have you, Mrs. Parks," she said as nice as could be. "But I can't imagine you would want to delay one second before you see your son." She even patted the woman's hand, where it still rested on Maya's arm, as if to remind her to move it. "I do hope you'll find your son well," she continued, as Mrs. Parks stepped back.

Daddy turned abruptly and walked with long strides up the street toward the bus. In spite of the excitement of all the meeting and greeting, he must have heard the bus's engine begin to rev up. He knocked sharply on the bus door and it opened. He stepped up one step and waved at Mrs. Parks to hurry.

She said a hasty goodbye. "This daughter of yours'll make a fine nurse and from the sound of it, there are plenty of people to nurse in your household," she said. She embraced Maya and headed for the bus.

When everyone was in the car there was a silence among us I couldn't stand. I wanted to ask something neutral. I asked Maya how she liked St. Mary's.

She seemed subdued, not bubbling over as she had been with her new friend. She answered without seeming to pay much attention to what she was saying. "The nuns are quite strict but most of them are very sweet. I think it's a good thing for me. I'm glad we don't have too much social life. There's lots of homework."

Mother half turned. Daddy was concentrating on his driving, his jaw set. I wondered if he was mad. I hoped not.

Mother said she thought the school had some parties with boys' schools nearby, and that they went to concerts. "You need to have some fun," she said.

"I don't think we'll have more than one get-together," Maya answered. "The nuns say it's not patriotic to use gasoline. I have lots of work, Mother, and I have to get good grades or I won't be admitted to a nursing program." As she spoke, she twirled a small strand of her hair around and around her index finger, coiling it up and then uncoiling it. I had never seen her do that before.

I was thankful Mother didn't start an attack on Maya's great dream of becoming a nurse.

"How's that lovely Stokes girl?" Mother asked. The Stokes girl had come last summer with her family to the Adirondacks. Mother and Daddy seemed to think if the school was right for the Stokes girl then it would be right for Maya too.

"Didn't I tell you in a letter?" Maya said. "She ran away at the end of October. I guess she didn't like it." Maya kept coiling and uncoiling her hair.

Mother turned around as far as she could. She looked right at Maya. "I hope you don't feel it's too strict for you."

Maya was getting ready to answer but Daddy spoke first. "Did Mr. and Mrs. Stokes bring their daughter back to the school?" he asked. He kept his eyes straight ahead and drove at his steady forty-two miles per hour.

Maya shook her head. "I heard she told her roommate if they tried to make her go back, she'd run away someplace where they couldn't find her," she said, still in that vague new way of speaking. "I wish we could have had that lovely Mrs. Parks come for dinner. She was such a sweet person."

No one said anything for several minutes. I was waiting for an explosion from Daddy. But he spoke in his hurt-sounding voice. "Mary Belle, how could you think of inviting a complete stranger, somebody you've just met on a bus, to come home with you for dinner? And particularly when you're here for the first time since September."

Maya bowed her head. Her finger stopped its coiling and uncoiling motion. I had the feeling she might cry. "I thought you'd all enjoy meeting this really nice person," she said, an intensity in her voice now. "Somebody who feels so sad about her son in the Army, maybe getting shipped off to the Pacific."

Daddy spoke low but I could hear the edge of anger in his voice. "It's one thing to talk with someone but that doesn't mean you necessarily want to invite them for dinner."

"I wanted her to come. I think you didn't want her because she was encouraging me to be a nurse."

Mother made a particular sound. "Oh Mary Belle," she said. "It's such a difficult profession and I don't think you realize just how difficult it is physically. With your asthma."

"I bet I wouldn't have any asthma in a hospital, the air's so clean. That's what Mrs. Parks said. And you know it's what I want to do." She paused, then added, "And that's that." She started in coiling and uncoiling again. I wanted to grab her hand and shout at her to stop.

"And who is this Mrs. Parks anyway, Mary Belle?" Mother asked in her reasoning tone. "You don't know anything about her. She could be making all that up, about being a nurse."

"She seemed so sweet and I felt sorry for her because her son needed to have some dental work done and she's got five other children at home and she didn't want him to have an army doctor do it."

I sneaked a look at Daddy, waiting for him to speak.

"And so you gave this complete stranger money," he said, in the way he had, barely moving his lips. He must be wrong, I thought. How did he know Maya had given money?

"You gave her money to help her pay for this supposed son's dental needs. I can't believe you could be so gullible, Mary Belle."

Maya hung her head. I saw that she had believed the woman, and she had given her money. I saw tears coming into her eyes. I didn't understand how she could believe just any story anyone told her.

Maya cried so quietly it was hard even to be aware of her tears. I felt sorry for her. But why would she even want to talk to someone at all, riding all the way from Peekskill to Schroon Lake. And she seemed to believe some of the most unbelievable sob stories. Right now, she seemed to agree that she had made a mistake in judgment, but I knew she had a way of seeming to yield but really maintaining her firm belief in the most outlandish things. The more outlandish the better, I sometimes thought.

I looked out the window, wishing I wasn't in the car at all. We were almost home. Mother shook out some of her supply of carefully folded tissues. She held them out over the seatback, and Maya, without looking up, took them from her. She dabbed at her eyes, and blew her nose loudly.

"Mary Belle, darling," Mother said in the tone of voice she used to keep herself from sounding aggravated. "It's only because we love you so much. We worry that you'll be too trusting with the wrong person and they might harm you in some terrible way." She waited for Maya to finish blowing her nose. "You don't want Aunt Charlotte and Aunt Jeannette to see you've been crying," she said. "They'd only worry."

If Netsie and Charlotte saw that Maya had been crying, they'd certainly think the absolute worst. Now that I was almost thirteen (only another six months) I knew some of these horrible fates that could befall a girl who was too trusting. Did Maya honestly believe that all people would be gentle and kind and that no one in the world had evil intentions? I leaned toward her, put my cheek against her bowed-over back, and gently patted her head. Her shoulders stopped shaking, she mopped her eyes and sat up straighter, and I knew she was getting ready to face the rest of the household.

Daddy drove up to the house quietly. I was sure he wanted to give Maya a chance to pull herself together before questions were asked. Mother opened the car door as silently as possible and got out, Maya and I got out, and the three of us went into the house as Daddy headed for the garage. Mother put her arms around Maya. "Once you have a child of your own you'll understand how your father and I feel," she said. "We love each of you children so much. Now I must help get dinner."

I carried Maya's book bag and her small case upstairs. When we got up there and into the room we shared, she put her hands on my shoulders and looked me straight in the eye. "You don't think I'm foolishly trusting, do you?" she asked.

I couldn't lie, but I didn't want to make her cry all over again. "I can't travel by myself yet," I said, "but when I can, I think I'd rather sit and look out the window or read a book. And I don't think you can believe everything people say." I wriggled out of her grasp. "I'll get you a cold washcloth and then I'll help you unpack," I said, and I headed for the bathroom.

"You're so sensible," Maya said. "I guess I want to believe what people tell me."

When Maya had put the cool washcloth to her eyes for a moment she smiled at me, looking as if nothing unpleasant had taken place.

[280]

"Oh, it's so wonderful to be home with you, Weezie," she said, throwing her arms around me and hugging me close. I inhaled the warmth of her body. I remembered those long happy days of childhood when my adoration of her had been unquestioning.

She broke away. "Tell me all about what you've been doing."

I was telling the story of *Casablanca* when Mother called up the stairs that Aunt Charlotte and Aunt Netsie would love to see Maya.

"I'll be right there," Maya called down. "I'll hear the rest later," she said conspiratorially to me, and she turned to the mirror to redo her high, rolled-over bang that served as a pompadour. I watched her as she brushed and arranged. Then she met my eyes in the mirror. "Does my hair look okay?" she asked. "I've got a new do."

I said it looked great even though I couldn't see much of a change. She turned toward the door and again embraced me in an all-enveloping hug. "I'm so lucky to have such a sweet, congenial sister," she cooed. "I love you."

I tried to put at least three-quarters of that same level of enthusiasm into an echoing declaration. It came out sounding awkward and phony. I would always rather show love than tell it. Maya's proclamations of devotion sounded forced. But how can I be so disloyal – mean, really? – I know she really did love me.

Maya paid a call on Aunt Charlotte in her room and then on Virginia and Nana in their adjoining room. Then she went to see Netsie in the kitchen. When she got to the table, everyone else was about to sit down. Chairs scraped; everyone got settled. Daddy said a spontaneous grace, mentioning at the end how thankful everyone was to have the family reunited once again.

Daddy carved methodically and accurately, each slice as close in size to the slice before as he could possibly make it. He chose not to speak as he sliced, devoting all his attention to the challenge in front of him. Mother served out boiled potatoes and green peas mixed with carrots; Jeannette brought from a warm spot on the top of the range the silver bread tray lined with a pure white linen napkin. Nestled within were fresh-baked baking powder biscuits.

Charlotte, who relished dramatic arrivals and departures whatever the occasion, arrived just as everyone was about to begin eating. There was a small flurry, Daddy acknowledging his oldest sister's presence at the table with a slight ceremonial dip of his head – he always carved standing up – the others greeting her with varying degrees of warmth.

"I've just had the most delightful visit with dear Mary Belle," Charlotte said, settling herself in her chair and fixing her napkin in her lap. "She was dear enough to come into my room. I wasn't sure I felt up to coming to the table tonight." She gave a delicate wave of her hand, small laced-edged hanky flourished quickly leaving a trail of lavender scent. The possible end of her sentence hung in the air expectantly. She was waiting, I felt sure, for reassurances.

"Of course you would come to the table on Mary Belle's first night home," Mother said soothingly, meaning to praise Aunt Charlotte.

Other voices joined in reassuring her, and she gamely carried on. "But then, dear Mary Belle persuaded me to please, pretty please make the effort," she continued, "and I made up my mind, no matter how I felt, I would get myself to this happy occasion."

Only Maya rose to the fresh bait. "Oh Aunt Charlotte, I hope you don't mind sitting with us," she said. "If you'd feel better, you could stay in bed and I'd be glad to fix you a tray of whatever you'd like."

Mother spoke up, before Charlotte could take up Maya's offer. "I know we've all had a lovely time getting ready for your arrival, Mary Belle. And we're so thankful and happy you're finally here."

"Amen to that," Daddy intoned from the other side of Mother, and kept on carving.

I was impatient to start eating. The aroma of the pot roast cooking away in its juices had whetted my appetite as soon as I got home from school. I hoped my sister wouldn't say something – anything at all – to spoil things.

Charlotte got the floor again. "Mary Belle, please tell us all about the Stokes girl – little Shirley. I hope you and she have become chums. You know I played bridge for years with her mother."

Maya looked uneasily at Mother and then at Daddy. "Shirley and I did speak to each other a few times," she began without emotion. "She's a lovely girl, but she's no longer at St. Mary's. She ran away."

I watched Aunt Charlotte. I knew the shock would register visibly, and it did. Aunt Charlotte liked to dramatize things.

Maya went on speaking, in the same bland but cheerful tone. "Everyone was very upset. And her family didn't make her go back. She told them she hated the school," Maya finished, then added, with a smile, "She said she felt as if she were in a prison."

I kept my head down, and focused on my food. I ate diligently, knowing Daddy was watching and keeping track of every morsel of food I ate. If I hesitated between bites he wouldn't wait long before he reminded me to "Pleeeeeze eat." I felt he had a mental calculator totaling the exact number of ounces of food I consumed as well as keeping track of all the amounts of the different food groups. I should not eat too fast either, in an attempt to get the eating process over and done with. That would bring forth a command to "Chew your food carefully and thoroughly. It's not healthy to bolt your food."

I was only listening by this time with half my attention tuned in to what Maya was saying. I wasn't interested in these school stories, and Maya's answers to everyone's questions sounded as if she were trying to say what they wanted to hear. The nuns were "sweet – most of them"; the girls were "awfully nice – most of them"; her room had "a lovely view"; the food was "quite good"; the work was "pretty hard – they have very high standards"; and finally, no, she had never been homesick – "maybe just a little when you and Daddy first left."

I knew that wasn't exactly true. She had written me a long letter saying how terribly homesick she was, that a lot of the girls were stuck-up, not very friendly, especially the old girls. And the new ones weren't any help: they were as new as she was and probably as home- sick, lonely and scared.

From the way it sounded to me, I knew I would never in a million years go to this prison of a school and I wondered why my parents had sent Maya there.

Now Maya was saying again that yes, the work was hard but she knew she had to pass many tough subjects to get into a nursing pro- gram. And at the mention of the word nursing they all pounced on her. They interrupted each other. They started in on all the old argu- ments I had heard forever: the drudgery (Aunt Charlotte); the hours (Netsie); the pay (Daddy); the blood and suffering and dying, and children dying (Daddy again); the sorrow, the ugliness (Mother).

"And will the people around you be congenial?" I knew congenial meant were the people in question just like us.

I couldn't understand why everyone kept trying to discourage Maya when she'd said for years she wanted to be a nurse.

I thought she was lucky. She knew exactly what she wanted to do; she had a definite goal and she could work toward it, look forward to getting there, and then do it. I didn't have much of an idea of what I might do with my life. I thought about getting married and having children but that thought made me feel too serious and it also made me think of being married to someone who turned out to be different from the way he seemed to be during that lovey-dovey time called courtship. How could you ever know you wanted to stick with some-one for the rest of your life? Wouldn't you only realize that after you'd already tried him out, at least a little bit? I kept this thought to myself. I knew it would only make the grownups titter at me. "My, you're cer-tainly thinking big thoughts for a little girl," was one of their pre-dictable remarks.

Maya was looking like she might start to cry again. I waited for a second or two of silence and then I changed the subject.

"I hope we have enough pot roast left over for sandwiches or hash," I said.

"I'm sure we'll have plenty," Mother said. "It was a six-pound roast."

"It's a fine pot roast, one of the best we've ever had," Daddy chimed in.

There were soft murmurs of agreement from Charlotte and Netsie at their end of the table. They turned from discussing perfect pot roasts to a discussion of methods for cooking the ritual bird – which method yielded tenderer meat, or better drippings for gravy, or a bird that kept longer and made for tastier soup. I saw that my deflection had worked. The Stokes girl, as well as Maya's life work, had been for-gotten for the moment.

I looked over at her. I wondered why she didn't make her mind up to keep quiet about her nursing career, especially with the whole fam-ily at the dinner table. Such angry discussions veiled in politeness gave me a sick feeling in the pit of my stomach. If only Maya could just not mention the word "nurse" or "nursing," or any of the other thirty or so words guaranteed to get the aunts, and Mother and Daddy too, all riled up. Why waste your breath?

It was time to clear the table, and I was glad to get out of the group. When Maya announced that she would love to clear tonight, I groaned to myself. Maya was agonizingly slow. And she was even worse drying the dishes. She had a way of massaging a plate, round and round with the towel, first one side, then the other, then back to the first side again.

I jumped up and started clearing. I prodded Dwight on the shoulder and whispered in his ear hoping no one would notice. "You're such a slowpoke; you're holding up everybody." He had been admonished by Daddy to finish all his meat and try to eat at least half of his potatoes. He stirred his potatoes around on the plate, spreading them out so it was hard to see how much he hadn't eaten. I pretended the plate was empty and removed it. Daddy didn't notice and Dwight gave me a grateful look.

Confusion, clutter, too many trying to do too much at once. Maya insisting she wants to help – she's had to help at St. Mary's – she feels she's been spoiled at home. "Not that I don't appreciate it, oh yes, of course I do. I feel so lucky to have you, Aunt Netsie, and you, Auntie Charlotte, doing so much for me." In order to follow her words through with an embrace of each aunt, Maya put down three stacked dirty dinner plates onto the pot roast platter, flattening several of Daddy's carefully carved slices of meat.

Daddy, headed for the sink, stopped in his tracks, pivoted abruptly back toward the crowded table. I knew he hated the stacking of dirty dishes. Why dirty both sides of a dish, he would remark. I saw his disapproving look, but he was silent as he lifted Maya's tilting pile. With a deft motion, he wiped each plate clean using one discarded paper napkin.

He moved the remaining slices of pot roast gently up against the butt end of the meat. I caught his eye at that instant. "This keeps your left-over meat from drying out too much," he said. I nodded. I was his deputy. He had his reasons for everything he did.

In his command voice, he said, "Now you ladies go back to the table. I've got this under control. Weezie and I will join you in a minute."

MAYA WAS different from the rest of us. I remember the scenes she caused, and I remember the feeling of embarrassment I always had when I had to sit through one of these scenes. She would say how much she liked something, for example, that to the rest of the family was considered unlikable. Her declarations were unnecessary, and she never seemed to have much of a sense of the stir she could cause in the family.

The talk about becoming a nurse was one of these topics, and it was linked to schooling. Mother would encourage her to apply to Vassar, where Mother's sister Rae had gone, or Oberlin, Mother's alma mater. Someone would pipe in with the fact that dear Pearl had lived at Oberlin, and someone else would mention again that Auntie Pearl had died of a broken heart.

The night Maya came home for the first time from St. Mary's was no different. When the conversation about schooling got going, Maya said, "I've been thinking Muriel's college is the place for me." Muriel was our cousin, Uncle Joe's daughter. Maya spoke quietly, as if there were no tension in this announcement, as if they were all having a pleasant chat about her college choices. "It combines nursing with a B.A.," she continued, "and it's affiliated with St. Clare's Hospital." For a moment or two everyone was silent.

Mother spoke first. "But Mary Belle," she said, sounding slightly embarrassed, "that's a Catholic college."

Maya kept her head down, looking at a small pile of tiny balled pieces of her napkin on her place mat. "They have a very good program. Nursing is nursing and I have a friend who plans to go there."

Daddy looked up at the ceiling. "I have great respect for Joe," he said, his voice solemn. "He never misses his mass on Sundays."

"Well, that's fine," Mother said. "That's what he's supposed to do. He was born and bred an RC. What would you expect?" Her voice had sharpness to it.

I noticed that my sister's cheeks were bright red. The finger and thumb of each hand were carefully rolling around and around in a circular motion two more tiny white balls.

Mother might as well not have spoken. Daddy continued to reminisce about his drives with Joe throughout the state of New York. "When Joe spots a Catholic church he often says let's go in and leave some friendly footprints; a few prayers couldn't hurt. I sit in a back pew. I love the peace and tranquility."

Mother made a tiny, impatient gesture. "There's just as much peace and tranquility in an Episcopal church," she said. "And the service is so dignified. We have all the same traditions." Her voice was softer but there was still an edge in it.

Maya looked up. "I love going to church where people bring their babies," she said with a dreamy look on her face. "Sometimes I go with my day-student friends from Peekskill."

"Don't you have an Episcopal service at your school on Sunday?" Mother asked.

"Of course we do. But I like to go to the service on Friday with my friends. The church is full of all kinds of people. They do a novena to the Blessed Virgin and we all say the Rosary together." Maya looked off into some distant place and said more firmly than ever, "Nursing is what I want to do and I know I can do it."

This last sentence lingered in the air as if she had spoken a curse upon the entire household. There was silence.

Then Aunt Charlotte tinkled her glass to get attention. "And now it's time for our dessert," she announced. "I have a special treat for our homecoming schoolgirl and for all of us." She glanced around the table to be sure she had everyone's attention. Then she pushed her chair back and swept out of the room.

You could hear the back porch door open and close and in another moment Charlotte appeared bearing her most special of all specialties, a towering, white-turreted creation, Charlotte's angel cake. A renewal of the religious wars was averted in the nick of time.

There were plenty of other homecomings – one with the latest boyfriend, a Navy guy she had met on that same bus and they almost got officially engaged on that bus. But it turned out to be a false alarm. And another one, the real thing for sure, a captain she came back from Korea planning to marry. She had the wedding dress. But that didn't happen either. For some reason she had a hard time making connections with anyone who was likely to be right for her.

It's strange to me that Maya was so little able to choose people who were appropriate for her. I've often wondered if she just chose the first person who would respond to her, and that always happened to be someone who wouldn't be good for her. My mother thought about it in terms of class, but I think it must have been more fundamental than that. Maya never seemed to come across someone who might bring out her strengths rather than her quirks. What if she was emotionally lame in some way, separated from her deep self, as if she were invisible to herself? What if she established these quick intimacies as a way of becoming visible to herself?

The grownups had a tendency to try to corner her, but that was impossible; she simply smiled sweetly and said things like, "But that's what I want to do." When I think about it, I can't remember her ever losing her temper. Sounds hard to believe but she had incredible self-control.

This I remember, and it was one of many scenes just like it:

"Mother, I do know what I'm doing and I'm going to be received into the Church." She set her lips firmly and her chin puckered.

I can remember, Mother was ironing and she kept slamming the iron down with a bang on one of Daddy's business shirts. "And that's another thing (BANG! iron iron iron BANG! iron iron iron BANG!) that makes me hopping mad. What's wrong with our church? (BANG! iron iron iron BANG! iron iron iron BANG!) Aren't we Christians too? We believe in the divinity of Christ and the Apostolic succession."

Maya was folding an ironed handkerchief into smaller and smaller squares. "But Mother, Christ said, 'Thou art Peter and I shall found my church upon this rock' and that's why we believe in the Pope in matters of faith and morals."

"And you'll never be able to go to church with us anymore. That makes me so mad I could step in it!" and she banged down the iron onto its metal stand with a clank. "Mary Belle, you're exasperating. And I thought we'd have such a nice visit when you came home."

BUT WHAT DOES Maya have to do with me? Nothing of me is invested in her. When I go looking for her in my childhood she's always

[288]

the same. Even now there's nothing about her that calls me to wonder about her. I grew up and left home. I used to try to be more charitable toward her, but she always seemed to cause me to be mean, in my heart.

It's hard for me to write about her. Even now, when she's been gone for so many years, something stubborn in me doesn't give way, and all my irritation and disdain come into anything I think of to say about her. She continues to bring out the worst in me.

Once when I was about three, we were playing and my finger got caught and mashed because of a game she had made up that involved a folding chair. Mother had to take me to the hospital, there was a lot of blood, everyone was discommoded.

Afterward they told me I was very brave. I had a beautifully bandaged left pinky, and I was glowing with praise for my grit and for keeping my hand still as the doctor worked.

Maya was contrite, overcome with guilt at having hurt me although she didn't mean to. She would never hurt her dear little sister, her dear darling Suba.

She sobbed at home, cuddled probably by Nana, maybe by Aunt Charlotte, who was still in her bridge clothes. Charlotte would have been exhausted after a long afternoon with so many ladies. "What's all this hullaballoo about? All this screaming, my nerves can't take it. I must lie down."

I came home in triumph. "Daddy will be so proud of you." And it was true. Daddy made a special trip downtown after dinner for a quart of ice cream, and I got to ride next to him, Maya still burning with shame, the disgrace of having caused such injury to such a perfect little sister. She couldn't say she was sorry enough.

I THINK ABOUT going to visit Maya one day when she was living in New Jersey. At that point she had only four of their seven children. I remember how impatient I always was to get going so I could get there and back again. I just wanted to get it over with.

I didn't go as often as I should. Going there depressed me. I felt guilty to feel depressed. She was the one with the hard life, trying to raise a flock of babies on a substitute teacher's salary. Paul was never asked to stay more than one year in whatever high school he happened to be teaching in, since he didn't have the proper teaching qualifications. Next year they might be in North Dakota.

Just thinking about her life made me feel trapped. She didn't even have a driver's license.

On the drive that late fall afternoon up the West Side Highway along the river, I vowed I wouldn't be bossy and critical of my sister's fussy methods of child-rearing; what she did was her business and I would stay out of it.

She was living in a tiny house with a cyclone fence around a yard of patchy grass and tipped-over plastic vehicles and toys. I pressed the doorbell and walked in.

The smell of unwashed diapers hit me. A baby was crying. Another tuned up from a crib in the living room. Maya came around the corner from the kitchen, holding the newest infant in the crook of her arm, with Mario, the oldest child, clinging to her skirt so tightly she could hardly walk.

"Oh Weezie, I'm so glad to see you," she said, and she flashed me one of her hundred-watt smiles. She was still beautiful but she looked exhausted. "Here, let's sit in the kitchen. I haven't had a chance to pick up in here." She turned and went slowly back into the tiny kitchen. I followed. She sat down at the kitchen table and Mario immediately started to pull himself up into her lap, grabbing at her breasts, at the infant, at anything he could get a grip on.

"Mario sweetheart, why don't you sit on Auntie Weezie's lap? She's a mommy too and she loves to hold little boys." A piercing howl went up from Mario. "Oh, precious, Auntie Weezie's feelings will be hurt and we know it's not kind to hurt someone's feelings."

"Let's get everyone dressed," I said, "and get outside. It's such a beautiful fall day." I could hardly wait to get outside myself; their house was always much too warm.

She leaned back against the chair. The infant, first girl and fourth baby in as many years, was sound asleep on Maya's knees. She didn't have much lap – a fifth baby was already on the way. She looked six months pregnant.

Another brilliant smile. "Going out would be a lovely idea," she said as if I had come up with something really original. "But Mary

Josephine should finish her nap. God willing, it could be another girl," she added, looking down at her belly. "But of course we're grateful for all the children God sends and we certainly don't care what it is." She paused for a moment and then added, "I haven't told Mother and Daddy just yet."

God doesn't send babies like he sends flowers in the spring, I thought. You and Paul have a little something to do with it.

"Didn't you tell me married couples couldn't practice birth control but they should exercise prudence?" I asked, trying to soften my tone. "Is this prudence?" I pointed toward her swollen belly.

"Oh Weezie," she said, "it's very complicated." She suddenly looked solemn. "Here, would you take Mary Josephine while I get the others? I think Joseph and Salvatore both need to be changed. Come on, Mario, you can help Mommy change your little brothers." The child's lower lip curled downward. My sister handed over the sleeping bundle. As she stood up, she leaned over and swept the boy into her arms. Her belly bulged out underneath his chubby knee.

I followed her into a bedroom. My head ached from the overheated, stale air. I felt exhausted just watching her heavy body with Mario dragging her down on her left side.

Joe, the middle boy, was jumping up and down in his crib, blond curls sticking to his head. The other three were dark, like their father. "Joe's my little WASP," my sister said. "Paul says there aren't many blue-eyed Sicilians. Joe must get those blue eyes from Daddy. Maybe he'll be a stockbroker, too." In actual fact, our father had never been a stockbroker. Did Maya know this? Hard to know what she knew, since she always seemed blissfully innocent of any and all information she did not choose to take in.

I offered to help with the diapers. "Oh Weezie, dearest, thanks so much. I love my little sister," she said, and she blew me a kiss which, as always, I pretended not to notice. Why did she always bring out my mean streak? She made me feel ornery. "I'm happy to do it. And the Blessed Mother always gives me the strength, every day, to be the best mother and wife I can be. I know it's not easy for Paul, working so hard in school and trying to keep ahead of his students."

She swept past me, lifting the diaper from my hand. I felt thwarted, unable to help, ever, even if it was her life, her choice. I watched her slowly douse the diaper up and down, over and over and over, as she went on talking about Paul's struggles.

"You don't know his parents," she said. She was working on another diaper by this time. "I love Poppy and Mamamia but they did put an awful lot of pressure on him and on his brother and sister too. They told Paul it would break their hearts and send them to an early grave if he entered the priesthood."

She finished with the diaper, put it in an industrial-sized waste container blocking the hall. "And Paul was –" she paused longer than usual – "not well himself. It's hard to understand some families."

"But Maya, Mother and Daddy didn't exactly encourage you to become a nurse either. Not to mention how angry they were when you became a Roman Catholic. I remember Mother actually slamming the door. I'd never seen her so mad."

Daddy hadn't been so outspoken about the situation. Then one day he completely flabbergasted me.

With his jaw tight, his eyes like blue ice, he said to me, "I can't stand to see the way Paul walks – like a Sicilian peasant. And married to my precious Mary Belle." He never mentioned it again. I was shocked at his snobbish attitude and yet I had nothing to say to or for Paul myself. I barely knew him.

She finished the last diaper and picked up the last pail. "They were afraid I wouldn't be strong enough," she said. "I think they were really worried for my sake, and Paul's parents were being – I hate to say this, it's not nice – they were being ... selfish. He tried so hard. His parents aren't very understanding, even today. We had a big fight with them this weekend. It was awful."

Her voice broke for a moment, and she went to the sink and washed her hands. As she dried them on a worn hand towel, she looked down to examine her nails. She always had beautiful hands, and as I looked at them there holding the towel I saw again what fine hands they were.

For a moment she seemed vulnerable. "Nobody could try harder than you do," I said. I sneaked a glance at my watch. "Come on. I'll put Joe and Sal's jackets on and get them headed out the door. It's such a wonderful day today and you'll soon have a yard full of snow and slush. I can carry Mary Jo and you can dress Mario yourself. He doesn't seem to want to come unglued from you."

She didn't move. Her smile beamed across the dark bedroom. "You're so sweet to want to help me like this," she said. "I know it's nice to go out but I haven't really had my lunch and I thought I could fix you a lovely sandwich. Or at least you can sit down with me while I eat. The children will be perfectly happy right here."

In the kitchen she lifted jars down from shelves and took a loaf of bread and some lettuce out of the icebox. Before I could say no, she handed me two slabs of Wonder Bread with something in between. I had never had peanut butter and jelly with lettuce and mayo. She made herself PB & J, no extras. I would have preferred that to my weird deluxe version. She sat down and carefully cut her own sandwich into eight tiny pieces. She took a tiny bite from one of the tiny pieces and began chewing slowly, smiling all the time. She was the only person I ever knew who could smile as she chewed.

Between tiny bites and tiny chews she said, "When we're done we can sit down in the living room. I have to fold some diapers." She kept smiling and chewing, very, very slowly.

I had not wanted a sandwich at almost four in the afternoon and especially not this sandwich. But I found myself nervously wolfing it down in about three enormous bites.

I left her chewing slowly at the kitchen table and went into the living room. I could hear happy children sounds from the bedroom and I stopped, staring out the living-room window. The front yard was in shadow. A chill was coming in around the loose-fitting window. I felt a wave of anger at my sister for keeping me in all afternoon. The day was over. A fiery ray of sun came out from under a black cloud near the horizon. The flaming ball slipped down between a garage roof and the etched lines of a bare maple across the street.

The living room was almost black. A green after-image danced on the opposite wall.

"Let's get some lights on in here," I said. "It's gloomy," and I started snapping on every light I could find. The children still sounded peaceful.

My sister came out of the kitchen, wiping her mouth with a Mickey Mouse paper napkin. She shoved the white mountain of laundered diapers into the middle of the couch. We sat down and started folding at either end.

"If you and Paul really wanted to be Lay Mission Helpers, and do something for the Indians," I said, "why didn't you postpone having another baby right after you had Mario? What's so complicated about prudence?" I had never pressed her on such a delicate issue before.

She spread her fingers and held them against her pursed lips. She spoke in a hushed voice, looking toward the front door as if she expected Paul to walk in any second. "I knew Paul still wanted to do some kind of work for the Church but when I suggested waiting – Oh, Weezie, he couldn't. I couldn't say no to him. When I even hinted we shouldn't –" She couldn't make a direct reference to the sexual act.

"You mean he didn't want to practice prudence even to do the work of the Lord?"

"I did try to remind him we'd wanted to dedicate our lives to helping the less fortunate but when I tried to say no to him, Weezie, he cried and begged me to give in to him. I didn't know what else to do. I'm sure you and Bruce never had any problems like this. At least you don't have any religious differences. The Episcopal church is pretty tolerant."

There was one loaded topic I'd never discussed with her. I looked over at her pile of folded diapers. I had folded at least four diapers to every one of hers but hers were much neater, like big envelopes.

I folded faster than ever. I knew Paul would be coming home soon. Maya always liked me to stay long enough to see him, and I always wanted to leave before he showed up.

I looked at my watch again. "I'm going to have to start back," I said. "I'll come see you again sometime soon, before the snow flies. Tell Paul I'm sorry not to see him."

"I hate to see you go. Would you do me one huge favor?" She stood up slowly, pushing herself up and away from the couch. "Would you mail this for me?" She handed me a postcard from the shrine of St. Dymphna, patron saint of the mentally disturbed and of hopeless causes. "I made a retreat there once before I was married. It was so peaceful in those little cells. I wonder why it was God's will that I couldn't be a nun."

She went over to the window and looked out. Street lights were on. The last pink glow in the west was gone. "I used to think the life of a nun was so hard," she said "Now I know they were on a fast elevator to heaven. This is the front line – the trenches."

I went over and put my arms around her. Her hair smelled of summer. Her arms held me tight. "I love you, Weezie. You're the best sister anyone could ever have. You and Bruce have done so much for us."

I could see my breath as I walked to the car. Under the street light I read her postcard.

Dear Mother and Daddy, We had a lovely visit with Poppy and Mammamia last Sunday in Toms River. The children got along so well and everyone slept on the way back. They like Paul at his new school and maybe they'll have him stay on next year. I'm feeling well and trying to get my figure back in shape. God bless you both. Much love, Mary Belle

Why didn't Maya want to play outside, run around, take any chances? Must have been her asthma, all her life. Mother and Daddy made poor Maya terrified of germs. No wonder she washed her hands a million times a day starting nurses' training.

Why did Maya need to tell me she loved me all the time? Sounded so phony. Mother and Daddy must have made her squash down any feelings of jealousy. "Mary Belle, you're going to love your baby sister so much."

I can only see Maya as someone against whom I defined myself from a very early age, and who has remained, for me, outside the psychic sphere of my self.

When she and Paul were living in Massachusetts, I went to stay with her for a few days. On the last night of my stay, I couldn't sleep and I went downstairs to make a cup of tea. Before the kettle had even boiled, Maya appeared in the doorway.

"I hope Paul didn't wake you up," she said. "He always does the laundry in the middle of the night." I can see that smile of hers. I used to wonder if she smiled even in her sleep.

She fixed us mugs of tea and came and sat with me at the kitchen table. Right away she started talking about asking Daddy for money. Paul wanted to go back to school, and she was going to have another baby. The way she talked about all this made me flinch. She sat there smiling, calmly and simply laying out why they needed money, as if money were a natural resource, available to everyone.

"Let me tell you something," I finally broke in. "You can't ask Daddy for money, because he doesn't have any." I wanted to shock her, but her face didn't register any change. I explained to her that my husband, his brother, and their father had "hired" Daddy, back in 1960, as a financial consultant. It was after Daddy came to me and Bruce, just before Christmas. Maya was in California at the time, soon after she and Paul had met.

"Daddy had to ask me for money to pay their oil bill," I told her. "If they hadn't had oil that week, the pipes would've frozen. He was forced to swallow his pride. It was awful. I felt so sorry for him."

It made me breathless, saying these things to her.

Her hands were poised over her mug. She looked as if she were shielding something precious.

"I suppose they wanted to protect me because of my asthma," she said. "When I was asked to leave the nursing program at Post Graduate, they didn't want me to get discouraged. And Grandpa's money—"

"What about me?" I said. "I had feelings too even if I didn't have asthma." She made me mad, so oblivious. I worked every summer to earn money to help get me through college and I got a scholarship, too. I got so tired of hearing Mother blame Daddy for spending principal. We're dipping into principal, she would warn him. But she never said to him, Why don't you go out and get a job?

Maya's innocence now, at this stage, was infuriating. "Why on earth didn't you ever think of asking them about their finances? I did," I said. "That's how I knew enough to apply for a scholarship. Where did you think the money was coming from, Maya? The pine trees?"

"I just assumed they were still comfortably off, living on Mother's inheritance from Great Grandfather. Whatever happened to it?"

"Three guesses. They spent it. Raising us, sending us away to school and college, feeding the aunts and Virginia and Nana. Daddy was never earning a steady income, you know that – or maybe you never bothered to think about it."

We had all kept up this charade for years.

My sister sat in silence. She had a way of opening her eyes wide when a situation was solemn. She looked as if she were staring at a ghost.

"Maya, you'll have to tell Paul that Mother and Daddy have enough to live on but that's it. If he had wanted to go back to school, he might have thought of it before you started producing so many children." I had touched a sensitive nerve. She seemed to snap back to life.

"It's God's will," she said "I've always wanted Paul to feel I'm there for him, no matter what. And I mean night and day." She gave her head a firm nod. "What about Bruce? I should think he'd be in favor of his brother-in-law getting a higher degree in English. I'll help him all I can, Weezie." She raised her eyebrows at me expectantly.

"You can't be serious. I'm not going to ask my husband to do any more for anybody in our family. He's already done enough. Why doesn't Paul screw up his courage and ask his own parents for some help? Let them loan him the money. I'm sick of people looking on us as some kind of welfare agency. I won't ask B. for another cent." I banged my hand down on the table. My sister's eyes were swimming with tears. She was shaking her head back and forth.

I was about to say, "There's no point in crying," but just at that second the cellar door opened right at my elbow. Paul staggered into the kitchen, his face hidden by a mountain of laundry. Once again, with his help, my sister had managed to stage-manage the scene so we were diverted from the heart of the matter. I wanted to scream at Paul to go back downstairs and let us get this all out in the open for a change.

A muffled voice came from behind the pile of clothes. "Mary, can you give me a hand?"

My sister's voice, smooth as honey, startled me. "Why, we can all fold the laundry together. Here, Paul, put it here on the table. You shouldn't carry such a heavy load; think of your poor back."

Paul bent to deposit his load of laundry, and let out a cry of pain. "My back. It's in spasm. Mary, help me." He crumpled to his knees, clothes spilling off the table onto the floor.

[297]

At once Maya was the brisk but gentle nurse, giving soothing instructions. "Here, I'll just slip this towel under your head. Now roll. Very gently. Onto your side. We'll put laundry under your calves. Weezie, quick. Get cushions from the couch and the pillows from our bed and a blanket. I'll get your pills, Paul. Don't move. I'll be right back."

We passed each other in the hall, me with pillows and blanket, she heading for the bathroom. She whispered to me, "Not a word of our conversation. He must be absolutely quiet. Nothing must upset him. I know you understand." She smiled angelically.

An hour later, Paul was finally settled in their bed, deep in a Seconal sleep. I was out myself the second my head hit the couch.

Sometime in the early hours of the morning, I got up to go to the bathroom and stumbled over what looked like a pile of blankets outside my sister's bedroom. It was my sister, lying on the floor, her head on a pile of laundry. Immediately she was awake.

"Ssshh. Don't wake Paul."

"What on earth are you doing on the floor?"

"I wanted him to get as much sleep as possible. I'm used to sleeping on the floor, Weezie." She grabbed my arm. "There's something I must tell you."

By this time she was on her feet. I saw that she was fully clothed. Her thick hair looked ready for the day. She gripped my arm tight.

"Weezie, I want you to know I hadn't really meant to have so many children so fast but I – we – couldn't help it. I sleep out here most of the time because if I sleep in the same bed with Paul he wants to – He wants me to do it. Every night, always. I can't refuse him or he cries and tells me I'll make him commit a terrible sin and it's my duty as his wife. You must understand, I haven't had any choice." She hung her head and started to cry. She made no sound but the tears were running down her cheeks. "I know it's not what it should be. But Weezie, he told me after we were married that he was asked to leave the seminary. They said he should never have thought of a celibate life. I don't know what to do except submit to him. It's God's will."

"Do you get anything out of it?" I asked. Even then I wanted to grab her and shake her. "Or do you just grit your teeth and let him have his way?"

She blew her nose in a tiny undershirt. "It's like what they said about Auntie Pearl," she said. "Remember? She put her hand to the plow?" She stood there fussing with the undershirt. "I married him, Weezie."

SOME YEARS LATER, when Maya and Paul and all her children were living in Texas, I asked her, in a moment of annoyance, over the phone – probably in response to one of those blanket statements she used to make about what was and wasn't God's will – what had made her convert when she didn't have to, and why she had left Skidmore in such a hurry.

She wrote me this letter and I kept it, because in some way it really did answer some questions I had always had about her. And because I always felt bad about my instant impatience with her.

> Well, Suba, I had some big problems. I know now it was God's Grace working slowly to lead me into the Church. You see, I had some serious mental problems at Post Graduate. I had them even before, at Skidmore, before I went to New York for my hospital work. I began to worry, walking down the street in Saratoga, if I saw broken glass, that some child would get hurt. I used to carry a little brush and a dustpan so I could sweep it up from the sidewalk and throw it into a garbage can. Sometimes I carried it back to my dorm. And then I started washing my hands – a lot. Sometimes I washed them ten times during the morning, before lunch. My friends began to notice. I said I had a skin condition so I was supposed to wash them with antiseptic soap. When I got to Post Graduate, I couldn't hide it any more. I tried so hard to do all the sterile techniques exactly right but I was always terrified my instruments would still have germs on them. I was afraid the germs would crawl down my arms or out from under my rubber gloves and onto the instruments. I was sick with worry all the time.
>
> So I scrubbed and scrubbed and scrubbed before an operation. I took so long the O.R. nurse told our Nursing Supervisor she thought I should see a psychiatrist. It was terrible. Almost before I sat down, he asked me, "When was the

last time you had sexual intercourse?" I almost fainted. And I hadn't even kissed a boy until Patrick and that wasn't until he gave me an engagement ring.

I was so disgusted and upset. I called Mother and Daddy and they told me to come right home. That's when I got really depressed. I thought it was the end of my nursing right then and there. But they were wonderful – they said I didn't belong in a place where some horrible doctor would ask a young, innocent girl such a question – and for no reason. You see, I was afraid to tell them about washing my hands all the time and the broken glass. I was afraid they'd keep me at home. But they knew how determined I was to become a nurse. So they called Dr. MacKenzie and he got me into the nurses' training program at Fitkin in Asbury Park. I began to do better. They went slower and the head nurse wasn't as tough on me. And I began going to the Catholic church a lot with the other nurses. Catholic churches are always open.

I could see I must control this urge to be absolutely clean. I saw it as a spiritual need – to be clean. I prayed that I didn't have too many germs and I began to have more confidence in God's will. Most of the other nurses were Catholic and once I started to go to Mass with them every day, it was such a comfort. I could go any time of night or day and the doors were always open. Masses were being said; a priest was always available for confession.

NOT LONG AFTER their final move to Texas, Maya was diagnosed with lupus (an autoimmune disease possibly connected with asthma medication) and scleroderma (a hardening of the skin, possibly connected with the lupus). We had her come up to us and the diagnosis was confirmed by the best rheumatologist in New York. The only treatment at the time was large doses of cortisone.

My sister confessed to me when she was in the early stages of her dual disease that her life with her husband had been a nightmare in the bedroom. Today it would be called marriage rape. Eventually no relations were possible because she was so sick, and by that time, she was afraid she had fallen in love with their priest – something I had suspected for a long time because she kept talking about wonderful Father Mac. What she admired in the man was pretty much what she had turned up her nose at when she was under our parents' roof. He was intellectually her equal, with a good education, someone she could talk to. I don't think she ever told our parents, certainly not Daddy.

Seventeen

Money matters. A lot of the story is about money.

Connie was brought up in a household where people had things they wanted. Things. Her parents were strict Baptists, but they believed in being comfortable and they had the money to do it. She loved to talk about her happy childhood – which seemed to go right to the day she met E.B.

My father was bright and promising academically (the story was that he was about to be admitted to Princeton at the age of fourteen), but because of his father's troubles and having to go to work at that point, he certainly didn't have much of a childhood. As a young boy, though, he was able to devote himself to book learning when the great majority of young people of twelve, thirteen, fourteen were going out to work on the farm or in a factory or the mines. (Child labor laws began to be passed in about 1910.)

Henrietta/Jeannette was the one who looked after him when he was little, and the habit of looking after him never died, even after she had staked everything on him and lost it. I ask myself how it must have been for her, involved with her boss, windfall money coming her way, and she's only ever thinking of her brother's advancement. He was the one who was going to save them. He was handsome, intelligent, strong and fierce. I never thought of him as fierce until I wrote it just now, but it's not inappropriate. He had a moral fierceness.

It doesn't matter that I can't imagine myself doing what Jeannette did. Maybe I lack imagination. There was something about my father that inspired slavish devotion. What my mother did, subverting her own gaiety in order to go along with his seriousness, would, I think, only have been possible if she were compelled in a certain way.

I think the way my father saw himself was the result of the way he had been taught to see money. What he was worth to the world was to him the same thing as a dollar value, and the fact that he didn't bring in any of those dollars, and particularly that he didn't bring in a lot of them, was as surely a moral dilemma as it was a practical one.

I think it was a mystery to him how a person as impeccable in his way of life as he was could fail to make a material contribution. In a way I think his whole life was a promise to himself, and the promise was strained to the limit all the time.

No one in my family faced the subject of money head on. It was considered ill-bred to talk about how much things cost. It was a huge, unspoken area that caused more and more tension every time my father got home for a few days.

Driving one day with my parents down to the bus stop in the middle of Schroon Lake's one main street brought the whole hidden subject into focus. My father had to go back to New York. I was the only child in the car; my sister was cramming for nursing school exams; Dwight was camping with his pack of buddies. We parked along the main street, in front of Al's, the local ice cream parlor that served as our Trailways bus station. I heard my mother say under her breath, "E.B., I need money."

There was a gap of silence. I'll never forget it. At that moment, I was watching the high school gym coach crossing the street. The sun made his dark, rippling hair glisten. He pretended to dodge the school principal's car with a sudden basketball jump, arms outstretched, and that was when I jumped myself. My father's voice exploded in the car.

"What do you mean you need money?" he said, controlled, harsh. "I gave you fifty dollars before our guests got here." I was sitting in the back and I could see the blue vein in his forehead pulsing. Mother was studying her rings, organizing them on her fingers.

"Well, we needed more groceries with guests, E.B., and I've got to get things for Weezie before she goes back to school. I've tried to be careful but —" I don't remember what else she said. The bus pulled up alongside us, double parking for its ten-minute stop. My mouth felt too dry to swallow. I stayed completely still. I was afraid I was going to cry.

With his left hand, my father opened the car door; with his right hand he dropped three twenties onto my mother's spread-out hands. Her hands disappeared under the rumpled green bills.

He leaned his head through the window, looking back at me. "Goodbye, Lueza," he said. "I'll be back to drive you to school. Help your mother."

He reached past the wheel and patted Mother's shoulder. "Be more careful," he said to her. "Remember what your own father said, 'Watch the pennies and the pounds take care of themselves.' You know things haven't been good lately in the Street." He turned and disappeared up the steps of the bus.

That was the first time I had ever heard money discussed between my parents. I remember sitting in the car with Mother, neither of us moving for what seems now like a long time. Then she put the money away, slid over, I got out, and when I was sitting beside her, she started up the engine.

I had to talk to her; I had to ask her something. Not about what had just happened, I would never have been able to refer to that. But I had to know what was going on. I had to fight against burying it right away with some bright remark about something insignificant. And I had to speak quickly, before she recovered enough to bury it. But I didn't know how to begin. We never talked about money; there was a family taboo in our genes. Even thinking of it made me feel as if I had a rock in my stomach. I spoke without looking.

"What's going on with money in this family?" I mumbled. But I made sure she knew what I had said, and I was ready in case she ignored my question.

She didn't speak up right away. I remember fighting my desire to laugh off the question, to change the subject. When she spoke, I was already thinking about the challenge I was going to have to give her.

"We didn't want you children to know, not yet."

"Tell me what's going on," I somehow dared to say. "What's the matter with everybody around here?"

"Grandma and Grandpa left money in trust for your education. Now it's gone."

"What do you mean gone?" I knew money in trust wasn't supposed to be touched.

I don't think she answered me. I felt as if I had been punched in the stomach. I don't remember any kind of an answer. I think we were just silent after that, all the way home. I keep seeing my mother's hands disappearing under the three twenty-dollar bills. But I already knew the answer, and nothing I learned after that ever made that answer any different.

This makes me think that the way somebody answers the question What did your father do? might tell the whole story about that person. Attitude about money, family's attitude about the father.

I was thinking about meeting other people's parents – even now, meeting the parents of one of my children's spouses, for example – and my thoughts went into this mode immediately. I'm talking to them, investigating the things that one speaks of tentatively on a first meeting with someone's parents, same generation as I am. And at some point, in connection with where I grew up, the inevitable question is asked: And what sort of work did your father do? A logical question and only natural.

But I see something about myself by the very fact that I immediately thought of that question, putting myself back into the way I felt when I went away to boarding school, then college, and was asked it many times. My stock answer came to be, Oh, he's done a number of things. He's been a newspaper reporter (sort of true except he was never directly employed by any newspaper), he's worked in banking and in the stock market (I couldn't bring myself to lie outright and say he was a stockbroker), and he's been a municipal consultant. And then I'd try to explain what on earth that meant and oh yes, that he had worked for the City of New York in the Comptroller's office. It was a hard question for me to answer. I was embarrassed, possibly even ashamed if I'm honest about it, that my father was somewhat of a rolling stone – a person who never found himself.

I could never admit that we lived on my mother's inheritance. I don't think I ever really acknowledged this fact to myself, of where the money came from, although I most definitely knew about it from probably the age of eleven or twelve. My mother told me often enough, and it made a serious impression on me.

I think what really struck me as I let the imagined scene with one of my children's parents-in-law unfold before my eyes was that I would still, at my age, be putting myself in the position of a much younger woman, a schoolgirl even, stuck somewhere in her deep past because of the stigma attached to a father who wasn't the actual money maker in the family. Strange that Dwight still feels this too, and is still angry at him for it.

The imagined scene about meeting people's parents also reminds me of myself visiting my roommate after our first year at college. Her family lived in the suburbs of Chicago and when my mother heard I was going out there she said I must look up her Harris relatives, the ones still very much connected to the bank. They lived in one of the most upscale neighborhoods.

I dutifully called them and by gum, they drove over to this modest home of my roommate's family, to meet Connie and E.B.'s daughter. They gave me the third degree – politely, of course. But I was grilled about the whole family and what each of the men was doing. (The women were assumed to be the homemakers.) I still remember the realization when they asked me, And what about E.B.? What is he doing? that he would definitely be found wanting because of the unusual variety in his employment. And also, just the fact that we actually lived in Schroon Lake had a lot of weight right there. I must have said that the aunts and my invalid cousin and her nurse lived right there with us, all crammed into this upstate farmhouse in quiet little Schroon Lake. I'm pretty sure they had once made a pilgrimage back east to Almanole, so they got the picture.

The question of whose money it was is important. I never mentioned to anyone – when I was growing up, and still wouldn't – the fact that it was my mother's money we lived on, but I've always been aware that that was the case. It was her money, and he went through it. Or: it was her money, and because he never really had steady employment, the principal was all spent. She mentioned it often enough, in passing. She used to say it to me in her ramblings to me about him. We'd be in the bathroom and she'd say, "Oh dear Daddy, I feel so sorry for him. He really should have been a college professor, and it doesn't help that we're living up here, but we didn't know what else to do." They didn't know what else to do because there wasn't enough money. She never said outright that the reason there was no money was that Daddy hadn't managed it well. She might say, "I just turned everything over to him," and let that speak for the whole debacle.

Did she say it to him? I seriously doubt she would ever have mentioned it to him. After his violent explosion on the way back from their honeymoon, when she tried to ask him why he had been fired and what he intended to do, she wouldn't have wanted to mention anything about their money problems, ever.

It was certainly a source of embarrassment and discomfort to me that we lived off my mother, that my father wasn't supporting us. It's a very important facet of my relationship with my father. I know I would never have had the temerity to say outright, "We live on my mother's inheritance. My father has never had steady, regular employment." I would have felt that to say this would have been a betrayal of this man I loved so much and felt so protective of, I realize, from a very early age.

BEFORE WE LIVED in Schroon Lake year round I didn't give much thought to what Daddy did. He told us he was in the market and he tried to explain in a rudimentary way just what made prices rise or fall – or drift, as I sometimes heard him say. Mother inherited the money from her grandparents in 1926. After the stock market's huge tumble on Black Friday in 1929, there wasn't a lot of movement in the thirties. But I assume whatever Great-Grandfather had left Connie was blue-chip enough so it bottomed out and finally held firm, creeping up but very slowly as the thirties wore on. There was a small boom in '37, then another slump. Aunt Rae, who held onto her inheritance, never dipping into it at all, saw everything begin to climb in the postwar years.

What on earth did Daddy do when he went off to New York City on the Jersey Central, when we were living with Aunt Charlotte in Spring Lake? And where on earth did he stay, if he didn't commute back and forth every night? Probably with Rae and Joe in Brooklyn. He'd come home and be very blue, look solemn and say, "Not much action," or "Another day of drift," and maybe throw in an acid comment on whatever the latest scheme was, coming out of "those crazy idiots in Washington."

From later conversations with Mother and Daddy I learned that Uncle Dwight hadn't held onto his inheritance either; he had used it to buy on margin – one of the high-flying energy stocks that was leaping ahead throughout the twenties. But after he lost everything in the crash, and Grandpa paid his debts to the grocer, the cleaners, the bank so they didn't lose their house in Chestnut Hill, Uncle Dwight had the gumption to go out and get himself a job in a hardware store. The job sent him door-to-door selling lawnmowers. He didn't live the rest of his life with false pride. And I know his wife, Ann, was proud of him.

Yes, I've avoided the subject of "And what does your father do?" since it clearly has been a difficult issue for me to face, even now. But there's no reason not to state the truth, and it does nothing to lessen the love I still feel for my father.

I continue to skirt this dangerous piece of thin ice, the possibility that I might state the fact that my father lived on the money his wife inherited in 1926, that he never held a job that could support us. He wasn't stupid but he was impractical and too proud. When I first wrote about him I made him a man who was a frustrated minister/scholar, working all his life on some great work of biblical scholarship – something to secure the faith for all time in spite of the modern world pressing in on all sides. A twentieth-century Casaubon.

Can't I come to grips with this subject? It's over thirty years since my father died and it is not going to hurt him at this late juncture. And he must know now how much I loved him, how much I wanted never to cause him pain.

ONCE OR TWICE, I did try to screw up my courage to pose a question like, "Daddy, why didn't you ever get a regular job with a regular salary?" or "Why did we wind up living in Schroon Lake where it was so impossible for you to do the kind of work you were suited for?" but I always backed away from it.

I can remember the panicky feeling I had in my stomach, a rising sense of dread that it would bring on a reaction so frightening I didn't try to imagine it, that he would hit me, or kill me. Or possibly that it would hurt him, wound him to the quick (that was an expression he used, about something Grandpa might have said to him, or Rae). I never wanted to touch that deep part of him where something had made him so fragile. The few moments when I posed such a question in my head and then didn't express it came during the long drives back to Wells College. It took eight or nine hours with gas stops, a wholesome lunch. I certainly had plenty of uninterrupted time alone with him. But I could not do it. Too terrifying. To ask why.

I want to take up the story when we were together overnight, forced to share a room because of a blizzard, when he slept on the floor. "I'm like an old dog," he said. "I can sleep anyplace." I liked being isolated from the family, just the two of us trapped by nature and then I would have asked him, why no steady, regular job, why had he used Mother's inheritance in place of that steady, regular job?

But I can't do it even now. I can't even invent it. I'm afraid of feeling like the helpless child again, incurring the terrifying anger, the loss of his love, the feeling that I had betrayed him. I'm unable to imagine the wounding. I know he had been hurt beyond repair, though I don't know, and I never will, who or what started it.

HE KEPT it all inside. I've always thought that was why he used to talk, silently, as he drove, his lips moving, and his hands, those huge, powerful hands, gripping the steering wheel or gesturing out suddenly, and then grasping the wheel again.

I see him, tight-lipped and muttering, waiting endlessly for my mother, who always had sweet excuses for why she was an hour, two hours late, sometimes more. He just sat there, dozing now and then, accepting this role of chauffeur for the woman who owned the house, the property, the inheritance. Why did he let himself get held by the balls? Why didn't I ask him? Never wanted to rock the boat, upset the applecart, ruffle his feathers – all those things my mother used to say meaning don't bother E.B., Daddy, no, the awesome Presence. Absurd. She held the purse strings but she didn't even try to open and close them herself. Was she afraid he would leave her?

Yes, it's all water over the dam, years and years ago.

It's I, the mature woman, trying to face that issue. I keep thinking about Daddy and me heading back across New York State on that long up-hill-and-down-dale drive to the Finger Lakes. I keep trying to create a scene in which I come to grips and confront him with that horrendous question.

While my father was still alive, I feared, as I've said, that that terrifying question could destroy his fragile ego. And I thought if I asked it, he might make the excuse that he was always worried, ever since the Texas era, about Connie having some sort of mental breakdown, that she wouldn't be able to face living on a small salary somewhere in a modest home, leaving behind forever those golden childhood and adolescent years when she was wrapped in the cocoon of her father's wealth and position.

I know for a fact that Connie felt guilty about making E.B. leave Texas. But somehow, and maybe this is because I had the chance to get to know her after Daddy's death, I know she was much more stable and strong mentally than he was; that he was always on the verge of taking off and perhaps disappearing forever, leaving all the women behind to make do. He would have said to himself, they're all better off without me, I'll send money when I can but they don't want me around and this is the only way.

And speaking of my mother's innate strength of character and of her ability to handle just about anything, that first winter in Schroon Lake was no picnic (Netsie didn't come to help us for another year or so) and Mother coped, with never a long face, a whine or a complaint.

I feel my father was not able to deal with his father's comedown in the world, that he was ashamed of his father but felt guilty about having such a disloyal feeling, and that he made the assumption that Connie would have crumpled under the disappointment of being married to someone who didn't make it in a huge financial way. Mother said to me more than once that she had the sense (and I think she said he made references to this now and then) that E.B. wanted to show her father that he, too, could be a big success in business, perhaps even bigger than her father.

MY MOTHER's grandfather was the big money man. He had made three fortunes by the time he was forty, according to my mother. His third and most long-lasting economic triumph was the founding of the Harris Trust and Savings Bank in Chicago. When my grandfather was eighteen he tried farming, then teaching school, but neither was for him. He went to Chicago, to his father's bank, started at the bottom to learn the basics of banking from the ground up, and was then dispatched to New York by his father to start an affiliated bank there.

He had a lump sum of money to start with, and the all-important connections. And he was good at banking: people trusted him. He made the bank successful. It was this bank that hired E.B. in 1919, and from which he was asked to resign in 1920.

Another thing I know is that from the early days of their courtship, Connie had made offhand remarks about the fact that her grandfather, who had really major wealth, was remembering her and her siblings in his will.

I see Connie as being innocent in her mentioning of the largesse to come in the not too distant future. She would have mentioned it when he confided his dreams to her about becoming somebody substantial, building up a great fortune a la Rockefeller or Vanderbilt, by wise investment and hard work. She wouldn't have been using this information as anything but a way of reassuring her beloved that she would stand by him and beside him in every possible way including giving over to him anything that came to her.

My mother's grandfather, who died in 1925 or '26, left her and her sister and brother each about seventy thousand dollars, which was not a bad sum at that time. It was this seventy thousand that my mother turned over to E.B. as soon as she got it.

I'm feeling shivery, clammy, talking to myself about this question. I appear to myself as Weezie, in the third person. She was afraid of him; she knew it would hurt him too deeply.

Is it the question itself that upsets me? What it implies about E.B.? Is it the shame I still feel? What is the shame? How often did Mother mention the money? How much did she undermine my desire to believe my father was a god?

E.B. avoided closeness to the point where no one in the family felt close to him. Not even me. Certainly not Connie's parents. I remember that no matter what project my grandfather embarked on around The Place, E.B. would never simply congratulate him on what had been done. Rather he would point out the flaws in Grandpa's planning, or his execution, or both, giving perfectly valid criticisms. This annoyed the hell out of Grandpa. "E.B. always takes the wind out of my sails," he would complain. Everyone in the family felt this about E.B., though most of us wouldn't have said it. He was no fun and he was too critical for his own good. And even if he didn't actually say something critical, he would look disapproving; his mere attitude indicated his distaste – his scorn, sometimes – of the way Grandpa had approached a certain project and carried it out. My mother was fond of saying that E.B. was someone who would never have read *How to Win Friends and Influence People*, and it wouldn't have changed him one whit if he had.

Someone who liked him might learn to respect him but would never feel he really knew him. For an outsider, which includes almost everyone – though when I was a child I don't think I would have felt it included me – there was always a deep moat around him and he rarely, if ever, let the drawbridge down far enough for anyone to cross over. Someone who liked him would probably have had the sense that he would never trust anyone enough to let them into his emotional inner self.

Uncle Joe, Rae's husband, spent a lot of time with E.B. driving back and forth from Brooklyn to Albany, and Albany to Schroon Lake, and he worked with him as legislative correspondent at the state legislature. If I think about the way Uncle Joe acted toward him, I remember how you had to approach E.B. Uncle Joe never seemed to take anyone very seriously. He never took at face value anything anyone said; he treated it with a light touch, as if it were all air. He became very fond of my father and I know came to trust him, and felt able to count on him. Uncle Joe wouldn't have said such a thing to my father directly. He would have made an offhand remark to show he appreciated his brother-in-law, something such as "Like good Irish whiskey, he'll deliver."

I remember Joe saying once that E.B. never went into a poker game unless he felt he could figure out every player's weak points – not necessarily as a poker player but as a man. (I was happy to know he had even played poker.)

I WANT TO KNOW what can't be known. What happened in those earliest years of their marriage, where things went wrong beyond the bank issue? What made my parents so discomfited by each other? If I look back to the first years, I have mostly questions.

I know they spent much of each of summer at The Place. Winters, in the early years, they lived in a Philadelphia suburb with Dwight and Ann. I'm sure Uncle Dwight encouraged my father to go to the brokerage house where he himself was working. Maybe Daddy was just there to manage Mother's money from her dowry, as well as to make contacts. Not sure.

I ask myself why E.B. would have been willing to live with Dwight, his brother-in-law, after he had been asked to leave the bank. What was going on with my parents at that point? They couldn't have had much money, since E.B. had just been fired. (The inheritance didn't come for another five or six years.)

He would not have seen Dwight as a threat. My uncle was boyish and lighthearted, made friends easily, very much the opposite of E.B. Connie's father had originally been impressed by E.B.'s serious nature, and by the fact that he had gone to work so young to support his family. He had even said early on, "I wish my son Dwight could be more serious, like you, E.B."

I think E.B. looked upon Dwight, in those days, as a sweet, pleasant young man who was not to be taken too seriously and whom he wanted to cultivate. Any possibility of a real friendship between E.B. and his father-in-law had been ruined by what happened at the bank. According to my mother, E.B. still wanted to stay in his good graces. But this idea doesn't quite make sense to me. My grandfather fired my father, and did it right before he married my mother. It seems to me my father wouldn't have dreamed of trying to get into the good graces of a man who would do such a thing to him. I know E.B. recognized that Schroon Lake was part of Connie's life; he was growing to love it too. I'm sure he understood that he would have to get along with this father-in-law, but it was difficult for him ever to pretend to like someone. It was my mother who was the peacekeeper; I don't think my father believed in keeping the peace.

I have clear childhood memories of sitting around the Sunday dinner table at Almanole, at the Big House, Daddy trying to laugh at Grandpa's jokes, trying hard to take any light teasing from Joe or

Uncle Dwight. I could sense tensions even way back then.

To go back to those earliest years of their marriage, my mother told me she and Daddy lived with Dwight and Ann for a year or two, maybe a little more. She told me they had a fairly close relationship, the four of them, in some small rented place in Germantown, outside Philadelphia.

I know my mother adored her brother, and they were cohorts when they were growing up. And I also know that the four of them had fun together at Schroon. They climbed mountains together, went on picnics, played bridge together, and went golfing. I remember them coming home from a golf excursion up to Lake Placid, laughing and joking, Aunt Ann and my mother tweaking the men by saying, "Now let the men drive." And then they all laughed uproariously. (The men had not scored very well that day, my mother told me afterward.)

I wish I could be a little bird, able to peer into that household in Germantown, watch those four young people just starting out, in the early twenties. I keep thinking how proud E.B. was, but he had to make do before they could set up their own household. And they must have been living on whatever money my grandfather gave Connie, as a dowry, to help them until E.B. got on his feet. I know that Ann had her own dowry as well; her father was also well-to-do.

MY GRANDFATHER would have had a hard time developing a close rapport with someone like E.B. He would have come to see him as too much of a dreamer. The very things that made him different and wonderful to me would have rankled in a man as practical, outgoing, and down-to-earth as my grandfather. He would have felt E.B. should have faced facts, picked himself up and found himself another position, never looking back. Whatever had happened was over and done with.

But from my father's point of view, I can't help feeling he would blame my grandfather for not having kept him on at the family bank in spite of the circumstances − on the strength of the fact that E.B. was now family. And furthermore, E.B. looked upon his dismissal by Arthur M. Harris as damning him in the eyes of Wall Street forever and forever. And even worse, that his father-in-law would blame him ad infinitum, rather than his sister, for what Grandpa would look upon as a very serious character flaw in his sister. (And now that I think about it, Grandpa probably didn't blame him, but E.B. took it that way. It set them at odds from that moment onward.)

But what about Dwight, Mother's older brother? My guess is that there was probably always an underlying tension between Uncle Dwight and his father simply because Dwight had not had to succeed on his own. He had had all doors opened to him and how was he using those talents? (How many times had my mother told me the biblical story of the father and his three sons and how he had given each of them twenty talents and how each of them had used those talents. It was practically Harris family lore.) There's Dwight, living the good life, playing golf, socializing in Main Line Philadelphia, buying and selling in the stock market starting out with that handsome sum from his father, already having a child still on his father's money, and when will he settle down, get more serious, start doing more good with his money besides simply making more and more and more.

Grandpa may have had hopes that E.B. would act as a more serious model for Dwight, his only son. Certainly a fancy college like Princeton hadn't settled Dwight down as yet, Grandpa must have felt. And neither had his years as a second lieutenant in the AEF. Grandpa had encouraged Connie and E.B. to start out with Dwight and Ann, and their baby. It would help all of them, Grandpa felt.

How well I recognized through the years that two men could not have been more different in temperament or behavior than my uncle Dwight and my father. Dwight was full of fun, had a host of friends from his Princeton days, had made a real love match with his lovely Ann. I could always sense the undercurrent of physical attraction between the two of them. It made me happy for them, sad for myself and my parents' distant relationship.

Uncle Dwight wore clothes well but casually. "It's because he's over six feet," said my father, always envious of taller men. I always thought Uncle Dwight was good-looking but I could see he was not handsome like Daddy. Daddy dressed soberly and conservatively, paid no attention to changing men's styles. He was still wearing a Homburg when other men had switched to the fedora. And the clothes were like the man. E.B. was not one to smile and make offhand remarks. He could be charming if he wanted to, but it wasn't usually with family that he showed his charm. In fact, it always made me uncomfortable when he acted charming, even though it was a relief to have him seem to be friendly. (It would happen when, for example, I brought someone home whom he liked – which was rare enough. But it was obvious to me that he was putting on this behavior to try to impress the other person, and it set my teeth on edge when it happened. But that's jumping a long way ahead.)

So what was my father doing, befriending Dwight, or allowing Dwight to befriend him? I'm sure there was something rebellious in Dwight, and maybe E.B. brought that out in him. I wish I could have known Aunt Ann and Uncle Dwight better. They were my godparents and we used to visit when we were living in Spring Lake, on the Jersey shore. I loved going there. The atmosphere in their household was mellow, warm and full of life, not like the feeling at Aunt Charlotte and Uncle Walter's in that damp house overlooking the Atlantic Ocean.

Uncle Dwight had not gone into banking, which his father had wanted him to do. "Trading in the Street – that's no real kind of work for a man. You're not creating anything," I remember hearing Grandpa say. I would guess that Dwight might jokingly have complained to E.B. about his father. I know Connie and Ann became close lifelong friends. They would play the piano together, they talked and laughed a lot, went shopping, went to concerts. I see the two of them with their hats at the same tilt, their white cotton gloves, heading off to catch the train into Philadelphia for the Symphony, a concert, a luncheon; Ann striding ahead on her long, graceful legs, Mother keeping up as best she could.

E.B. benefited by associating with Dwight's friends, too, in a business way, and this would have added another level of cordiality to their relationship. I see I'm reluctant to call it a friendship. By the time I was old enough to know anything there was no warmth between the two of them. Uncle Dwight was always jovial and funny, very much like his father, and E.B. was on his own. But in those early days, they did have something like a friendship. Dwight had the life E.B. would have thought was appropriate for himself. I think my mother must have been wrong: E.B. wasn't trying to get into her father's good graces; rather, I think he must have wanted to get in on the way of life, and he saw Dwight as a connection to that way of life without the embarrassment of having too much to do with Grandpa.

With his father-in-law, I think E.B. was forever embarrassed, once he had been fired by him. It was this that caused his habitual resentment. He must have created, in his mind, a separation between the father and the son, in order to be able to associate with Dwight in Philadelphia. In that way E.B. could get his footing in a world he very much wanted to be part of and felt he should be part of by birthright.

When they were all just married, and living together, Ann already had a baby and was in love with motherhood as well as with Dwight. She would have encouraged Connie to have a baby – a possible source of friction between Ann and E.B. My mother told me she had wanted a baby for years when Maya finally came along. E.B. wouldn't hear of it. He said, No children until I'm well established. As I've said, the way he made sure there would be no children was that he would not sleep with her. That's one of many things that helped create the relationship I was born into in 1931, eleven years into their marriage.

Eighteen

AFTER LUNCH the last day, Dwight and I worked separately. I was in the attic going through Daddy's desk. The bottom drawer was locked but rusted, and with a well-aimed blow of a hammer and heavy screwdriver I broke it open. I felt a rush of adrenaline, prying into Daddy's most private place. Even Mother had left this untouched.

I reached into the drawer, pulled out a diary bound in brown leather, edges worn to dusty redness. Stamped on the cover, in peeling gold leaf, E.B.T., and underneath 1943. As I handled it my fingers got stained with bloody-looking smudges from the dried-out leather. Inscribed on the front page in slanting, heavily looped writing: To Eden – Yours, Esther. My hands froze. I wasn't going to turn the page without Dwight as witness, even though something in me desperately didn't want to reveal to him what I knew might be in this diary.

I called to him. He was in the old northwest bedroom, the room he had shared with Mother during his pre-adolescent years, right below me.

"What's up?" he called back.

"Come have a look."

He was up the attic steps two at a time. I put the diary on top of the desk, open to its inscription. He glanced over my shoulder.

"Esther," he said. He poked his short index finger at the name.

I wasn't sure why I had even called him, except we had agreed we would show each other anything important we found. Now I didn't want to look at it with him there. "Let's put it on hold," I said. "I wanted you to know about this but we'll attack it together, later."

"I really don't give a damn about the old man's personal stuff," he said. "Why not toss it?"

I started to protest, then thought why not toss it, he was right. He didn't want to know, and I didn't need to know more than I already knew.

I handed it to him. "You toss it," I said. "I can't."

Without a pause he winged the diary square into the INSTANT OUT carton and headed back downstairs.

I got back to work. My hands moved mechanically. I saved almost nothing. Below me, Dwight was attacking books, heaving them across the room, by the sound of it. As I worked, I knew, somewhere back in some hidden recess of my mind, that I would not be able to resist looking at the diary. But now I'd do it alone.

The inscription kept appearing in my mind. Stupidly, I remembered Antzie once telling me handwriting with fat loops meant a highly sexed person. I kept seeing Daddy's name in that handwriting.

In the war years, Daddy worked in the Comptroller's office for the city government in New York, and did freelance articles for Uncle Joe's paper, the *Brooklyn Eagle*. He rarely got home. Trains were too full of servicemen and higher priority travelers, buses were packed, driving was out of the question with an "A" gas ration card. His job got more demanding; offices were shorthanded with so many men in uniform. People on the home front doubled up on jobs. He found a boarding house at 21 Minetta Lane, in Greenwich Village, run by an elderly couple named Gretzman.

I remember some of his letters. In one, he described his vigorous morning walks to the Comptroller's offices at City Hall. He drew tiny sketches. I remember one he did of himself sitting at a table loaded with food, other boarders hunched over their plates. I could see how much Mother looked forward to his letters full of funny stories about the city. I did, too. Mother used to read parts of them aloud at the dinner table.

Up where we were, in the North Country, we didn't have blizzards. It just snowed and snowed and snowed. The first flakes drifted lazily down, looking uncertain but gaining in seriousness as the storm built, slowly and quietly; no histrionics of wind or bluster. The intense cold was more of a threat. Wind inevitably followed the snow, pushed by a frigid Canadian high. You had to breathe in short breaths, and the cold pinched the inside of your nose. The household of women managed on their own well enough. Connie and Jeannette were able to keep the coal- and wood-burning furnace stoked during the day and banked through the night, and we all slept buried under mounds of blankets, quilts, afghans, even bearskin car robes. Timmy Herlihy, from next door, kept the woodbox in the kitchen filled with hard-wood, daily replenishing the supply from the new woodshed fully stocked by E.B. in the fall months. E.B. had also filled to the rafters the old woodshed off the living room with fireplace-width logs, and we kept a fire burning from the early hours of the morning until everyone was tucked in for the night.

The winter of '43, the winter my father got the room in Minetta Lane, was one of extreme cold, and because of oil shortages we had a few holidays when the school building was too cold for classes.

I might not have felt his absence as keenly as I did if Mother had-n't fussed and fretted about it all the time to me, especially with Maya away at school. She seemed in a continual worry when his letters did-n't come as often as she would have liked. She wasn't usually a com-plainer but I remember thinking that year that she seemed bothered more by what I considered inconsequential things. Her fears seeped into my own thoughts about Daddy and I couldn't shake them.

That winter, I was old enough to stay after school, play with town kids. They had a great hill for sledding. The town allowed a back street to be closed, and the snow plow was kept off it. Water from one of the town's few hydrants made the surface slick, glazed.

Dead of winter, 1943. The sun is down. My feet are numb. I've been sledding for hours and it's time to get home. I can see the family car up the hill. Exhaust fumes uncoil at its rear. High and square, the '32 LaSalle is the most old-fashioned car in town. As I get closer I can see Mother behind the wheel, head bent; she's reading by the light of the dashboard.

"Did we get a letter from Daddy?" I ask, climbing into the car. I remember this. I couldn't see her face under the brim of her hat. When she spoke, she sounded strange.

"I can't understand it," she said. "My last letter came back. Look." She held out an envelope with Daddy's name on it, the Minetta Lane address, in her handwriting. How rude the black pencil lines drawn through the address looked, and there was a pale purple stamp in the lower left corner – a pointing index finger and the box checked next to Addressee Unknown.

I didn't know what to say. "Why don't you call him tonight at that boarding house?"

"Just be quiet." She was bending her head, listening to the sound of the engine as she shifted gears to pull out into the street. I couldn't see her expression. The engine made a full-throated, healthy sound, and began to rumble evenly.

I said, "Are you sure you had the right address?"

"Of course I've got the right address," she said sharply. "I've been writing since October. Don't you think I know where to write my own husband?"

"But why not phone him?" It seemed stupid not to try.

"That's the last thing I'd do. He'd be furious." She shifted into second gear, accelerating faster than normal, and the wheels spun, throwing snow behind them in a cascade. I remember I started talking, telling her about coasting, how much fun to have lots of kids to play with. I felt I wanted to protect her, as if she were a fretting child. Up to this moment, she had always been imperturbable, the comforter, the placater, the peacemaker.

I kept talking, making conversation. It made me feel even more uneasy, but I didn't know what else to do. Something was very wrong, but I couldn't fix it. And neither could she. I babbled on, my voice raised above the whine of the car in lowest gear to give traction on ice.

"Weezie, scrape the windshield for me," she said. Clouds of steam poured from her mouth. It was freezing in the car.

I scraped with my nails, made a circle of cleaned glass.

"I hope and pray he's all right," she said. She seemed to be talking to herself. "It's not like E.B. It's exasperating. Something's wrong." She turned to me suddenly. "Have you done your homework?" she demanded.

I was embarrassed. She must've known I couldn't have done homework if I'd been sledding all afternoon. Besides, the next day was Saturday.

She was so upset she wasn't concentrating. It wasn't like her. A car right in front of us stopped and Mother had to hit the brake hard. The heavy LaSalle skidded into the bumper of a double-parked truck with a smart jolt. My head snapped, and I slid forward, bumped the dashboard with my knees.

"Dammit," she said. "Are you all right?" She hated jerky driving, never did it. And she never swore, not even "damn."

I was all right, and she jumped out, looked at the two bumpers, jumped right back in. I had never known her to have any kind of an accident.

"No harm done," she said, and she pulled around the truck, spinning her wheels again – another thing never done. "Are you all right?" she repeated and then went on, without looking or waiting for an answer, "Why can't people signal? It's so inconsiderate." She paused. "I'll call Rae and Joe tomorrow. See if they've heard from him."

I couldn't wait to get out of the car when we got home, and upstairs to my room, away from her.

The next day she was impatient to get downtown so she would be at the post office when the mail came in. Had she called her sister? I don't think so. I don't think she would have wanted them to know, either, that she didn't know where her husband was.

Dwight and I went with her downtown, and Dwight waited in the car while she and I went in. The post office always smelled of cats because the postmaster, Mr. Lockhart, kept any number of them and they made themselves at home. Mr. Lockhart called out, "You have mail, Mrs. T." I was at Mother's elbow as she set the combination, opened the small brass door.

She waited until we were out of the post office, then sorted through the mail. By the look on her face I knew there was nothing from Daddy. Silently, she held out two letters, each with a purple finger pointing, same box checked. I looked at these letters and felt them physically. I didn't know what to say. I was afraid, but I was also angry. Where was Daddy?

Again I tried distraction. "Twelve cats today," I blurted out. We had a game of counting cats at the post office and comparing counts. But she ignored me, walked fast up the street, looking straight ahead. I ran to keep up. She was talking under her breath, but I knew she was talking to me.

"Now I'm worried. City offices won't open till Monday. No, better not bother them."

"Why not call the boarding house?" I asked, again.

"You know he doesn't like me calling long distance." She slowed down, looked over at me. She sounded as if she was apologizing. "I don't have their phone number," she said.

I remember kicking an ice ball, skidding it up the icy pavement. We were at the car, windows frosted white, square roof sticking up higher than every car along the street. Dwight was drawing pictures with his fingernail on the window.

I pushed him toward the middle of the front seat. "My turn to ride on the outside," I told him. "You got it coming down." I could still overpower him easily, and I didn't resist the temptation.

"Weezie rode on the outside in front two times last week. Not fair," he howled. "I get the whole front seat, down and back." He tried to shove me out the door.

"Stop fighting," Mother snapped. "I can't stand that constant squabbling. You'll both spend the afternoon indoors if you don't stop it now." She started the car, gunning the accelerator. She drove home very fast.

THE WEATHER stayed bitter for another week. The LaSalle's ancient battery died from the cold and we managed to get along without a visit to the grocery. The Herlihys brought our newspaper from the paper store, milk and butter when we ran out, meat once or twice. Mrs. Herlihy called one morning to see if we needed anything and must have asked about getting our mail for us.

"Pick up our mail?" I heard Mother ask, as if she hadn't heard. (She had ears like a cat.) "Oh Belle, thanks, we're not expecting anything important. You've done enough. Thanks so much," and she put down the receiver.

I knew she was ashamed to have anyone else see Addressee Unknown on her letters addressed to Daddy. She wouldn't let me go on foot either, though; she was worried I might get frostbite. Whatever mail came in sat in our box, warmed by a cat.

One morning in the bathroom Mother said, "I'm sure the gossips have been talking about those returned letters of mine. You know how Mr. Lockhart likes to talk. I'm sure there's an explanation." She rinsed her mouth, spat into the sink. Her tone made me feel as though I had suddenly gotten older, and I was embarrassed because I didn't know what to say.

When we finally had a thaw, Mother got a jump start from the Herlihys and drove into town.

I REMEMBER running in from school one afternoon, looking for something to eat. Mother was putting away groceries, slamming cabinets and cupboard doors. Her eyes looked red but she wasn't crying.

"Your father's very sick," she said, almost not opening her mouth.

He was such a strong man – able to chop down trees, make them fall where he wanted them to fall, lop off the biggest branches with only a couple of strokes of his axe. He could walk and walk and walk, never changing his pace or the length of his stride, never breathing any harder going uphill or down or pushing through the heaviest undergrowth.

I remember how scared I was, the sick feeling in my stomach, as I stood there, waiting.

"I had a phone call from a woman who's been taking care of him," she said. She kept opening and closing drawers, banging cans, rattling dishes. "A Mrs. Edel. She lives near the boarding house. She said your father got sick there but refused to go to the hospital. You know he won't spend money on himself."

"Why didn't she let us know sooner?" I didn't understand how it could have taken so long to find out. Mother looked at me for a moment with a strange expression, and ignored my question.

"He has a terrible case of mumps," she said. "Very dangerous for a grown man. Can settle in his glands, in the groin." Her voice trailed off the way it did whenever she approached the subject of sex.

That part was too hard to think about. I went back to my question. "But why didn't we hear sooner that he was sick?" I knew I was irritating her but I couldn't keep quiet. "Is he going to be okay?" And what did mumps have to do with sex? It made no sense but I knew Mother was not herself. She was shaken and she was mad. Daddy had never been sick one single day that I could remember.

"Mrs. Edel had a doctor, a friend of hers, come in. Your father was too sick to know anything. I'm thankful she took care of him. Maybe she's a nurse, a friend of the Comptroller." She banged the stove lid and started stirring the fire. "Get me a few sticks from the woodshed," she said. "This fire's almost out."

We didn't hear directly from Daddy for another two weeks. Mrs. Edel called two more times to report on his progress and each time Mother was angry after she hung up the phone. I was annoyed with her for being so mad. Daddy was going to be all right, even if he hadn't let us know where he was. And the nurse had done us such a favor.

The days were noticeably longer by the time Daddy was able to come home to Schroon Lake. He was thinner but his voice was as strong as ever.

"Can you imagine my getting a childhood disease at my age?" he said. He slapped his knee as if it were some kind of joke. He was almost fifty, his hair gray but still thick and full on his head. He and Mother got into an argument about whether he was strong enough yet to shovel out the driveway, or sweep the snow off the roofs when we had a heavy late March snowfall. He gave in to her – unheard of. After a few days, he went back to New York.

With Daddy gone again, Mother started talking to me more. I had once loved going downtown with her. Now I felt trapped, forced to listen to more complaints about the returned letters, how Daddy hadn't let us know sooner, who on earth Mrs. Edel might be. She said over and over it was wonderful of her to have taken care of him when he was sick. In the next breath, she would say, again, she couldn't understand how Daddy hadn't let her know.

I repeated myself, too. "You know Daddy never wants to worry you about anything," I would say. "Then he got too sick to call. And he hates to use long distance." I stared out the window a lot, wishing she would stop talking, saying the same things.

She went over and over the questions. Why hadn't Rae and Joe known about Daddy's illness? How had Daddy gotten from Gretzman's boarding house to Mrs. Edel's apartment if he was so sick; Mrs. Gretzman didn't even know Mrs. Edel, had never heard of her before. She finally did phone the Gretzmans to ask about Daddy's things. That was the only question she did ask. (Daddy had already picked them up by then.) But she kept harping to me about all the loose ends, as she called these troubling questions.

"You can't imagine how embarrassing it was, in this small town, getting those letters back like that," she would say. "Not to mention your aunts' asking me every day and every night if I'd heard from E.B. Everybody knew I didn't know where my own husband was." Her knuckles looked white against the black steering wheel. I looked back out the window.

More than anything else, I noticed her driving. It had become erratic. I remember one day being startled, as I brooded out the window, at the sudden sound of the horn. She was honking at an enormous lumber truck creeping up the hill in front of us. Its load of logs was slewed over to the left edge of the truck, chains sagging. "Why doesn't he pull over?" she said. She honked again, harder and longer. "I still can't understand why your father didn't make one phone call to say where he was." She shifted from second to high, pulled around and passed the truck. I remember staring into massive logs a nose-length away.

I wanted to say, "Why didn't you ask Daddy when he was home?" but I was afraid to. I couldn't wait to get out of the car.

After a while we started having spring weather and I could ride my bike again. One day Mother asked me to ride into town to get the mail. I rode as fast as I could, wanted to hurry back and go to the lake to watch the ice break up. Huge blocks of it would be cracking off, grinding and crunching against each other. I wanted the lake bright blue again after all those months of sterile whiteness.

Mr. Lockhart stopped what he was doing and walked over to me where I was opening our mailbox. He asked me if Daddy liked living in the big city. He had never said anything directly to me my whole life.

"My father's home," I lied. It was none of his nosy business. I pulled out a bunch of mail.

"He's got nice handwriting," Mr. Lockhart said. I slammed shut the mailbox, turned away and headed for the door.

After I was out of sight up the street, I shuffled through the mail. There was Daddy's up-and-down handwriting, his elegant signature in the upper left corner. Underneath, a new address, no more Minetta Lane. It said c/o E. Edel, 13 Cornelia Street, NYC.

My mother told me that Daddy explained his move by saying that the boarding house had no room anymore because the two Gretzman sons were back from the war, wounded, still recuperating. Housing was extremely tight in the city; the *Times* and the *Trib* said so at least once a week – rents frozen at prewar rates, absolutely nothing available. Daddy said he was lucky to have a place cheap, handy to City Hall, plenty of good wholesome food. Mother seemed to accept the change. At least her letters weren't being returned anymore.

LATE IN THE SPRING, about the time Grandpa and Grandma usually started their drive north from Florida, Grandpa had a stroke and died. Mother didn't go down for the funeral. Her sister said it was too complicated, too expensive, and what about the children. She wanted to go, but she finally had to agree with Rae. It was a sad, mixed-up spring. She stopped talking about Mrs. Edel and I put my father's living arrangements out of my mind.

I spent that summer working at the souvenir and soda shop in town. (I had turned twelve in May.) Two weeks before Labor Day, city offices closed and Daddy came home. One afternoon Dwight and I got him to go with us for a paddle across the lake and around the island. The sun was low in the sky as we came walking up the hill, and it slanted into our eyes as we crossed the back lawn. Loud voices were coming from the direction of the porch. I didn't recognize any of them.

Daddy walked faster, got to the house before us. When we caught up, he was coming back down the steps. There were three strangers behind him.

"Weezie, you and Dwight say how do you do to Mrs. Edel," he said, "and to Morris and Sarah. They stopped to say hello en route to Montreal."

People talked all at once, then Daddy broke in. "Your mother and I want them to pay a real visit, stay by the lake. Mrs. Edel was a friend in need."

Mrs. Edel gripped my hand. Her arm was white, and you could see the hairs on it. Her hand was thick-knuckled, with strong fingers, no rings. She wore long spiral silver earrings; they jiggled as she looked at me from dark, deep-set eyes.

Mother stood in the kitchen door. "Go up and change. Get out of those damp suits," she said. "Put on a dress, Weezie. Dwight, a clean shirt. And brush your hair, both of you."

In dry clothes, hair neat, hands washed, I was about to head down when Mother, at the top of the stairs, took my arm and led me into her bedroom. Dwight was already in there, sitting on the bed. She told me to sit down too, and she closed the door.

"I know you'll be polite to Mrs. Edel," she said. She hesitated a few seconds, then added, "She's Jewish, like Mr. Moses (the head of the camp next door). We're all very thankful for her kindness."

Of course we were polite to Mrs. Edel. She was interesting, different, talked fast and with enthusiasm about life in Greenwich Village, her job as an editor in a publishing house, bringing up her children without a husband after he walked out with a girl half his age. I remember her cooking. Talking and cooking exotic dishes, talking while she sewed. She gave me the names of books to read, found an illustrated copy of *Anna Karenina* in the bookshelves in the living room. "You're old enough for something worthwhile," she said. She told me to use nicknames for the long Russian names. Keep going.

I labored through Tolstoy all through their visit, struggling to figure out what was going on with Anna, handsome Vronsky, mean old Karenin. No wonder Anna fell in love with Vronsky, but how could she run off, leave her child? The book upset me but I didn't quit, and then I began to love it.

Their drop-in turned into a two-week visit. Mrs. Edel's car had had to go to the shop, and the necessary parts were hard to come by because of the war.

The day they were leaving I was up early, as usual, reading, on the lowest step off the back porch, in the sun. No one could see me; my head was well below their eye level. I kept out of sight so I could read in peace.

Daddy had gone downtown early to get the newspaper. Now he was back, sitting in the chair with the new slipcover that Mrs. Edel had made. I could hear him rustling pages. Then I was in Venice with Anna and Vronsky, sad that they were quarreling.

I was interrupted by the sound of high heels clicking on the kitchen linoleum. They changed tone on the wooden porch, and then I heard Mrs. Edel's voice.

"Eden, you're up with the sun. Sleep well?"

Eden? I was back from Venice with a jolt. No one in the family called him anything but E.B. Mrs. Edel always called him Mr. T.

"Pretty soundly. How about you, Esther?"

Esther. Right out of the Old Testament.

"Oh yes, this air's so pure," she said. "Wonder how the kids made out."

"Glad they could come. You can be proud of them."

"I am. They needed a change."

"Esther, you look rested for the first time in a dog's age." Silence. Then Daddy's voice again. "I don't know about this fall. Depends on things at the Comptroller's office."

"You'll find work in the city. Nothing for you here. Let me know when you can."

"Of course." The paper rustled, high heels clicked across the porch. I heard the sound of the glider settling under her weight. I could hear cooking noises now, in the kitchen.

I sat frozen on the bottom step. I had never heard this tone in my father's voice. He sounded like someone in a movie, talking to his leading lady, so young.

A bang from the kitchen. Mother had dropped the stove lid into place, too hard. "Gently, Connie," he usually said, through gritted teeth, followed by, "It'd take at least two weeks to cast another." I waited. He said nothing.

"Oh dammit," Mother cried out. She must have thought she was alone. It was so unlike her. Until this past winter she had hardly ever raised her voice.

"E.B., I didn't know you were back with the paper." Now she sounded like Mother. "Can you get this fire going? Kindling's damp. Is that Mrs. Edel, up already? Good morning. Hope you slept all right. I slept like a log."

"Oh, I had a divine sleep," Mrs. Edel said. "Nothing like mountain air. Can I help?" I heard her stand up and take some deep breaths. I pictured her in her tight red sweater. Her breasts stuck out like Betty Grable's. Mother's voice came from the kitchen.

"You relax. You have a long drive."

"This vacation's been such a treat. I can't thank you enough. I hope you and Mr. T. will visit us in New York."

[329]

I heard scraping of chairs. Mother had set the breakfast table out on the back porch. I heard her voice, louder now, on the porch too.

"We'd love to," she said. "Wouldn't we, E.B.? I'd love to go to the city for a visit." There was a pause. "What about some porridge, E.B.? Will you please say grace?"

ESTHER EDEL was the first Jewish person I ever met. She was the first exotic person I was with up close. She had a throaty voice; those huge, deep-set, dark brown eyes; thick, almost black hair, wavy, worn in coils low on her neck. She moved in a fragrant, musky cloud. And she wore makeup, even mascara, like the movie stars in the Maybelline ads. She plucked her eyebrows; her real eyebrow hairs didn't match up with pencil lines arched above her eyes, obvious in bright sun when I took her paddling in the canoe. She didn't know how to paddle or row. But she did many things well, fast and easily. She whipped up slipcovers for the old easy chair that was popping its stuffing; made me a peasant blouse and skirt; cooked dishes I had never heard of, like spaghetti, eggplant parmigiana, kasha, potato pancakes. She filled the kitchen with exciting, strange tastes and smells. She spoke rapid-fire, startled me by her directness about being divorced, raising her kids alone, being happy when her two-timing husband left. "Good riddance," she said, blinking black lashes and rolling her amazing eyes.

Where did they stay? I don't remember. And where were the aunts when Mrs. Edel was cooking? It's a blank. All I can say is that Charlotte would not have liked Mrs. Edel's cooking – too foreign, spicy, rich. And I can't recall Jeannette when Mrs. Edel was there. They must have kept out of the way.

E.B. carried his Victorian sensibilities with him throughout his life, in honor of his mother and of all his forebears. He had a basically conservative nature, in the political sense as well as in the sense of preserving and maintaining whatever was worthwhile, solid, enduring. He must have been fascinated by Esther Edel, drawn to her because she was so much the opposite of the women in his circle of family and friends.

The most I ever heard from his own lips about her was that there was a great deal of sympathetic Communist propaganda spouted by her two teenage children, and maybe by her, too, during the evenings while he was living in their apartment.

Why did he continue to stay in an apartment where the atmosphere was so uncongenial, to say the least? Living space in New York during the war was precious beyond imagining. E.B. would have been hard pressed to find another room. And what if Mrs. Edel, herself, was the main attraction, even if they never actually had a fully realized sexual relationship? And who's to say they didn't have a relationship?

My father always spoke in reverent tones about the tenderness of women. His attitude toward me reinforced my original view of his Victorian attitudes regarding sex. An affair with Esther Edel would have been an exciting transgression. Certainly she was a woman who knew her way around. I didn't quite understand at the time when she came up for that visit what it was about her that was so different, but I know now that she was sexually alluring. She had a full-bosomed, womanly shape. She had a heavy-lidded, glamorous kind of attractiveness. I didn't even think of it as being sexy at that time; it was more mysterious, dangerous.

I SHOULD NEVER have picked it up again. Oh, if I had never picked it up again. One more thing I'm sure I wasn't meant to know. It's worse than reading intimate details. I walked quietly and bent over the carton. I pushed things aside and saw it, dark and crumbling at the edges, that diary. It had fallen flat, and the gold-leaf initials, shadowed by the side of the carton, didn't gleam but they were tooled deep in the leather. I reached for it without thinking. Again my fingers felt the dried-up leather, and I breathed the scent not of my father but of old bindings, and of the heat under the attic roof.

How long did it take me to open that book again, look again at the up and down handwriting, and leaf through the pages. Long enough to see dust motes rise from them into the late slanted light from the window. Empty pages. Creamy pages. Dates never marked. Not one appointment, not one notation. No trace of my father came to me by the opening of his book. The inscription sat on that endpaper, waiting. The whole emptiness of a life, it seemed to me, was in that book.

I looked up and found Dwight watching me. He was holding a

Golden Book of Airplanes, closed on his finger where he had been looking at it.

"Look at this," he said, opening the book to show me a drawing of a fighter plane on one of the pages. It was one of the models I had helped him build. He must have made the drawing as a young boy.

I looked at it. He was tickled at having found it. I said something but my mind was on the diary. He was talking to me but I wasn't paying attention. I held up the diary.

"You caught me," I said.

He scowled at me. He was starting to speak but I butted in.

"I know what you're going to say," I said. I didn't want to hear it in nasty, low terms, the way he had said the movie star had kicked Daddy out of bed. "I know they were probably lovers," I said, "that year Daddy had the mumps."

He seemed to hesitate. Or is that just the way I see it now? He seemed to pause on the verge of speaking. I was about to warn him. I was in no mood. I said, "Don't say something horrible, Dwight."

At the same time he said, "It wasn't mumps."

The whole rest of the conversation was both of us talking over each other. I couldn't walk away. I couldn't scream. I couldn't put my hands over my ears. So I talked.

He said again, "It wasn't mumps," as if to make sure I had heard him.

Then I said, "You weren't there. You were only eight years old."

But he went on, without stopping, talking under me, talking over me. "He tried to commit suicide," he said.

"You don't know anything," I persisted. "You can't say anything." I didn't think about what I was saying, but it's still in my mind, and I can hear him going on, as I threw sentences at him about how much he didn't know, couldn't have known.

He said Daddy had tried to commit suicide and that he was already living with Mrs. Edel when he did it, and she was the one who found him. Saved him. Wanted him to live. He said he knew because Daddy told him. I was sort of yelling. I didn't know where it was coming from, the yelling. It wasn't really loud but I couldn't stop. I wanted to know why Daddy had told him. Why would Daddy tell him that? Why wouldn't he have told me, if it were true?

"It's true," he said. "He only told me in passing. He was giving me the lecture on what a failure I was. I was eleven years old. He told me I was no good and that I was going to end up like his father, dead on the railroad tracks. Did you know that, Weezie? Did you even know his father killed himself?"

That got me quiet. I was stunned. I started trying to listen to what he was saying.

"He said his father was a coward for committing suicide," Dwight said. "He blamed his own father for everything and yet, at the same time, he excused him, rationalized his failures by blaming family misunderstandings, the decline of the silk trade all because of socialists, their strikes, and particularly Helen Gurley Flynn. I remember how scared I was. But I talked back to him. It might be the only time in my life I really out-and-out talked back to him." He trailed off. I waited. He was standing in debris, things in disarray. Up to his shins, as I remember it. I wanted to shake him. I wanted to say to him, You're a grown man. Grow up.

"So what?" I said. "Don't you do the same thing?"

"Damn right I blame him. That's what I said to him. I said why didn't he just do the same as his father and get it over with."

The yelling came up in me again. It was like fainting in order not to be present. It was a roar that didn't drown anything out, but it gave me something to pay attention to instead of what he was saying.

He kept talking. I was speaking lines of family lore and he was reciting between the lines the things I didn't want to know.

He said that Daddy told him then about the mumps not being mumps, and about living with Mrs. Edel. Dwight called her Esther. Esther Edel, not Mrs. Edel, as I've always thought of her. He had lost his job at the Comptroller's office, he had lost most of the money Mother had given him, and he was living in this woman's apartment, Dwight said, unable to pay and, Dwight said, sleeping with her.

"He told you all this? You were only eleven years old. Why would he tell you all this?"

That stopped him. But not because I had caught him in a lie, even though I hoped I had.

"That's what he used to do, Weezie," he said, as if I had finally understood the hell that was his childhood. "He would talk to me in ways that were completely inappropriate. He didn't care what he said. Sometimes when he was angry, I think he didn't even know what he was saying. It just came out of him."

"He never told me any of these things," I said, unable to push the welling of jealousy out of my voice.

"You never made him mad enough."

"He got mad at me sometimes."

Dwight shook his head and turned to leave the room. "He got mad at you," he said, " but he let you off because you were always trying to be friends with him to protect his ego."

"But you tried too," I protested. "Didn't you?"

He turned on the threshold. He was smiling. "Didn't know you understood that," he said, and he lumbered off down the stairs.

BY THE TIME Dwight and I headed out late that afternoon for Cecil's the rain clouds were about wrung dry. The sky had that intense look that comes with the beginning of a sunset beyond local weather.

Dwight started the car, pulled in front of the gas pumps. He jumped out, walked to the front of the car, shook Cecil's hand. They started chatting about this and that, peering into the engine, tapping things, screwing and unscrewing caps and plugs, doing men's, engine things. Dwight looked exactly the way Daddy had looked at filling stations from here to New Jersey and back; same stance, same deep interest in what Cecil – or whatever garage man was rooting around the insides of his car or truck or tractor – had to say. Dwight and Daddy were alike in so many ways. The smell of gas made my eyes fill with tears. It brought back all those car trips, all that preparation, all that engine lore.

On the way home from Cecil's I couldn't get the idea of Dwight and Daddy out of my mind. I couldn't get a hold on how close they must have been. I had never thought of it before. I wanted him to talk about it more, but I didn't want to bring it up. I thought if I talked to him about something else, we could get to it, to the way Daddy had told him things, treated him like an equal, so young, and Dwight not even wanting him to.

Everything he said about Daddy sounded mean. Even the story about the trip to California, the way he had told it in that skeptical tone of his, had sounded like a recitation of Daddy's worthlessness.

I brought up Nashville, the drive to Nashville. Daddy could have forbidden him to go and that would have been the end of it.

"He drove you to Nashville," I said. "What if he did that because he wanted to help you?"

He didn't answer. I wasn't sure he had heard me. He was driving with one hand, the other arm out the window. I looked at him, waiting for a response. I could see something in his profile that looked like that boy who used to come into the house silently sometimes and go into his room and close the door.

"Dwight?"

"Leave it alone, Weezie."

It was as if Daddy was right there with us, sitting between us in the car. I reached across and touched Dwight's arm. He flinched and I quickly pulled away. "We never talk about him," I said. "We never have talked about him, even when he was our common enemy."

He gave a short laugh. "You never thought he was your enemy, Sis. Try to remember. He's always been a hero to you."

I couldn't argue. Something in his tone warned me, even more than his words did. We didn't speak for the rest of the ride. When we got to the house we parted without a word. He went to the back porch, where he had been sleeping nights, and I could hear him shuffling through something that sounded like papers in his duffel bag. I went upstairs and ran a bath. It had been the most difficult day of all of them.

Dwight knocked on the bathroom door, said he had something he wanted me to read. "I banged this out after you called me about Mother," he said through the door. "I knew I'd never be able to tell you about this. Still can't talk about it without bawling."

Typical that he would wait till I was in the bath, then have to talk through the door. For a minute I was so irritated I couldn't think of anything to say.

"I'll leave it on your bed," he said. "I'm turning in. See you tomorrow," and I heard him move away.

What I found on my bed was an oak-bark folder with a sheaf of handwritten sheets of paper that began without title or salutation.

DWIGHT WROTE:

First day of school. September, 1945. I was ten. First day was always a half day. I had ridden my bike and had permission to stay in town and play with my friends. I'm sure something had been said as to what time I was expected to be home but I don't remember what.

Late afternoon. A bunch of us were having an apple fight in the ruins of the old Leland House Hotel. Concrete walls of the foundation and some front steps, walkways leading up to the empty pit of the old basement. Tufts of crabgrass, dandelion long gone to seed. Almost fall, high clumps of goldenrod and stalks of that tough weed with the feather-like seeds – milkweed – pushed through the dirt and leaves. Burned rubble had been cleared away long ago. The grounds had grown up; lawn was tall grass with small trees – hardwood and evergreen. There were some untended apple trees at the back of the property, with gnarled trunks. The stunted apples made for great apple fights.

I didn't like apple fights. I didn't have a good throwing arm. And I was afraid of getting hit in the eye, having an eye put out. I'd heard stories over and over of someone who'd had their eye put out by a rock or a stick, or a branch snapping back. And there was Francis Swinton in your class with his eye knocked out by his brother swinging a golf club. Those apples were hard as marbles and they hurt wherever they hit you.

At dusk I told the other kids I had to go home. No sooner had I said it and started to go after my bike than someone said my father was there. He was driving the old 1931 LaSalle.

I always hated it when Pop came after me. He always seemed to deliberately do things to embarrass me in front of the other kids.

I approached the LaSalle. He glowered at me, snarled through clenched jaws, "Get home." His manner frightened me. It seemed somehow different, more menacing.

I assumed he would drive me home, yell at me a lot in that louder-than-thunder voice of his. But no – it was worse than that. He fell in behind me and followed. Oh no, I remember thinking. I hope nobody sees me with him following. Maybe he'll only follow a little way and then pass me and go on ahead home. He kept following. He didn't pass me. He drove along behind with the old LaSalle in low gear, grinding along, the engine muttering in its own unique language.

Down the main street of town – people staring – over the bridge of the Mill Pond, by John Young's Garage (it hadn't burned down yet). Past the Post Office. By the Brown Swan (the Word of Life hadn't bought it yet). By Ed Kelly's Funeral Home. Past our church, the house of Miss Richardson, my first grade teacher – (she and Forrest Harrington hadn't gotten married yet). He kept following me. Past the Hoffman Road. Past Gillings Garage. Better now; not so many people to see this humiliating scene. Past the Leavitts'. Past Hanmer's Cabins (no one outside to see me). Past Borman's. I could barely pedal up the hill, but I made it. The LaSalle was halfway off the pavement but the shoulder was too narrow, cars couldn't pass when there was oncoming traffic. They honked at Pop, then roared past when they could. Past Jenks' place. Past Helen Robinson's (she was not in sight). Past Junior Gochie's (I hoped he wasn't outside. He picked on me a lot anyway). Past Caldwell's (David wasn't outside. That was good). Past the Charlie Hill Road and over the top of the hill. Easier riding then. The LaSalle still there – close behind.

Almost home. Over the tunnel at the boys' camp. Dark there with the big pine trees on either side. I heard the LaSalle engine speed up. The car pulled alongside me. The passenger window went down. I could hardly see him. His voice growled out, "Go over to the barn." The car passed me at the Moses' driveway, turned into our barn ahead of me. I heard the crunching of my bike tires on the gravel of the driveway to the barn. It was almost dark.

The barn door was open, the car inside. I approached. My mouth was dry, my stomach ached. I was quivering in fright. What was he going to do to me?

I couldn't see him. His voice came out of the darkness. "Get in here." I could hardly walk. Almost paralyzed with fear. I went inside.

My eyes began to get used to the dark. He was on the left. I saw only a form. I could barely make out any features. As I got closer to him I made out his face – it was contorted in rage. I got within his reach. His left hand reached out and closed on my right shoulder. His right hand was clenched around a piece of kindling about eighteen inches long. He slammed that kindling against his chopping block. That wood stump was solid, like a rock. It made a sound like a shot. I jumped. He squeezed my shoulder until it hurt. He hit the piece of kindling against the chopping block again. I almost fell down. I looked at him. His lips were pulled back baring his teeth. That was almost all I could see of his face. He banged the kindling against the trunk one more time even harder. I could hardly breathe. "This should do it," he snarled.

And he hit me with the kindling on my left side between my belt and my knee. He swung from way back. And he hit me again on the same side. And he told me how bad I was. And he hit me on the other side back-handed. And he cursed me. And he hit me. And he hit me. And he hit me. And he yelled at me. And he shook me. And he hit me – forehand – backhand – and roared at me how bad I had been – and he hit me and he hit me and he hit me. And he asked me something. And I couldn't answer because I was so petrified and I hurt so much and that pissed him off so he hit me more – forehand – backhand. Again and again and again. And I didn't cry and maybe because I didn't it made him more furious.

The Bastard! The Bastard! The Bastard! The Bastard! Oh God when will he stop!

I never cried. Finally he threw the kindling against the wall, and screamed at me to go to the house. I could hardly move from the pain and the fear – but I did, shuffled out of the barn and to the house – away from him – the Beast.

I don't remember exactly what happened next except that I was in the bathroom upstairs and was going to take a bath. I was undressed to my underwear. Mother knocked and I told her to come in. She saw my buttocks and legs. They were purple-red from my beltline to my knees, almost bleeding in spots. "Did he do this to you?" I still couldn't speak, just nodded. I have no idea what, if anything, she said to him about the episode.

I don't know to this day what I did to deserve the beating. That day all I had done was stay late in town.

At the time, my bruises were kind of a badge that I nonchalantly displayed when I took a shower after PE at school. I remember Bob Welch looking at the bruises, eyes bugged out. "My old man really beat the shit out of me," I remember saying.

I didn't think about it for years. Happened to be watching TV – something about adults who had been abused as children. I was affected emotionally to a degree that really surprised me. I sat sobbing as I listened to their experiences, all of which were worse than mine: their abuse went on for years. I don't know if I was crying for them or for me – maybe a little of both. I cried at times as I wrote this. Strange, it was over 50 years ago.

I did the only thing I knew how to do. I wrote one word, "Sorry!" on a piece of paper, slipped it in on top of the pages, sticking out like a bookmark, and tiptoed out to the kitchen. I left the folder where I knew Dwight would see it when he came in in the morning to make the coffee. After that I went back to bed, cold and exiled. Things happened that you didn't know about, and not having known made you feel worse when you did find out. I was afraid of Daddy when I was a child, but Dwight's life had been awful because of him.

And it did ring some ancient bell where I somehow had a very vague recollection of my mother telling me (when she was living with B and me) that she knew that Daddy had hit Dwight (now, that seemed to be putting it mildly). When she told me that, I was so stunned I didn't want to talk about it, and I know it was painful for her even to mention it.

Why did he do it? I think it's really two questions: where did the rage come from, and what triggered the beating? To answer the first question, I would say that my father, who believed that his life was a series of things that had happened to him, would have seen my brother's birth as ill-fated. Because of the difficult birth and the weakened condition in which it left Connie for months, my father didn't get his ranch – the very thing he was convinced would have allowed him to prove himself in the world. I think Dwight's birth started to symbolize that disappointment, which slowly mounted into rage. After harboring this feeling for ten years, he learned in 1945, when my grandparents died, that there would be no money coming from their estate. It was the end of the windfall dream. At this point any minor infraction on Dwight's part could have triggered the violent release of that rage, so unreasonably centered in my brother. I think there is no need to speculate further.

WHEN I LOOK BACK, I have a sense of my own privilege in the family hierarchy, and I felt it at the time, too. But it didn't come to me, I worked for it. I can see that I was very competitive. Even now, writing about my siblings I find this tendency to show them in a lesser light, and to prove, however mildly, that I was more mature than they were, or more intelligent, or more acceptable.

I didn't pay enough attention during our childhood. I didn't take seriously what was going on with Dwight. I wrote him off. I was aggravated by him. Why wouldn't he now be angry with me? I did nothing to try to save him. I guess no one did. And I was only a kid myself.

THE NEXT MORNING, Dwight said nothing about it. We drank our coffee as usual. He acted as if the night before had been like any other. I took my cue from him and we did the final chores, together or apart, a little shy with each other at first, but soon back to our usual exchanges about this old hat, that old photo.

That was our training. That was the way a household full to overflowing with temperaments expected itself to go along. Even Dwight, who, at least the way I remember it, openly rebelled, had learned the lesson to the core. And we went on, saying nothing, embarrassed, both of us I'm sure, even to think about the abuse, about the beating, about the eternal question, Why?

And where was Mother? Where was Mother?

And where was I?

Nineteen

EVERYTHING LEFT in the house and outbuildings was for the auctioneer, who would be there in another hour. We called our families, washed up, and met in the kitchen for lunch. We admitted to each other how exhausted we were. But we congratulated each other. We had done the impossible, sorted through everything in the house, grounds, outbuildings. Now we had only the auctioneer and Mother's memorial service, which was to be the next day.

Dwight was moving bacon slices with tongs, transferring them from the center of the skillet toward the edge. "I see you're using the correct cooking method on the bacon," I said.

He looked sheepish. "I know I scorned Pop's system but y'know something? Bacon tastes better cooked slow, damn it."

"Got a few quirks myself," I confessed. "I save soap slivers. And I turn out lights when I leave a room." I went to the sink, ran water until it was cold. "This well water's still the best. I'm glad Daddy won that argument." I filled my glass, turned off the faucet.

"There's a right way and a wrong way – I thought I'd yell if I heard that one more time. Now I say it to myself." He shook his head. He was lining up bacon strips in parallel lines on a folded piece of paper towel. "Look at me. Can't dump 'em all whopper-jawed."

We carried our plates out to the porch – bacon, lettuce, and tomato sandwiches, cold beers in bottles.

Dwight took a bite of his sandwich and grinned. "Delicious," he said.

I took a bite. He was right. I remembered the smell of bacon on cool summer mornings before the heat had dried the dew.

When we had finished eating he got up and carried our empty plates into the kitchen. I followed with the beer bottles, trailing after him, wondering if there was anything I could say to him. He ran water into the basin in the sink, immersed the plates and utensils. I handed him glasses that were on the kitchen table from earlier in the morning. There was a group photo propped up on the window sill of one of the kitchen windows where I had left it the morning I discovered it. On the back was written "To my dearest little sister, Constance, from your devoted Rae. August 1942."

I picked up the photo and looked at it carefully. "I remember this photo pretty well," I said. "Do you?"

I walked over to the sink and held it out for him to look at. He paused in his dish washing, studied the picture.

"Sure," he said. "I can't believe I would have worn that leather helmet in August."

"Mother could hardly pry it off your head even to go to bed."

"That's all I wanted, to be a pilot. Dad poked fun at me. You'll outgrow that silly notion. Made me mad." He shrugged, went back to work.

"I don't remember, Dwight. We only squirrel away our own stuff, I guess." I thought I was wise in the ways of the world that summer. Eleven years old. I was grinning a buck-toothed grin, not as painfully embarrassed by my less than perfect teeth as I was to become.

"Hey, Beavertooth," Dwight teased me, flicking a few drops of soapy water in my direction. How I had loathed that nickname.

I laughed. "Shut up, Babyfoot," came flying out of me right back at him. "Listen, Dwight, we have to talk about Mother's memorial service."

His hands were submerged in the dishpan, suds above his wrists. "I'm not saving this dishwater," he said, and he overturned the battered metal pan. He rinsed his arms free of suds, then bent over, splashed water on his face.

"Well, Sis, it's all yours," he said, reaching for the hand towel. He wiped his face, patted his beard dry. When he looked up at me his eyelashes and brows were still wet. "My hiding places are all gone, Weezie. This place is up with me, I'm finished. Going home. Talked to Vera. Wes is home."

"You mean you're not –"

"Soon as the auctioneer's out of here, I'm gone." He dried his hands, put the towel aside without looking where he was putting it, leaned back against the sink with arms folded over his chest.

"Like father, like son," he said. "I did a lot of the things to my kids that our father did to me. Things I hated when he did them to me. I improved as time passed, though. But Poor Wes was my training ground and his teen years were bad. I realized my methods were awful. Fortunately, in spite of me and Pop, Wes has turned out to be a very decent human being. He and I discuss his turbulent times and he tells me it wasn't all me – maybe that's just some of the decency in him showing."

I wanted to rush to him, give him something I had failed to give him. But then I looked at him. He was not lamed; he was strong.

"Got to get back to my life," he said. "Mother's memorial's all yours."

I picked up the dish towel and reached past him for something to dry. He caught my wrist and held it.

"Leave 'em," he said. "It doesn't matter anymore," and he let go of my wrist and left the room. I heard him going up the stairs, then I heard the scraping of the metal wastebasket being pushed aside so the bathroom door would close.

I didn't leave them. I dried them, slowly, carefully, and put them away. Not because I had to but because it was the last time.

Twenty

For fifteen years after my father died, Mother had kept the old farmhouse in Schroon Lake, where she had spent every summer of her life (except for that terrible summer in Texas). In those later years she went back in mid-June and stayed until the early frosts of October.

Her house aged along with her. There had never been money for anything but essentials – a new woodshed when raccoons dug into the old one; a new cellar under the frigid downstairs bedroom; the living-room fireplace and the chimney at the top of the stairs.

I used to go up to help her shut the house every fall, stay several days while we closed up together. It was always a sad time, memories rushing back. The mountains were wild with color against the pure blue Adirondack sky.

The morning would arrive to head south. We always drove back to New York in tandem. She drove herself even her last summer, age eighty-seven.

That last time was the same as all the others. I had everything we were taking with us near the front door, and started loading my station wagon. Mother liked to take her personal stuff in her own car. She would check and re-check to make sure she hadn't forgotten anything, even though her memory was excellent.

"Don't rush me. You know I'm slow," she called downstairs.

"I'll scrape the windshields," I said. "We had frost." I closed the front door loudly so she would know I wasn't downstairs tapping my foot.

I started the engine in her '69 Nash Rambler and scraped the windshield, my breath coming out in clouds. As I walked from her car to my own, something brushed my hair. I reached up. It was a rusty-orange maple leaf. It had floated from the ancient maple in the side yard. I looked up. Other leaves were letting go, silently drifting down in the chill morning air. Leaves kept floating down, letting go from each twig, touching the stiff, whitened grass with a whisper.

Mother had moved in with us when Daddy died. Fourteen years

now. They had been living in the farmhouse until he had his stroke, in the fall of 1970. She stayed with us during the time he was in limbo in the hospital in New York. He lingered seven weeks, and when he died she moved in with us. She fit into our lives by then, and our children adored her. She was a great listener, never bossy.

"No fuss," she said. "I won't take one of the children's rooms." Old-style apartment maids' rooms were made for tiny people with few possessions. There was space for a narrow bed, a small bureau; there was a sink in one corner, and an ugly, institutional metal closet that clanged when you shut it. She kept a row of books, her current reading, lined up on a shelf on the wall side of her bed, along with a box of Kleenex, extra wool socks, her Bible, and a yellow-and-blue stick of Camphor Ice. In the morning, she fired her nighttime accumulation of used Kleenexes across the room into the wastebasket with deadly accuracy. Her covers would still be tucked neatly around her. "I get under my covers like putting a letter into an envelope," she liked to say.

One night she suddenly needed oxygen. There was no place for the equipment. "I don't want to do anything inconvenient," she kept insisting. B and I moved her to the hospital to be safe. It turned out she had pneumonia.

One day, when I got there at the usual time, I paused in the doorway of her room in the hospital and saw her lying with her back to the door, head sunk into the goose-down pillow we had brought with her from home. The form in that bed was so slight it could have been merely rumpled blanket. Nurses said she was the perfect patient. "She doesn't even move at night," they said.

Now, she lifted her head, spoke toward the wall.

"I'm still breathing," she said, "and I don't need the bedpan, thank you." Something made her turn her head. When she saw me she settled down again. "They're sweet but I wish they wouldn't hover," she whispered. I reached for her hand; her grip was warm and firm. "I'll finish my nap," she said. She was asleep in seconds.

I went to the window. The view was too familiar: a small rectangle of gray sky, a slate slab of river, hideous high-rises on the New Jersey shore, gulls wheeling over the river. I settled into the recliner by the window, drowsy in the hospital heat.

Back at Schroon Lake, in bed, lots of pillows behind me, I heard Mother's step. She was coming in the door with a tray of food. Her fresh, just-out-of-the-bath smell enveloped me as she bent to feel my head for fever. That first winter we lived at Schroon (before the aunts came to live with us and before I went to the hospital) I had serious ear trouble, excruciating earaches; I would spend a week in bed and they would go away – though they always came back, worse than before. There was no specialist for over fifty miles on narrow, icy two-lane roads. The farmhouse was drafty and hard to keep warm, and Daddy was away a lot so there was often no one to go for medicine.

"I just heard a chick-a-dee," Mother said, sitting gently on the edge of the bed. "How's the patient?" She spooned me full of homemade soup, perfect toast, as much as I would eat, orange juice just squeezed, a dessert of multi-colored Jellos with a puff of whipped cream on top. Often a surprise lay waiting under the folded white linen napkin. *Life* magazine on Fridays, full of the world; cartoons she had cut from the papers; a new paper-doll book; favorite comics ("Can't hurt. It's a rest from books").

Mother never seemed to get tired. She was up before dawn and she worked all day, shoveling snow, keeping a wood fire going in the kitchen stove, keeping the furnace fed with coal, scattering ashes on the walkway to the road, driving miles on icy roads for mail, groceries, medicine, extra treats. And cooking. Breakfast, lunch, and dinner. She seemed to do everything happily. She never made a point of any of her hard work. After we children were in bed she would be playing Beethoven sonatas, Chopin études, Joplin rags on the piano.

A food trolley rumbled up the corridor and stopped at the door. The aide knocked, too loud. Instantly, Mother was awake. "It's getting dark," she said. "I don't like you going home late." She waved toward the door. "Must've dozed off. Why didn't you wake me?"

I stayed while she poked at pale chicken surrounded by gluey gravy, an ice-cream scoop of mashed potatoes, listless mixed vegetables. "I know I'm supposed to eat," she said. "Food's not exciting in plastic." As if she were taking medicine, she took a bite from each category, and chewed hard. After several rounds, she put down the plastic fork and wiped her mouth with the crackly napkin. "I want you to get me out of here," she said. "I won't be hooked up to machines."

She had been in the hospital over a month. "I didn't want to come here," she reminded me. The pneumonia had cleared up. B and I pulled strings, got her home.

Even after all that, she insisted on her usual summer at Schroon. "Now this time I'll clean up my house before I pass out, or bust," she vowed – a vow she made yearly. She drove herself up, as always, and I followed behind, and stayed a week to help her get organized.

We laughed, more than anything else. Digging into drawers, pulling out old photos, ancient Christmas cards, invitation lists to long-ago parties, old bills, clothes Maya and I had worn when we were still dressed in matching outfits. Mother's burst of morning energy was gone by early afternoon so we made little real progress. But we took long walks to the lake, and we talked.

Mother called her life a mixed bag. She talked about her childhood as if it had been an idyll. She had had a Victorian upbringing, strict, but full of love, and financially solid. She had married Daddy at Almanole, in June of 1920. "Married in the right place, off on the wrong foot," she said. "Somehow things got off the track. I'd love to write it down," she would muse. "Call it *Wrong Foot Forward*."

That last autumn, as I shut the door before the tandem drive back, Mother took hold of my arm. "Do get this all down," she said, making an all-inclusive gesture with her head. "Everything's changed so much. Don't forget." Her cane thumped across the porch. She didn't look back.

MOTHER HAD been brought up in a Baptist family that was strict enough to make sure she took the Pledge against alcohol at the age of twelve. In her last years, the certainty of that way of life seemed to ease somewhat. She would enjoy a little sherry with me at sunset sometimes, and every now and then she would muse on subjects her upbringing had taught her were not for musing.

One morning she interrupted her usual silent progress through her oatmeal. "I'd have thought the world was coming to an end if we hadn't gone to church," she said, and she pounded her fist on the table as she added, "every single Sunday." She paused, picked up her spoon. "But I don't know what happens when we die. I'm supposed to believe we go to heaven but I don't know."

That last autumn of her life, she needed more and more sleep. She used her cane no matter how short the walk. "There's nothing stupider than an old person falling," she would say. "It's simply false pride." She was blessed with strong bones. Her eyesight was keen; she needed glasses only for reading. And she remembered everything and heard everything she wanted to.

Late one night B and I had a shouting argument. It escalated out of nothing, triggered by the news that the roof of the woodshed up at Schroon Lake was near collapse from an early snowfall. B exploded, roared against spending a nickel on that relic, as he referred to the farmhouse. "Why doesn't she sell the fucking place?" he shouted.

Next morning, the two of us were deep into the *Times*, coffee at our elbows, when Mother, up and dressed earlier than usual, came into the kitchen. She perched at the edge of the stepstool, balancing herself with her cane and the toes of her Tretorns. We both glanced up, surprised to see her before my husband shot out the door.

"Good morning, Connie," he said. "How'd you sleep?"

She folded her hands on top of her cane, looked him straight in the eye and said, "You know, I'm thinking of selling that fucking place."

We laughed till we cried.

A week later, she had trouble walking to the bathroom by herself. She had to pull herself along the invalid rails we had installed in the narrow back hall. She had an appetite only for ice cream; she was too tired to chew, she said. Even homemade soup was too much.

I got impatient. Christmas was near; everyone was busy. I wanted to get out at night but felt guilty about leaving her all alone. "Go," she would say, with a sweep of the hand. We got practical nurses for nighttime. One snored so loudly sitting up in the chair she woke Mother. Most were efficient but brusque, working for the salary.

This was my mother. I had to remind myself that she had always had time for me when I was growing up. We compromised with a one-way room beeper. She never made a sound.

She got a cold she couldn't shake off. Antibiotics and deconges-
tants were added to her assortment of capsules to balance heart and
blood, blood pressure and water retention. She would line them up
morning and evening, a row of tiny, elongated Easter eggs, and down
them one by one. "Goody goody! Three more to go," and she would
force down another one. "That's it," she would announce when the
last one was gone, and she would slap the table in triumph.

One night my husband had a late business obligation. I was happy
to be home, and to spend the evening with Mother for a change. As
she headed for bed, I walked beside her, on the pretense that I needed something in that direction. She almost never asked for help of any
kind and I tried to respect her wish to stay as independent as possible.
Once she was in her room, I left her to take off her dressing gown and
slip into bed.

Minutes later I heard her voice, strong and clear, "Lueza, I need
you."

I shot for her room. She had tried to get into bed but her legs
refused to obey. She was frightened. I put a hand on one of her legs.
It was trembling. I helped her lie down, and sat in a chair by the bed.

I asked if I should call Dr. Schachtel. We still had a true family
doctor, someone who would make a house call.

She waved her hand. "No. I want rest," she said.

She lay still, on her side, seemed to be listening to her body. I took
her hand. It felt tiny, but had almost the strength of her old grip.

Footsteps in the hall and a minute later my older daughter, Jody,
came in. The other three children were scattered, couldn't be home
until Christmas, a week away.

"Hi, Granny," Jody said quietly, and she sat at the foot of the bed
and massaged Mother's feet.

Time passed, impossible to know how much. I had a sense
Mother's end was near. She breathed normally for some minutes after
Jody sat down but her breaths got shorter and shallower. At one point,
she lifted her head and said in a firm voice, "Jody, I hope you have
great success in your acting career."

She seemed to be dozing; her breaths were shallow but regular. My
husband and Dr. Schachtel came in. Jody had called the doctor before

she came into the room. When she heard their voices, Mother opened her eyes, tried to lift her head.

"Dr. Schachtel, how are you?" she said. "Won't you have a chair?"

He reached down, stroked her forehead, held her hand briefly, long enough to get a pulse. "I'm here if you need me, Connie," he said. She shook her head, closed her eyes. She dozed again. The men sat in the hall.

Her breaths got shorter and then I heard that frightening sound they call the death rattle. She lay still, completely quiet except for that frightening sound. There was no sign she was in pain or discomfort. She held my hand firmly but she seemed to be slipping into a deep sleep. Her breathing slowed and stopped. Then her grip loosened.

My parents stayed energetic well into their seventies. They were healthy and strong. Mother gradually aged. My father (I thought of him now as E.B. but still called him by the childish Daddy) stayed physically powerful. He maintained his erect carriage, his sure step, his steady tireless stride, and his healthy appetite. The aging in him was mental. He started to have memory lapses, when his distant gaze lasted many minutes and he didn't return completely to his surroundings for longer intervals. He might have dropped off to sleep, but his blue eyes were open, seeing something remote, his lips moving just slightly. When he did return, his speech would be indistinct, and this used to unnerve me. His diction had always been precise, his sentences full and grammatical, no matter whether he was describing a bird only he had been quick enough to catch on the wing or trying to explain Einstein's theory of relativity to a ten-year-old. Now his mumbled words made no sense. "Yesterday the winter − trucks − my axe − the gas bill's today."

Did he know he was drifting a little farther away each time? He didn't acknowledge these lapses and none of us ever mentioned them, even among ourselves. He still drove, and although it seemed insane to let him do it, we all did. Some automotive angel must have kept his mind alert when he was behind the wheel.

I drove with him early one hot summer morning to the town of Ticonderoga. He said he had to replace the brake shoes on the truck and no one in the town of Schroon could be relied on to get the right ones. He seemed to drive as always, totally focused; my eyes were on him, as inconspicuously as possible.

We were quiet for the early part of the drive, winding as it did along the shore of Paradox Lake. He kept a steady thirty-five, pulling over to the right on the short straight stretches and waving his big hand to allow the line of vehicles backed up behind us to speed past in triumph. "Darned fools," he would always mutter.

"Do you remember anything of the time when you absolutely reject-ed me?" he asked out of the silence between us. I was startled by his voice. I was thinking I was glad to be alive, safely beyond those wild rides I'd had on this road careening along, bleary from beer, hurrying home with someone I barely knew at the wheel, entwined in someone else's arms trying to keep his hot hands at bay, at least in front of the other passengers. I felt a stab of guilt, sure Daddy had read my thoughts, and was about to give me a verbal scolding for my teenage deception. A bit overdue, I thought, annoyed at his dragging up ancient history

"I was a rebellious teen, like most," I said in answer. "Tough on Mother, too."

"You acted as if you wanted nothing to do with me," he said, as if he hadn't heard me. "You only wanted your mother."

I was thinking I hadn't wanted her any more than him, and I was about to say so but he continued.

"For weeks on end," he said, and his voice sounded as though he was back in that distant time. "You were about two. I was so hurt."

Could he still be hurt? And angry as well. It had been thirty-eight years. I looked more closely. He was serious. His eyes watered up, his knuckles whitened against the wheel.

"I was too little to know what I was doing," I said sharply. How dare he make me feel guilty about this. "A lot of kids only want their mothers at that age." I wanted to say, Don't be ridiculous. You were always too sensitive.

But I didn't say that. He seemed fragile, helpless, terribly needy. The anger didn't leave me, but I moved over to him, put my left arm around his still solid shoulders, gave him a half-hug as hard as I could, and kissed his smooth cheek. (He'd made a point of shaving before we left – I'd heard him, in the gray dawn light, behind the closed bathroom door, fast, efficient, using probably no more than a teacup's worth of lukewarm water.) With my right hand, I grabbed the mighty biceps he had flexed for me so often, like Popeye, and squeezed hard.

"I love you," I said, "and I always have, even if I was being naughty back then. I never meant to hurt you, ever. Please forgive me." I leaned my head on his shoulder, pushed as close to him as I could.

A horn blasted from behind us. Daddy had slowed way down. He pulled over and coasted into a cleared, level area piled with gravel and sand to be sprinkled on the road when fall rains and frost made them slippery. Another line of impatient drivers accelerated past us, some staring at us, probably wondering at the odd couple we made.

He seemed unaware of them. He had stopped the truck and he cut the engine. He sat looking straight ahead, and made two huge fists, pounded them gently at three and nine o'clock on the wheel. Then he tilted his head back against the seat and at the same moment exhaled a great sigh.

"Thank the Lord," he said. "I'm so relieved." No smile, but there was a lightness to his voice. "You can't imagine how that has weighed on me all these years. Now I'll shut my eyes for forty winks."

HE ALWAYS SAID our name was Norse.

It's my mystery; what made us different from all other families. I never had the conversation with my sister, because she never seemed to think that way.

He caused a circulation of sadness in the living being that was our family. He caused a kind of maiming in my mother, and cowed my brother before Dwight could even learn to walk. As for me, I learned from him to leave my self aside and be a consoling presence.

I forgive him by remembering his circumstances, and by remembering what he gave me, and by being old enough now to understand something, the way you can understand something better when you come to it again. I remember that given the circumstances and his personality, he did the best he could.

I wrote that and hated it. "Did the best he could" is a concept that would not have satisfied him. But it's what's left; it's what there is.

And how do I forgive myself for letting pass the chance to talk to him, to try to know him? Whether he wanted to be close to me or anyone, or he didn't, it's no consolation to me to be told or to think he didn't want to be known, and that's why I wasn't truly close to him. I was the one from the beginning who knew how to be close to him in the only way he seemed to allow. I know how much I didn't try, in later years. I ran. I fled. I kept my self from him.

I suffered him.

I loved him, but it was a love lodged in me. It didn't grow or shrink. It didn't have anything to do with times we were together in his later years and he was so difficult; and it didn't have anything to do with the long stretches when I would make the token call once a week and put the children on the phone.

The myth was important to me. When he said to me, toward the end of his life, in a rare moment of emotion, that he had been a failure, it made me as angry as it made me sad. I always knew the myth of all of us was phony, but I loved the myth. He worked the way he could work; he felt it would have been a step down to take a steady job. And I was glad he didn't take a regular job and that we didn't live in some subdivision of a large city. Who would I have become without this setting of such exquisite beauty, Schroon Lake and The Place? I was proud of his stubbornness. But only part of me was glad and proud. And as soon as I could leave, I was gone. I changed my life.

Understanding isn't always comforting. All the things I can't change haunt me. I don't think it's a question of forgiveness. He was mighty, he was impossible, he was handsome, needy, rigid, intelligent, overpowering; he was a storehouse, he was a mine. He was my father, Thirkield, Thunder in the Field.

Epilogue

I'M IMPATIENT. I want to get down. My dress is stuck to the backs of my legs, glued as I am to Mother's hot lap. Mother seems not to notice the heat. She's busy focusing a pair of binoculars, trying to spot Maya in the clusters of girls on the huge playing field.

She turns to Daddy, leans over to glimpse his mimeographed sheet of events and girls. He leans over and whispers something into her ear. Before she can respond, he jumps up, strides to the end of the row, quickly descends to the ground, and disappears in a crowd of parents and coaches.

Mother's binoculars are trained on the crowded field. When I'm sure I've spotted Maya I point, to show her exactly where she should focus.

"Don't point, Weezie, it's not polite," she whispers in my ear. I close my fist and shake it in a pointing motion where I want my mother to look. But each time, I'm wrong. I want to run down from the stands, mingle with other brothers and sisters standing along the edge of the playing field, jumping up and down to cheer on their favorites.

Daddy is returning. He holds out a proper program. Mother is still staring through the binoculars. I take the program but I can't read yet. All I see are long lists scattered over the page.

Daddy leans across me. "Here, Connie," he says to her. "Let me tell you when Maya races. Have you found her yet?"

Mother shakes her head.

I know I can find Maya if I get closer, down there on the ground. And I'm sure I'll be able to find my way back if they'll only let me go. I see a drinking fountain. I must have a drink and I want to go alone.

I take a great breath. "I'm thirsty and I see a fountain over there," I say. I thrust out my fist. "Can I go down by myself? Oh, please."

There's an agony of delay. My father looks at me solemnly. He looks over toward the water fountain. "You must come right straight back here," he says, and he points his finger straight downward at where we're sitting. I nod my head firmly.

"Do you think it's all right?" Mother asks him, over my head.

I slide off her lap. The slight breeze makes my legs feel momentarily chilly. Mother's lap is damp, the light blue cotton darkened and crinkled into deep creases. She smoothes and straightens her skirt, her face filled with uncertainty. She waits for Daddy to answer.

"You'll find your way back up to us?" Daddy asks me. I nod fiercely.

"And don't put your mouth directly on the spigot," he warns me. I nod again, but I'm already moving, off the far end of the bleacher. Before I move down to the next level, I look back at them. Their eyes are fixed on me. I give a very quick wave and step down, almost jumping from one level to the next.

Before I know it I'm on the packed-down grass, surrounded by surges of girls and parents and smaller children all moving in eddies around me. I know I must keep my attention fixed on the far end of the bleachers in order to find my way to the fountain. I glance back up toward where my mother and father are seated, to help fix my position, and I can see they've lost sight of me in the crowd. Their faces turn this way and that. Only I myself know exactly where I am at this moment. I feel the excitement of this, and an edge of fear. But I know I can find the fountain by myself. I slip through the darting, bloomered girls, avoid the stern-looking people with whistles, quickly move ahead of the slow-moving adults.

I see a line of girls, red-faced and sweating, and at the head of the line the fountain. Will they allow me to use their fountain? I get in line, step purposefully forward as if I belong right there. No one says a word to me. It's as if I'm invisible.

I'm at the head of the line. A moment of panic. What if I can't reach the water bubbling up out of the spigot? I grasp the star-shaped metal handle and turn it, holding onto it as hard as I can to help lift myself just high enough to gulp down a big drink of water. I move away, water trickling down my chin spotting the front of my pale green dress. I wipe my dripping mouth and chin with the back of my hand. No one can see me, tell me, "That's not ladylike."

I've forgotten about looking for my sister. I'll see her later, after the races are over. I make my way happily back up to where my parents are waiting for me.

ACKNOWLEDGEMENTS

This book has had several incarnations. The earliest version was stimulated by memories of what had been for me a setting of idyllic physical beauty and unending imaginative possibility: my grandfather's summer place on Schroon Lake, in the Adirondacks. His big house was set on a hill, a good walk up a gentle incline from the lake.

Summers, until I was seven, we stayed in the former tenant farmer's house, across the road from dark and mysterious woods. Almanole, Grandpa and Grandma's house, was out of sight but near enough for me to get an early taste of independence at the age of six, when I was allowed to visit my grandparents for breakfast. From Grandpa's porch I could look far and away across the lake, toward his mountains, which receded in ever steeper and higher levels until the biggest of them, Pharaoh, commanded them all.

Memories of the setting, as it was in the early thirties, are the ones that come to mind, as well as changes that came as my grandparents aged and died. And the war came then too, not long after our family, for reasons unknown to me at the age of seven, made the decision to live year round in Schroon Lake. It was a big shift in my perspective, particularly as it coincided with my beginning grade school.

Writing about these times as I remember them from early childhood stirred other memories, memories that brought out near-forgotten flashes, moments of tension between my mother and my father. I loved both my parents; they were both right; they were both wrong. I have finally written what I feel is the best possible description of the story of our lives all together.

I have used real names and fictional names. I have not wished to embarrass any of the (very few now) living members of the Harris/Thirkield/Pearson/Early family circle. And I have no wish to embarrass anyone in Schroon Lake who may wish to remain anonymous.

Mary Alma and Arthur M. Harris, *my mother's parents*

Aunt Rae and Uncle Joe Early, *my mother's older sister, by seven years, and her husband*

Muriel Early, *Uncle Joe's daughter by his first wife (who had died)*

Uncle Dwight and Aunt Ann Harris, *my mother's older brother, by three years, and his wife*

Bill and Mary Harris, *their children*

Connie and E.B. Thirkield, *my parents*

Mary Belle Thirkield (Maya) – *my sister*

Paul, *her husband*

Dwight Thirkield, *my brother*

Vera, *his wife*

Wes, *their son*

Aunt Charlotte Pearson, *my father's oldest sister (by eighteen years). As children we called her Aunt Char.*

Uncle Walter, *her husband, who died in 1941*

Virginia, *their invalid daughter*

Nana Gordon, *Virginia's nurse (Her name was Alberta but everyone called her Nana.)*

Aunt Jeannette Thirkield, *my father's older sister by sixteen years*

Pearl Sherman, *my father's older sister by fourteen years*

Phillip, *her husband, professor of English at Oberlin College*

Constance, *their child*

We lived in New Jersey, part of that time in our own small house in Plainfield (my sister and I were both born there) and after that was sold, in the early thirties, off and on with Aunt Charlotte and Uncle Walter in Spring lake, New Jersey. Summers we went to Schroon Lake.

In January of 1935, we moved to San Antonio. My brother Dwight was born, prematurely, in March of '35. We stayed in Texas until some time in the spring of 1937 and in the summer of '37, we were back again in Schroon Lake.

The winter of 1938, from January until probably June, we lived in Brooklyn with Aunt Rae and Uncle Joe and then went up to Schroon Lake for the summer. From the end of that summer, we lived in

Schroon Lake. I lived there until I was married in June of 1953.

There was an exception: for the school year, September of '41 until June of '42, we lived again in Spring Lake with Aunt Charlotte, now widowed. I attended fifth grade, and my brother first grade, at the local public school; my sister was at Manasquam High School. The bombing of Pearl Harbor took place while we were there and we witnessed some ships torpedoed by German submarines right off the coast. Aunt Charlotte's house was directly across from the ocean.

The arrival of Virginia Johnstone and her three children (David, Elisabeth, and Gerald) was a major element in our feeling at home in Schroon Lake year round. Summer places are very quiet after all the summer residents and tourists have gone home. It wasn't that my mother needed a lot of things going on. But she did need a friend.

ORIGINALLY I had incorporated more of the family members into my stories of those days from my early childhood. I want to mention family members who did not make it into the final version of this book.

MURIEL EARLY, my oldest cousin, had endless patience with me and my sister. I was fascinated by her because she was beautiful. She had long black hair that she arranged in many styles – pulled back in coils, poofed up on her forehead in a roll, and sometimes stored at the back of her neck in a brightly colored snood that was like a fishnet. Like her father, she was very tall and she had his unflappable nature. She was never bothered by the persistent questions young children can ask about everything under the sun. And she had Uncle Joe's gentle Irish wit, never barbed or sarcastic. I was also fascinated by Muriel's array of boyfriends – counselors who paddled over to our float from the boys' camp next door. They came in search of Muriel and lolled on our float in their tight, bright latex bathing suits – tanned, hairy, and handsome, all of them. They took turns swinging me with a one, two, three and flinging me as far as they could from the float. I loved it.

Muriel smoked, though not in front of Grandpa or Grandma, who would not have approved. She knew she could trust me not to tattle on her. And she would sometimes give me a thrilling drag on her cigarette. I would try to puff it into smoke rings, something Uncle Joe could do easily with his heavy blue cigar smoke.